don't follow *the* her*d*

by m. davey

Information address: Post Office Box 3096,
Burleigh Town 4220,
Queensland, Australia.

E-mail address: natural@naturalway.net.au

Web site: *don't follow the herd* can also be ordered at: www.naturalway.net.au

ISBN: 978-0-646-49293-3

WARNING

This book is the result of the author's healing experience. It is also the experiences of some of Elias Schindelar's many clients.

The contents of this book should not be viewed as advice.

Any advice, suggestion or information from Elias Schindelar to his clients – or that which was derived from books, journals, newspapers, articles, web sites or any other source – that appears in this book was for the sole use of the author.

Self diagnosis is dangerous.

Readers are urged to seek assistance from qualified health care professionals on all health issues.

“

it is your right to
enjoy good and natural health. take
back the powers you were given at birth and
do not become a slave to systems. only
the body can heal itself. this is
the law of nature

”

– elias ludwig schindelar

INDEX

Continued

DISCLAIMER

- **Elias Ludwig Schindelar provided much of the information in this book. This information is not private or confidential, and it does not belong to him. It is available through various sources throughout the world.**
- **This book is the result of the author's experience and should be viewed as such. Information and remedies were applicable and appropriate at the time.**
- **This book was not written to specifically target circumstances, individuals or specific companies.**
- **Self-diagnosis or treatments for any type of health issues may be dangerous.**
- **Do not disregard, avoid or delay in obtaining advice from qualified health care professionals because of something you have read in this book.**
- **If you have or suspect that you may have a health problem, contact a qualified health care professional.**
- **The information in this book was not written to replace advice from health care professionals and it should not be construed as advice.**
- **This book is not to be used as a reference guide or for teaching purposes. There may be errors.**
- **The contents of this book are the personal views and opinions of those who contributed.**
- **The author, editor, Elias Schindelar and contributors do not accept any liability and cannot be held responsible for any injury, loss or damage incurred by use of or reliance on the information or from any error or omission in this book.**
- **Readers should take responsibility for their own health. There can be no guarantees concerning health outcomes.**

ACKNOWLEDGEMENTS

I sincerely thank and deeply appreciate the contribution Elias Schindelar made to this book over the last six years. Without him and his information it would not have been possible. He volunteered numerous hours of his valuable time for which I am truly grateful.

I wish to thank Mr and Mrs Schindelar snr. for their patience and setting up meetings with Elias. I deeply appreciate their support.

With sincere gratitude I greatly acknowledge and appreciate the knowledge and understanding of my editor. Without the countless hours of valuable time he kindly volunteered over the last six years, this book would not have been possible.

There is no doubt in my mind whatsoever that had I not met Elias at that precise moment in time I would not be alive today. I would not have survived my illness without his knowledge, understanding, patience and natural therapy.

There are no adjectives that would adequately express my gratitude to him. Elias gave me the rest of my life to live with quality and he gave me an alternative to healing – natural therapy – a priceless gift.

THANK YOU

I sincerely thank the following people
for their valuable contributions:
John Litchen;
Walter Last;
Kevin Wilton;
Iris Indorato, Hon. Consul of Germany;
Dr. Vera Schribiner;
Lyn McLean; Soy Online Services and
Macquarie University in New South Wales.

Sincere thanks to Neroli Endacott for supporting me in an effort to shed light on the problems of Foetal Alcohol Syndrome. Thanks also to the Foetal Alcohol and Drug Unit; Department of Psychiatry and Behavioural Sciences/University of Washington School of Medicine and the United States Department of Health and Human Services for making Chapter 5 possible.

Thank you to the wonderfully generous folk who gave their stories. Many did so during one of the most vulnerable times of their lives. I sincerely hope others in crisis will draw strength through their honesty, commitment and self-discipline.

I have much to be thankful for and I am truly grateful everything happened the way it did because it is in times of adversity that we learn life's lessons and the dynamics of our strengths.

I greatly acknowledge the divinity of the universal Creator.

INTRODUCTION

A SECOND CHANCE

Struggling in the darkness,
entombed, wasting and polluted.
Afraid and desperate for freedom.

In the recesses of my mind
I tip-toed the corridors,
while life around me continued as usual.

Alone, humbled and tired.
Last breath approaching.
Deceived by life's fickle promise.

Illness unyielding,
I lived as I must.
Disillusioned in the shadows of torment.

With hope and patience,
in pursuit of the evasive "light",
that for many years lay in its shroud.

Life is a mystery.
An array of tests.
Numerous questions, but no answers.

In hope I waited.
Faith rewarded.
Fragments of truth unfolding.

Until now,
they lay hidden.
Locked away in secret crypts.

My being lies in nature,
a gift of my birthright.
To learn, embrace and share.

This is my rebirth.
Time so precious.
Much to accomplish.

On guided wings,
I leave my cocoon.

"

the best time
in our life can be
when we reach the gates
of despair. only if we are strong
and maintain the power to think
for ourselves can we unlock
the chains and stride
ahead to new
beginnings

"

– the author

Chapter 1

TICK TOCK TICK TOCK

whoever would have thought one sick bird could wreak such havoc ...

Peering through the oval window of the aircraft I gazed at a cloudless sky. Over the years, I had made many such journeys in my quest for good health. I wondered if this would be just another waste of time and effort. I looked normal but felt like a caged animal silently screaming for freedom. One can walk away from almost any situation but there is no escape from incurable disease and there is no escaping the mind. It was only in times of meditation that I found myself temporarily free of my deadly illness. No one knew how I felt.

We tend to think if one looks okay, they must be. Illness had thrown my life into disarray and I detested being sick. Until now I had direction. But that was my former life. I was robbed of many aspects including artistic flair. Other than family, art, music and creativity were passions and the core of my being.

As time wore on the severity of the illness engulfed my body. The need to survive and breathe overshadowed all else. I obsessed over wellness and craved oxygen. Sickness is demeaning. In retrospect, I had taken good health for granted because I did not think disease would strike to the extent it could render me useless. Life had been good. Suddenly, in a single breath, the freedom that accompanies good health was gone.

A major change had taken place and I had to adapt to a new way of life. I became creative in finding ways of hiding my ill health from others. With practise, I became good at it and things that had once been important no longer mattered. But hiding the fact I could not breathe properly was difficult because sometimes I gasped. I was viewed with suspicion. I sensed what others were thinking:

Stop smoking lady. But I had never smoked. Pretence was a struggle because it had not been part of my life. Never for one moment did I try to fool myself or my family into thinking I was well. Slowly I became a prisoner in my home and body. But I did everything possible to look like the average person because if someone knows there is a serious problem they usually sympathise. And I loathe sympathy.

Many offered help and prayers which was lovely, while others gave me names and telephone numbers of doctors, specialists and therapists who had helped them. I followed through on every suggestion because it had obviously worked for them. I was desperate and grateful for any help. Being ill was lonely. I grew envious when I spotted a runner or power walker.

Climbing the aircraft steps had been an effort and the perspiration flowed freely. I closed my eyes as my mind wondered back over my life. I had been searching for someone who could help me conquer my illness for quite some time.

The "medical merry-go-round" lasted several years and this was to be my final opportunity because I was growing weaker. Running out of alternatives I sensed the curtain coming down. I had exhausted all avenues. It was March 3, 2003. Winter was rapidly approaching and I had been given six months to live. I felt tired and really ill but remained ever hopeful.

Looking back over my life I remember having pneumonia for three weeks at the age of three. At four, my left leg was bent stiffly at the knee from rheumatic fever.

A religious order ran the local primary school and I began prep. at the age of four. A beautiful young lady taught us to love our Creator and all things good. We listened intently as she recited legendary biblical stories but her portrayal of angels, saints and the Holy Spirit were my favourites.

She was vibrant with a straight back and a brisk walk and she possessed the grace of an angel. She said to adopt an invisible spirit who would guide us through times of adversity. She said the spirit would be with us always and we would never be alone. Little did I realise she was teaching one of the greatest lessons of our lives – that of faith and hope.

I had lived on sugar cane farms all my life. From early childhood I had dark circles under my eyes and an embarrassing grey birthmark the size of a hand in the middle of my back that looked like dirt. I had tried to remove it many times with a huge, hard bristled brush my mother used to scrub the kitchen floor.

Our family was fortunate not to have contracted poliomyelitis in the late 1940s as did many of our contemporaries, but during my teenage years I suffered the usual viruses. At 18, I was injured in a car accident and later suffered horrid migraines.

By 23, I was married and the mother of a beautiful baby. I thought bringing up children would be easy because I only ever looked at life's big picture. I thought all I had to do was to bring them up opposite to my childhood. After all, I had experienced more by the time I was 14 than in all the decades since, although it seemed an eternity at the time.

As a child I had felt old and I did not understand why. It seemed as though the weight of the world was on my shoulders. I learnt much about human nature the hard way but was too young to decipher it. I knew who not to trust and whom to rely on, the difference between a regime and a lifestyle and religion and faith.

My spiritual guardian had sat on my left shoulder and seen me through the toughest years of my life. There were questions that had no answers. Most adults would not even have to think about such matters let alone deal with them. But what I learnt as a child has stood me in good stead throughout my adult years and no matter how tough situations become I will not give in until age catches up with me or the unforeseen occurs.

When our first child was one month old I placed him in his crib after his final feed of the day. As I was getting into bed a tingling sensation ran through my head. My nose and mouth felt numb and soon I lost vision from my left eye. I felt facial movement and fetching a mirror I watched in horror as the left side of my face moved upward. The eye was tightly closed and sitting to the side of my head. The side of my nose was where the corner of my eye used to be and the corner of my mouth met the side of my nose.

Now flattened, my nose spread centimetres across my face with two big holes that were once nostrils. My mouth continued to move until it became a thin line up my face. Frozen with fear, I lost control of my tongue and was unable to speak, but I made glottal sounds.

I vividly recall the overwhelming terror I felt as my facial skin tightened. The situation was insane. I was responsible for a newborn. Being a first time mother in the bush was enough to cope with and I could not understand the unfolding ghastly scenario. If this was another of life's lessons I was learning it the hard way.

Within seconds I had mutated into a hideous looking monster but I still had my mind and clear thinking. Petrified, I panicked over the welfare of our baby. But it was all too much and in utter dismay I hopped into bed and switched off the light.

Unheralded, nature stepped in through the darkness and within seconds another transformation took place. Anxiety, fears, thoughts and memories were erased from my mind. I became but a shell without feeling or emotion.

I felt my spirit leave my chest and hover above the bed in a "space" that was now saturated with brilliant shafts of white light. Detached, thoughtless and uncaring, I observed my twisted-faced self lying motionless below.

Time stood still. In that "place", time had no meaning. I began swirling into a giant black abyss with brilliant blue trails. Suddenly, its spiralling jaws opened and inhaled me into oblivion.

The following morning I woke to the welcoming sounds of our crying baby. I felt as if I had been on the front line of a battle zone. With a fuzzy brain and blurred vision I rushed to a mirror and saw my face had returned to normal and by the end of the day my head felt fine. To this day I will not watch movies if the characters have had their faces altered to look like monsters.

After several months I spoke with a general practitioner. He said I should have sought medical assistance that night because I had suffered a blood clot in the brain and this can happen after child birth. But I had been too afraid to even talk about the incident and brushed it under the carpet. He said I was fortunate because it could have been fatal. I was grateful to be alive and that my face was normal. Since then my appearance has never been an issue. As long as I feel well and body components are correctly positioned, I will be *more* than happy.

Two years later we had another child. When the baby was one, I experienced another blood clot on the same side of my face. But life was busy on the farm so that episode was brushed under the carpet as well.

I contracted the mother of all viruses during the 1970s: the Hong Kong flu. I coughed day and night for six weeks. It weakened my immune system and every year after that I got influenza during winter and coughed for months.

After waking one morning I could not stop fainting and it continued throughout the day. Unable to walk, I crawled. I had Meniere's syndrome. It was so bad and it plagued me for several years. An ear, nose and throat specialist told me to manoeuvre my head into a position that produced a spin and hold still until the dizziness wore off.

I did as he said and that was the end of the major attacks. He said the fluid in my inner ear was not level and by holding my head steady during a dizzy spell, it would correct itself. He said to compare it to the oil in a builder's spirit level. I am very grateful because there are those who do not recover from this syndrome.

One year during the 1980s, I experienced months of coughing with an over-productive lung. Tests were carried out but a diagnosis proved elusive. I slept upright in a chair at night. At one stage, completely exhausted from sleep deprivation, I was admitted to hospital and given a small white tablet at 3pm. Within minutes the cough disappeared. At 9pm I had another tablet and that night I had a beautiful sleep. The following morning the cough was gone. This had to be heaven.

A nurse, who was also an acquaintance, said the drug was "heavy" and the doctor had not made a diagnosis. She added: "If you take another three tablets you will be completely addicted and your life will be hell because the more you take, the more you will crave". I threw them down the toilet and went home. Within hours, the cough returned. The nurse said the cough could be the result of an allergy and pointed me in the direction of an allergist with a good record. After the usual gamut of blood tests, he said my immune system was poor because of viruses and I was to visit his rooms each morning for intravenous vitamin C. He said: "Within two days you will feel so well you will be jumping out of your skin".

After five days I was having trouble walking. Dizzy spells and nausea were ferocious. Each morning as the solution entered my blood stream I blacked out. The allergist contacted the manufacturer who said the base ingredient of the formula was sucrose (processed cane sugar). He said I was allergic to processed cane sugar and to avoid all processed foods. I flew home and did as he suggested. Within days the cough vanished.

Life on the farm was good for a few years but then my joints began to hurt. Severe pain moved to and from different parts of my body and organs. As symptoms worsened, the state of my health was causing major problems. Washed out from lack of sleep, I felt and looked dreadful and dark circles under my eyes looked awful. Medical tests proved futile.

One night before drifting off to sleep I experienced sounds in my brain and put it down to being overtired. Within days the number of sounds multiplied and grew louder. I was terrified because my father had died a vegetable from surgery that had gone horribly wrong after suffering an aneurism in his brain.

I feared for the welfare of our young children and this stress compounded my problems. I was terrified of ending up in a mental institution and loathed brain surgery with a vengeance because after seeing what happened to my father, I thought it was all trial and error.

The sounds evolved into explosions that were so loud they hurt. They were like electric shocks and sleep was nigh impossible. But the brilliant visions they produced were magnificent. Every conceivable colour including rich flushes of gold and silver, disgorged from a chasm which appeared to be high in a mountain and cascaded into luminous waterfalls. Each night I was treated to a magnificent spectacle but it was a shame they hurt my brain so much. One night I experienced 26 and one was so strong it threw me off the bed and on to the floor.

Through fear and exhaustion I visited a doctor the following morning and asked if he had other patients with similar problems. He said he did not. He admitted me to hospital and placed me under heavy sedation for five days. I had no idea what chemicals were in the injections. I was totally smashed and needed a break. But the welfare of our children was foremost on my mind.

The relief was fantastic. I did not ask questions and was grateful for the calm in my brain. I went home with prescription medication. They did an exceptionally good job because my symptoms disappeared. In ignorance, I swallowed them without question.

After a few months life was back to normal. I assumed I could stop the drugs so threw them down the toilet. This was not the smartest thing I ever did. The noises returned with a vengeance and they now banged away in my brain both day and night. I craved the medication. I thought I was sick before going into hospital but those symptoms proved minuscule compared to those that followed.

Going cold turkey was not a good idea. I knew nothing about the side effects of the drugs. I was well and truly addicted and under *their* control. My weakened muscles flinched and sometimes I had trouble standing and walking. Symptoms escalated and all the while I had a family to care for. My kidneys and joints hurt. The medication was only a stop-gap treatment. Doctors did not know what was wrong and it was horrible because I had a drug addiction as well as an undiagnosed brain problem.

I resumed the medication and the urge to increase them was overwhelming. Life was hell and I needed help. I visited a "house" whose owner, I was told, treated clients such as myself. I explained my desperate situation to the practitioner. With laughter like that of a roaring bull, he said: "You addicts are all the same. You get hooked and expect someone to bail you out of your predicament. Well it doesn't work that way". Again I explained my initial problems but it fell on deaf ears. The final words from the person behind the desk were: "Yeah, yeah, yeah, the world is full of people like you". This was another valuable lesson. I got myself into a situation through ignorance and vowed it would never happen again. Doctors treated me the way they were educated: with drugs that had horrendous side effects.

There were few alternatives in those days and research as we know it today was almost non-existent. I placed all my faith in the system because that is the way it was done. I felt isolated because I could not discuss the problem and there was no one I could go to for help.

But I had an idea. With a sharp blade I shaved off a tiny corner of the tablets for two nights. Then on the third night I shaved them twice. I continued doing this until they were reduced to almost nothing. It took eight months to wean myself off the monsters. I now have first hand experience of the pain and suffering endured by drug addicts. Drugs have a grip like the jaws of a crocodile.

I began going on afternoon walks in an effort to regain muscular strength. But the mountains appeared to dance, while sugar cane paddocks floated in the air. Dotted white line markings on the bitumen roads rose and fell. Snakelike they slithered before me while the feeling in my head was that of inebriation.

Brain scans, x-rays and blood tests proved futile. I looked normal and this came against me. The medical profession began to view me with suspicion: were the symptoms real? Was I attention seeking? I sensed the infamous brick wall going up. But I was a private patient, paid my accounts so they tolerated me. Migraine headaches also plagued me and the only relief were pain-killing injections which sedated me for 24 hours.

I flew back to the city to see the allergist who had diagnosed my processed cane sugar allergy about the problems I was having with the sounds in my brain. After several tests, he said I had chemical deposits in the brain from sprays and fertilisers that had been used liberally in the sugar cane industry at that time. The heavy use of chemicals was notorious. He said he had many patients with chemical poisoning and they all lived on farms or within close proximity to agriculture. He said I was very fortunate to be alive and the levels of chemicals in my brain must have been very high to produce such symptoms.

Another crop growing area also practised aerial spraying for pests and as a result, 15 people (mainly children) contracted cancers. Liquid fertilising was also common practice and many native birds and animals died in farming communities because of its potency. Some farmers lost their sight after tiny droplets wafted in the wind and accidentally settled in their eyes.

In my mind's eye, as a very young child, I can still visualise my father spraying a yellow undiluted transparent chemical liberally on the cows, totally unaware of the dangers. The chemicals were used to combat buffalo fly infestation. I can still see the tiny droplets rolling from the hair on the underbelly of the animals and into the bucket as he milked. The substance was DDT, a powerful organochlorine insecticide. It was used extensively during the 1940s and 1950s.

The compound is stable, accumulates in the soil, and concentrates in fatty tissue, reaching dangerous levels in carnivores high in the food chain. Restrictions are now placed on the use of DDT and similar pesticides in this country. But they may be present in imported foods, fruit and vegetables where our restrictions do not apply.

Several incidents of chemical poisoning came to the fore in the 1980s but were rapidly quashed. The allergist said the Australian government would not allow him to have the blood of his patients tested for chemicals. Samples were sent to America and the results took four months.

In the meantime he advised me to visit a clinic in Texas in the United States that had a program for detoxifying Vietnam War veterans suffering the aftermath of Agent Orange poisoning. I decided against it because I was too weak to travel. He gave me the program and I did it on my own. I found it difficult because I had to drive 130km daily to attend a gymnasium that had a sauna.

Even though I felt like a dishcloth, I exercised to generate body heat. This was followed by specifically designed one-hour saunas. After 72 saunas more blood tests were done and there was an improvement, but not enough. Chemical levels were still too high so I had to repeat the program. I was grateful to the allergist because his knowledge had saved my life. But four people in our local area were not so fortunate.

Life was improving to a certain degree. I was drug and allergy free, and my head felt fine. I had spent valuable years of my children's lives trying to get my health on a level plane. By the time I did, both children had left home. This was a dark period but through the many dramas that life handed out, I maintained my love of music and I had studied art for several decades. My love of the arts, music and architecture balanced life.

The empty nest syndrome made its ugly presence felt. With sweaty palms and apprehension I began college to study French cuisine. Passing all exams with honours, becoming qualified was important to me. I needed to know if my learning capacity had been affected by the chemical poisoning. Luckily, it was not.

Eventually we sold the farm and built a house on acreage with a commercial kitchen and I established a catering business. The work was fantastic, I met lovely people and I loved what I did. I created a special line of food. Within a few weeks the planning paid off and I was getting engagements, many of which I had to refuse because I could not keep up with the orders. I revelled in my new life.

One crisp May morning a kookaburra landed on a low bough in our garden and thinking it wanted to be friendly, I went out for a chat. With stooped shoulders it sat motionless but the sounds coming from its lung were like that of a baby's hard plastic rattle. It was difficult to comprehend a living creature could make such a metallic sound. The following day it lay dead about 100m from the tree.

Thirteen days later on May 25, 1996 at 3pm I began to feel unwell. Within one hour my body grew stiff and I had trouble walking. I felt dizzy and a fever began to rage. On the third day I began fainting and went to hospital for five days. Winter had arrived. The area was in the grip of a major flu epidemic and a doctor said I was another victim. My lungs were productive and I coughed day and night. I felt weak from sleep deprivation and there were times when my mouth would fill with blood without warning. The disease was insidious.

I left the hospital with raging fevers. Within six weeks I developed chronic sinusitis, had trouble breathing and was given asthma drugs. But my situation worsened. I had bronchitis and tests revealed I had contracted chlamydia psittaci (bird flu). A lung physician said I had inhaled the disease from the kookaburra in a single breath even though I had stood three metres away from it for only a few seconds. We checked the dates and they coincided. The sick kookaburra also gave me a blood disease.

Weeks later my health deteriorated and I went into hospital with pneumonia and whooping cough. Things did not look too flash and some of the coughing bouts were nasty. Whilst on his morning rounds I asked the doctor if I was going to die, he said: "If you believe in a higher order you had better start praying". I knew I was in trouble from the onset of this ghastly disease therefore his comment was not surprising.

After a week, I went home and began tracking down people who had contracted the dreaded bird flu and found one had recovered completely after a few weeks. Another lady said she recovered but was having difficulty breathing and was given asthma medication. The third had to have a lung removed and was left with asthma-like symptoms. The fourth had died.

Matters were not in my favour. I had been sick for 42 weeks and my immune system was smashed.

I visited a lung specialist in another city. After several tests he said the bird flu virus and the accompanying blood disease were still present in my system. He said people contracted the disease if they came within four metres of an infected bird. There was nothing anyone could do to help and I would have to learn to live with it.

I lost my catering business and in the years that followed chronic sinusitis almost drove me to distraction. I worked on my health, ate what was considered to be healthy and exercised. It paid off. My health began to improve and I thought there must be something I could do that did not cause stress and did not have deadlines to meet because catering was out of the question.

After much research I created a range of all-natural and chemical-free skin care products and a line of specialty soaps. Once again life was good. I met new and beautiful people who embraced the new products. They were just as enthusiastic as I because they no longer had to pay enormous prices and they no longer had concerns about chemicals on their skin.

One day during August 2001, I woke with a dreadful headache which progressively worsened during the course of the morning. My head hurt so much I had difficulty holding it up. Hurriedly, I packed a bag and called an ambulance and went into hospital with a suspected brain haemorrhage.

Drugs were offered but I refused them because I needed to know what the problem was. Blood tests revealed I had three strains of mosquito-borne diseases – two of Ross River Fever and one of Barmah Forest. I left the hospital but the symptoms continued. Days turned into weeks, headaches were violent, fevers aplenty and I had trouble breathing.

My symptoms escalated. I ballooned from excess fluid. I was so huge I had difficulty rolling over in bed. Internal heat and nausea were crazy. What felt like crawling spiders under my skin began in my heels and slowly crept up my back and to the back of my head. My skin was sore and it felt tight to the point where I thought it would split, but it was normal to touch. Perspiration lingered for hours and my head constantly thumped from high blood pressure. My breathing capacity progressively worsened.

My blood was tested regularly. Symptoms of chlamydia psittaci reared their ugly head and I knew I was in trouble. One test revealed hepatitis. Drug-induced lupus showed up in another and rheumatoid arthritis in another.

Diseases began to read like a shopping list. This came as no surprise because by now my joints were sore and swollen and I had to shuffle when I woke in the morning. The heat and profuse sweating continued. I had trouble breathing and craved oxygen.

My skin care business was at a standstill and doctors were baffled. Two areas in my lungs were very sore. I got to a point where I had to lie down after having a shower to recover from what was fast becoming an ordeal.

I arrived at the gates of despair in March 2002. They opened to one brick wall beyond another. Without a doubt my situation was fast becoming grave. Good days were few and far between and I was afraid because without breath there cannot be life.

Luckily both children were living away. I did not want them to see me looking like a swollen toad and I thanked the Creator the disease was mine alone. With hope I prayed, begged and pleaded with my spiritual guardian to send a glimmer of light. But there were no answers and weeks turned into months.

I coughed up copious amounts of gunk because by now I had emphysema and bronchiectasis. I constantly researched and through the health department discovered a professor of medicine in another city who specialised in tropical diseases.

On September 11, 2002 after three months of continuous testing, he told me I had contracted another type of bird flu virus and its bacteria had invaded both lungs. The name of the bacteria was pseudomonas aeruginosa. It multiplied at the rate of millions per day and appeared like minute, transparent fibres.

The bad news: it protects itself with a yellow bio-film that no drug can penetrate, therefore the disease was incurable. He said my condition would worsen as the invasion continued.

I asked him what time I had left. He said I was as good as the next bout of flu or six months at the most. He insisted I go home and get my things in order and organise a wheelchair and oxygen tank. He said I may have contracted the virus from an airport.

But another medical professional said this virus may have been the result of an injection I had had in March that same year and another I was given the previous year that was supposed to give protection from influenza during winter months.

Seated across his desk there was nothing I could do but silently retaliate against what the universe had divvied out. But the professor was such a lovely man and I felt sure he understood what I was thinking. He picked up his gold pen and lowering his head he continued his report, thus allowing me time to adjust to my supposed fate. This was so unexpected. I was into solving problems. Damn it, six months – that was unbelievable!

Gathering my wits, I told him I was not at all interested in dying. I wanted to overcome my illness and simply get on with my life. I felt I was too young to die and there were things I needed to do. I had been ill for long enough. I made mention of a theory I had read about – urine therapy – and asked his opinion. He threw up his hands and with laughter from deep within his belly, said: "Urine therapy? My God, I'd sooner die!"

"That's okay for you. It's not your head on the chopping block. Don't forget people get drunk on something similar every night of the week. And this is not going to cost anything," I replied as he chuckled. We discussed other remedies and I said I would begin urine therapy while I continued my search for freedom. He warned me about certain herbs and said some could cause death. He wished me well and added: "If it can be done, it will be you who will do it".

The drive back to my home town was lengthy and as I knocked over the kilometres I felt I was on another planet. The words "six months" reverberated through the corridors of my mind. Could this really be happening to me? I could not imagine death because I was obsessed by finding someone who could help me overcome my illness.

I wanted to do things, create, and listen to beautiful and timeless classical music. I wanted to live and witness my family evolve. The human body was born to live, it is resilient and will do all it can to stay alive. I had overcome other adversities in the past and I was determined to conquer this sod.

With that thought firmly embedded in my brain, I began my newly found therapy. Yuk – it was not easy (no wonder is costs nothing). But I was desperate to live and prepared to try almost anything.

From the very first half cup I managed to swallow the feeling was euphoric. Within four days the improvement was miraculous. Within a month I was scrubbing walls and my business was in full swing once again. How about that – six months indeed!

Again I began the rounds of doctors, specialists, therapists of all descriptions, naturopaths, herbalists and faith healers. I even had hot spoon therapy. One person I went to for help wanted to put me in a bath tub and cover me with ice cubes for seven hours. He said pseudomonas aeruginosa did not like the cold and required a warm environment in order to survive. He also said if I felt cold, I could use a blanket. Thank you very much ...

Until now I had tried every suggestion that came my way but this sounded bizarre so I declined the $800 ice experience because I thought hypothermia would probably kill me. Then I decided to try magnetic therapy because I had read favourable reports on the subject. I felt light headed after the first treatment and thinking it was normal, I continued. But after each session the dizzy turns increased to the point where I was fainting so I discontinued the treatment.

After three-and-a-half months of urine therapy my health improved. Then in late December we visited an animal park. After a relaxing lunch we waited until 3pm: crock feeding time. Feeling tired I sat on a log. "Come on, croc time", came the call. I tried to stand but was unable and I felt something hit my lung like a blow from a sledgehammer. I could not breathe and the intensity of the previous symptoms felt as if they had doubled. Things were not going to plan.

Sometime later a lady called to purchase some natural skin care products and Frenchmilled soaps. During our conversation she said she had been in dire straits with her health and could not find anyone to help her.

After much searching she said she found Elias Ludwig Schindelar in Malanda on the Atherton Tablelands. He was doing brilliant work with natural therapy and suggested I give him a call. She had been visiting with him for five months and was on the road to recovery.

I telephoned Mr Schindelar the moment my visitor left and

spoke with him personally. I told him how I felt and explained my symptoms. I said I had been ill for a number of years and that a short shelf life had been predicted.

He said: "I know what is wrong with you. You have viruses. You must fix this. You can kill these viruses but you must come and see me immediately".

The screeching wheels of the aircraft kissed the runway. Descending the steps, I gasped for breath. This was tropical Cairns in March: picturesque, green and steaming. Nothing mattered. I was bursting with hope. Was this the spiritual light I had so often prayed for? In eager anticipation I embarked on one of the most incredible chapters of my life. Thank you universe ...

"

the nerves are the life
and the death of the body

"

– elias ludwig schindelar

Chapter 2

ELIAS LUDWIG SCHINDELAR – MEDICAL MASSEUR

"

when you know
what you are talking about,
you can speak freely

"

– elias ludwig schindelar

Elias was born in Sindelfingen, Germany in 1965 and from early childhood aspired to become a medical practitioner. He read prolifically. At the age of 12, a book on the powers of natural healing affected him profoundly. It became his introduction to natural therapy.

He graduated from high school at the age of 17 but needed a special dispensation from the German government because he was considered too young to enter university. His wish was granted. On the first day of medical college he and his fellow students were given a tough assignment because they had to prove themselves. Their professor insisted they learn the name of the 1,024 muscles of the human body and every bone within the skeletal system with 100 per cent accuracy.

The exam was set for the following week and it did not have

multiple choice answers. They were told: "If you have one incorrect answer your request for entry into this academy will be denied".

He studied hard, passed the exam and needless to say was one of a few who earned his entry to Stuttgart University, and later Stockach on Bodance. He said he was pleased they had to learn the muscles and bones in a week because it cut out a lot of learning time later. He also said he shared his studies with those who genuinely wanted to be there.

The structure of his studies was in the form of a pyramid which was built on four levels. A sound base of mathematics was essential. The second level was physics followed by chemistry, then anatomical science. He said without mathematics it was impossible to understand chemistry and physics. To understand anatomical science one must understand the mechanisms of mathematics, physics and chemistry. But in order to understand the functions of the body, it is imperative to connect all four subjects.

In the third week of his studies he made an important discovery: prescription drugs do not heal the body, they create other problems and compound those that exist. And it is for this reason he graduated with government accreditation as a Medical Masseur, Homoepath and a Medical Bath Master. Even though he also has government accreditation to administer drugs, he chooses not to. Elias is also qualified to withdraw blood, test it and then read the results.

He worked in, and ran hospitals, managed a sanitarium and taught anatomy and nerve system functions at university level. Those who funded the university discovered he did not endorse the use of drugs. To the contrary, he was a strong advocate of all things natural. Through his studies he had learnt that with natural food and natural therapy the body could heal itself.

One day he was approached by his dear friend who was the university director. It was a sad day for both of them because the director was instructed to terminate Elias's contract because he did not endorse the use of drugs.

He was offered a huge salary from the government to run a mental institution in Germany but declined the position because he firmly believes that with natural therapy, and pure and natural foods, people who suffer mental problems can heal themselves. He believes people deserve the right to heal naturally. He added: "I believe in freedom – not restraint".

He set up private practice and his reputation as a highly successful natural therapist spread rapidly to the extent that he was treating up to 250 clients a day. He worked from 5am until 11pm. The waiting list was enormous and appointments were booked six months in advance and he would only see those with difficult and life threatening problems. But if someone looked really ill, he would not turn them away. He said he could not say: "Come back in six months because for some it would be too late".

After many hectic years in private practice he decided to lighten his load. He felt he needed a quieter lifestyle and fewer clients. He left Germany and eventually settled in Australia.

The area he chose was Malanda in northern Queensland because it is not too close to an airport or city. The air is crisp and clean, the weather mild, and it is close to the ocean and outback. Then after five years he proudly became an Australian citizen.

Elias said the basis of his work was correcting messages to and from the brain via the nerve system. But he has never been "popular" with the established institutions because he did not operate or prescribe drugs. He said: "There is no need to operate on most problems. For example, (with) curvature of the spine, I gently remedy the problem by working with the nerve system without causing damage. The client does not suffer pain, they do not miss work and the result is usually very successful."

He continued: "It is very easy to help the body cure itself of problems, diseases and viruses, but it is much better to prevent them". He added: "Disease prevention plays a major role in natural therapy because we are what we think and the state of the body is a reflection of the foods we eat and our lifestyle".

The course that Elias studied was deleted from the medical curriculum in Germany about 1990. He said Medical Massage as he learnt it was lost forever. No courses are available in any curriculum that he is aware of that offer natural healing through nerve massage the way he does it.

Working with the nerve system is his favoured method. He maintains the nerve system is: "The core of our being and the life and death of the body". He said: "Teachers should train new medical students to focus heavily on the nerve system because many nerves are severed during surgery and this should never happen".

During the time it has taken to write this book, I have met those who cannot comprehend or believe that any one person can fully understand and treat every part of the body from the top of the head to the soles of the feet as Elias does. But the manner in which he studied enables him to do just that. His unique style of natural therapy connects the brain and body through the nerve system and together with natural foods, most clients can enjoy a total recovery if they choose.

Accident trauma is his favourite work but forensic science is his passion and he intends to make it a lifelong study because it plays an important role in his work. He said it was imperative to know how accidents, illness and diseases affected the body after death. Without such knowledge it is impossible to achieve 100 per cent accuracy when administering natural therapy.

For example: if a client suffers brain damage from a motor vehicle which has overturned several times, he must determine with 100 per cent accuracy the number of times it has rolled. And he has the ability to do this through his knowledge of physics and forensic science and his understanding of the nerve system.

He must define every detail of the accident and modify the therapy, enabling the client to make a full recovery. He added: "I must be able to work out precisely what happened during an accident in order to help the client's body to heal itself through natural therapy. They are unable to tell me because they were unconscious at the time".

His philosophy is: "I do not heal people. No person has the ability to heal another, although there are those who think they can. But they are wrong and it is probably their ego working overtime". He went on to say: "The way I work is not a secret. Anyone can do what I am doing if they study the way I did. Knowing what I do about mathematics, physics, chemistry, anatomical and forensic science, it is impossible for me to work in any other style".

His work is not only three-dimensional, because he brings in a fourth – that of time. This is the length of time he can work on a particular area. Some treatments may take up to 30 minutes while others 30 seconds. It depends on the illness or problem and how much the body can tolerate at that particular time. It may be dangerous to overwork a specific area.

He said many have tried to find out how he worked and they became cranky when they realised this technique was not one that could be taught in a few minutes. For example, if someone has dislodged a vertebrae, and even if it is out by only one millimetre, he does not have the physical strength to push it back into position. Instead, he corrects the nerve messages which radiate to and from the brain within the muscles adjacent to the injury for a specific length of time and applies a specific amount of pressure. Only then can the vertebrae be positioned correctly. He said there were no secrets – the answers lie with physics. His style of Medical Massage deals only with correction and absolute accuracy.

The treatment of each client is different because every person has a unique problem. He mainly works on the back where there is less fat, the nerve system is shallow and it radiates from the spinal cord. He seldom works to the front of the body because there, nerves are much deeper. They are situated on an angle and below the ribs.

He does not advertise. He said: "The majority of my clients have heard about me from someone else. Most of those who visit have discovered drugs will not heal them, nor will they save their lives. When someone is really ill they will always find the money for a plane ticket". He added: "When people are really sick they search the world for help. If I show one person how to heal themselves without drugs, they tell others". Many of his clients travel half way around the globe for his unique therapy and do so regularly until they heal. But they are clients with self-discipline.

Elias usually does not work with those who have had radium or chemotherapy but on the odd occasion he has broken his own rule. He said this form of therapy may have a damaging effect on the nerves, blood and vital organs and there was nothing he could do to correct it. It also damages the skin on his hands within minutes of working on a client who has had this type of therapy.

If a client has a difficult disease or problem, he will only work with them when he is absolutely certain they are extremely self-disciplined, honest and totally prepared to work with him.

He said there could be problems because 95 per cent of his clients visited him in a "state" when all other medical treatment has failed. Sometimes it may even be too late for their body to heal itself. He has helped thousands of people to overcome life-threatening illness and they think he is marvellous.

But there are also times when clients visit Elias with diseases and irreparable damage from prior drugs, procedures or other therapies. And even though he is up front and honest, and tells clients the truth, his honesty and his will to help have sometimes worked against him. Sometimes after a client dies, Elias has to deal with families in a state of high emotion. Most are saddened and accept their loss with some form of dignity and gratitude. They may feel that by taking their loved one to Elias, they left no stone unturned and that they did all they could to prolong life.

But after the death of a loved one, some people can change therefore, nothing remains the same. Some have gone out of their way in an effort to blacken Elias's name. They have tried to make his life, and the lives of his family, hell on earth. There are those who have gossip mongered, spread horrid and unfounded lies, while others have harassed and stalked him for months after the event. This is how some people deal with grief.

Some may not accept the fact it was all too late to begin with. But they went to him with hope, when all else had failed, and because he has a fantastic track record of helping those who help themselves.

Alas, the tall poppy syndrome is alive and well in this country because where there is success, there may also lurk jealously, hate and deceit. And it is Elias's success that has attracted those who have sought to destroy him. There are those who have invested much of their time and effort trying to invent ways to bring him down.

But Elias is more than familiar and capable of dealing with this side of human nature because it is part of his work. It is also a part of the character of the individual who chooses to live their life in this manner. This character flaw can manifest as an addiction which may also pave the way for future dis-ease. But those of strong character already know that what does not kill only serves to make them stronger and more dedicated.

Elias has had to adjust to the Australian way of thinking. In Europe, the level of discipline was much higher than it is in this country. Most Europeans exercise self-discipline with regards to self-healing. They cannot afford to be sick for too long because if they lose their job there are usually six highly qualified people to take their place. Therefore they do all they can to heal quickly.

In Europe, 97 per cent of his clients healed themselves totally. He treated all problems including leukaemia, bipolar, all viruses and cancers, Parkinson's and Alzheimer's diseases and infertility etc., and many other diseases he regards as difficult. But in America and Australia the figure drops abysmally, people are not healing diseases he considers simple. This is the reason he no longer accepts everyone who walks through his door. He said it is not possible to take on the client's responsibilities because the ultimate in the healing process begins and ends with the client.

There are those who visit two or three times and if they feel better that is good enough for them. They do not concentrate on a complete recovery because they are either impatient or it is not important enough. Elias said he has had many clients who had visited him for a year or two and if they had not fully recovered, they complained. They do not realise the body takes years to heal itself. But they are quite content to visit medical practitioners for years with the same problem, for example diabetes, and take drugs without complaint.

It seems when some people begin natural therapy their expectations alter. They become impatient and expect to heal overnight. Many do not continue and claim natural healing does not work. The problem arises when they discover that in order to heal they must do the bulk of the work. Elias sets his clients on the right path but he can only do about 3 per cent. The remaining 97 per cent is up to the client.

Many find this difficult to comprehend because they have become accustomed to thinking prescription drugs will do all the healing for them. Drug taking is part of the Australian way of life – a culture.

And this is easy because people do not have to think for themselves and they do not have to change their lifestyle. But results are not in their favour. There are those who have healed and live their lives stress free by following the laws of nature. In cases such as these, they no longer need to visit Elias unless problems arise.

There is nothing supernatural or magical about the way he works because it is the culmination of a lifetime of intensive study, personal sacrifice, discipline, dedication and focus. Those who understand the theories of natural therapy and have followed Elias's history and the way he works, know his reputation is impeccable. He works in conjunction with nature and has had tremendous success. He works alone and enjoys total freedom.

Even though he is a brilliant academic, he is very much in touch with the average person. His door is always open to those who are in need, provided they are prepared to work with him. There have been times when he has seen those in need any time of the day or night regardless of what day it is. Prior to one particular Christmas season I asked Elias if he was going to take some time off for a holiday or maybe relax. He replied: "That would be very nice, but if I get a new client with a serious illness, I will have to stay home and treat them because sometimes immediate treatments are imperative if they are very ill because their time may be running out". He always makes himself available if necessary and always says: "No problem". He is a servant of the ill. Elias is very giving. I consider myself extremely fortunate to have a natural therapist of his calibre living in this country. There are thousands of people who have to trek half way around the globe to visit him.

Together with nature, the body and mind is the essence of healing and the spirit in which Elias Ludwig Schindelar works.

Chapter 3

THE HIGHS AND LOWS OF NATURAL HEALING

The following chapter contains extracts from a daily journal I kept to record my progress after my first treatment with Elias. I was so certain he was going to help me heal that I felt a strong need to track daily events and the way I felt. My intuition was fuelled by the conviction in Elias's voice when he spoke about natural healing.

After my first visit to the Elias Schindelar natural therapy clinic, there was no doubt in my mind I was going to overcome my illness. I promised myself I would do whatever I had to in order to survive and be healthy.

At that stage death was near. My lungs were my biggest enemy. I had difficulty walking and speaking and most times I could not finish a sentence for lack of oxygen. Both lungs ached from the pseudomonas aeruginosa bacteria, a legacy of a second bird flu virus which also left me with a blood disease.

I had bronchiectasis, emphysema and chronic sinus compliments of this bacteria. I was battling two strains of Ross River Fever virus and Bahama Forest virus, drug induced lupus and hepatitis. My blood pressure was high but I refused medication. I was overweight from inactivity and fluid retention because my kidneys were not functioning correctly.

Fluctuation of heat caused by the viruses followed by profuse sweating was the order of my days. When it was heavy I wrapped myself in towels. I felt uneasy and washed out from sleep deprivation and sweating. I only slept between the hours of 6am and 7am when at the point of exhaustion.

My hair had been falling out for 15 months and my fingernails were growing paper thin. I had been really ill since 2001 but it all began in 1996 with the first bird flu virus, chlamydia psittaci from a sick kookaburra.

If I were a horse I would have been taken up a dry gully and shot.

04/03/03: Monday 10.30am (my mother's birthday) – my first visit to the Schindelar natural therapy clinic. Lying on a massage table I relaxed to Chopin. As Elias entered the room he said: "Hello". I felt extremely embarrassed and asked him to excuse my excess weight and explained the dark area on my back was not dirt, but a birthmark.

He began massaging my back. I felt anxious and thought it was unusual to begin working on me when I had not explained my problems. "Excuse me Mr Schindelar, I need to discuss my problems with you". "One moment please. I need to see what your problems are", he replied as he continued working. I stopped talking.

He stopped working and began by saying the dark area on my back was not a birthmark but the result of liver damage from childhood diseases (I vividly remember having pneumonia at age three and rheumatic fever at four). He said it would disappear with time as the body healed.

I would also lose the excess fluid and my body would take care of the unwanted weight as I recovered. He said in order to heal I must eat natural food, practice discipline, have a strong mind and I must not take drugs or supplements. No drugs or supplements? Fantastic!

He said I must eat fruit only and have three lemons in three litres of water daily. He said all fruit was good. The list included pumpkin, choko, eggplant, all squash, marrow, avocado, cucumber, capsicum, tomatoes along with three birdseye chilli a day. Chilli thins and purifies the blood, cleans the arteries, lowers cholesterol, lessening the risk of heart attack and stroke. I am to eat five dates three times a day after meals and at bedtime. No cooking? This is going to be a romp in the park!

He said anything that contained a seed (excluding legumes, sprouts and grains) was a fruit and to eat lots of grapes because they contained natural insulin.

He answered all my questions simplistically and spontaneously and I felt I was in the hands of a person who was in total control and knew exactly what he was talking about. He spoke with such conviction. He worked on my back the entire time and said he felt the effects illness had on my body by massaging the nerve system. I did not have to explain my illness or the way I felt.

I said I had tried every type of drug and therapy that was offered by all types of practitioners and therapists. I explained I had been very ill for a number of years and had forgotten what it felt like to be well. So desperate was my need to recover, I even tried urine therapy and magnetic therapy. He said: "I am not surprised because when people are desperate to live they will do all they can do to survive".

I told Elias I was losing a lot of hair. He said: "When the body is sick it will shed everything is does not need. A tree loses its leaves in times of drought and the body works on the same principle. With time, as you get better your hair will grow back".

I asked if it was possible to regain good health by eating fruit with water and without nerve massages. He replied: "Of course, but it depends how sick the person is and it depends if time is on their side. Many have healed themselves naturally, as long as they possess discipline and are honest with themselves and eat natural food. But nerve massage helps the body to heal much quicker".

He added: "Some people are close to death when they come to me and are running out of time and they must improve quickly in order to survive. In cases such as this, nerve massage is imperative". This was very reassuring, exciting and words cannot explain my relief. I was actually going to get better. Fantastic!

Even though Elias is brilliant in his field, he simplified answers to my questions in a manner in which I had no difficulty understanding.

He said I was to come back and see him on Wednesday. I wanted to get better quickly so I asked if I could come back the following day. He said: "No, you must not. You must stay at home". When I asked why, he said: "Tomorrow, you will know". His spoke reassuringly. An inner voice said: "Do not doubt. Do exactly as he says".

Driving away from the clinic I thought of the many culinary courses I did over the years. I thought of the countless hours I spent studying in order to achieve the highest marks possible for exams because it was important at the time. Now it seems, in order to heal and be healthy, I will have to throw everything I ever learnt about food nutrients out the window and begin learning again.

I thought giving away the food I had eaten all my life that prevented good health was not going to be an issue. There are *no* alternatives. It was either find a cure or die – simple! I had a very short shelf life and was not in a position to negotiate with death.

05/03/03: Fruit diet well under way; severe pains in the stomach to the extent where I had difficulty standing; spent most of the day in the toilet and smelling like rotting hyenas on the savannah; no wonder Elias told me to stay home!

06/03/03: Elias said nerve massage altered the normal functions of viruses. By massaging the nerves, he corrects messages to and from the brain in order to stimulate the immune system to function efficiently.

I asked if I should visit the next day but once again he advised me to stay at home. Cannot wait!

07/03/03: Another day in the toilet; much pain; no wonder Elias said to stay home; too sick to eat or drink.

08/03/03: The sweats are not as vicious; just want bananas; dizzy and nauseous; need sleep; stomach bloated. Today's massage was very deep, hard and it hurt.

09/03/03: This is not so flash; nausea; much bowel activity; need sleep; all over the shop mentally and physically; this illness is terrible: feel as though I am in a tumble dryer. I remember a quote: "We must get worse before we can get better". This is not an issue, it is something I must and will go through. And it is just the beginning. I wondered how long it was going to take.

10/03/03: Diarrohea aplenty; heaven help those around me. I told Elias how I was feeling so he concentrated on my colon. He said the toxic chemicals in my liver were making me ill. He is doing all he can to help. This is good. I have no doubts whatsoever.

11/03/03: Very little sleep last night but a good day.

12/03/03: Elias worked on my kidneys and said the swelling in my hands would vanish with time. I asked about products made from the leaves of certain trees. He said leaves may contain sulphur which was necessary for the tree to function normally. But it builds up in the human system and may become detrimental to health.

I am to revisit in three months and to phone if I have problems.

13/03/03: I am so relieved to have found someone who can help me. A great weight has been lifted off my shoulders because I do not have to think about death and just concentrate on getting better. Thank you universe!

14/03/03: Not a good day; blood pressure fluctuating; phoned Elias; he said I was safe between 100/65 and 160/110 when relaxed and in a horizontal position. He explained that different viruses lived in different parts of the body and one was in the centre of my brain. This is the area that governs blood pressure.

I was to drink more water and eat lots of dates. He said after treatments I would have good and bad days and this would continue for at least six weeks after therapy. The viruses would then begin to die and I should improve.

16/03/03: Chaotic last night; two nightmares going on at the same time; heat from the viruses is hard to deal with; sweats are long and cold; incredible hunger; terrible pain in my right hip; have difficulty walking – feel like a chook on polished lino, but all I need do is to remain upright.

17/03/03: No sleep last night; hip pain severe; knee is very sore; blood pressure unstable; heart revving; skin is sore; profuse sweating; diarrohea; phoned Elias; he said to soak a towel in a mixture of one litre of water and 100ml of vinegar and place it on swollen areas. I am to eat watermelon and pears only for three days. He said the pain was coming from another virus in the kidneys.

21/03/03: Body is going absolutely berserk; toxins on the move. Excellent!

22/03/03: Very good day; introducing more fruits into my diet since the three days of watermelon and pears; few heat turns; the four large red lumps on my right shin disappeared by nightfall.

24/03/03: Began natural therapy at 65kg; losing weight; do not stray too far from a toilet; arthritic pain in my right knee is improving; viruses are on the war path.

26/03/03: Slept in until 8am; tremendous; the body is working hard and must adjust; far cry from the one hour sleep I was getting before I started natural therapy; a good day. Thank you Elias.

27/03/03: Blacked out at 2pm from low blood pressure; maybe I am doing too much, too soon; no heat turns; a few minor sweats but my skin is crawling from viruses.

28/03/03: Beautiful sleep; this is so good; feel as though I have won the lottery; cannot wait to get over this terrible illness and do as I want.

30/03/03: Worked the markets after a good night; low blood pressure.

31/03/03: Spoke with Elias about my low blood pressure. He said the problem was coming from my kidneys and advised me to have a hot bath daily for three days with 1.5kg of sea salt added to the water. I did this just before bedtime. It was a good idea because my heart was racing. Felt washed out; have pressure in my head.

01/04/03: Had a disturbed night due to the salt bath causing the kidneys to eliminate toxins faster; not well; nervous all day so skipped the salt bath; sore shoulder; kidneys working hard.

03/04/03: Had two minor explosive sounds in my brain, reminiscent of the 1980s; chemicals may be moving in my brain.

05/04/03: Disturbed night; heart racing; felt the blood rushing through my body; 58kg; weight loss is slow; excellent.

06/04/03: Another bad night; blood circulation crazy.

09/04/03: Laboured breath all day. Elias said I must have a lot of patience; I have difficulty coping with my breathing. My universe darkens when I have such problems. I get so tired on the days when I am short of oxygen.

The shorter the breath, the greater the battle. So difficult to be positive because there is no one close by with whom I can discuss my problems. No one understands how I feel.

I do not want to phone Elias with every little problem because I do not want to be a nuisance. I had a visit from two women today. One was an academic in the fields of medicine and psychology. They asked about my therapy.

The academic said my restricted breathing was coming from my mind. She added: "The more you think about it, the more you will not be able to breathe. It is all in your mind. I do not know how you can remain on such a strict diet. The discipline you possess must be so great".

She added: "Fruit does not contain protein which is vital to muscle maintenance and if you continue eating only fruit, your heart will eventually fall out of its cavity because the muscles would not hold it up". Thank you very much for sharing your knowledge and support!

The other was a sceptic. She said: "You have given this therapy enough time to work (one month). You are losing so much weight and it is not working. You should start eating properly. You have no guarantees it is going to work". The weight loss she referred to was unwanted excess fluid.

I explained that Elias was the only person who offered any hope of recovery and I was going to continue doing exactly as he said. They did not understand or believe the grim alternative and they do not understand the properties of fruit. I explained that fruit contained protein, but they did not want to know. They have no concept of natural therapy.

I must make changes to the way I think. I must be careful of what I say and to whom I confide in. Elias's natural healing does not include drugs or supplements and I felt I left myself wide open to criticism and ridicule.

My family advised me not to entertain the opinions of others who were not in the same situation. They told me to continue doing exactly what Elias said because he was the only person who had explained the illness and the cure.

I spoke with a lady in another city who was also visiting him. She said the arguments against natural therapy would be great because it was new to many. She said not to listen to anyone because they would always try to talk me out of what I was doing through their fears and ignorance. She advised me to remain focused and said natural therapy was not a quick fix. A lot of hard work and discipline is essential.

I felt much better because my friend is experiencing excellent results. I have now refocused, feel doubtless and clear minded. My friend said the road to good health would be long and bumpy because I had been sick for so long.

10/04/03: Slept well; my ankle is very sore so I went for a walk hoping to bash a bit of sense into it; high steps are making life difficult; my lungs are giving me curry. They can please themselves what they do because now I am focused.

11/04/03: Symptoms continue; had a salt bath hoping it might help. This is a difficult time because I am craving food and would love a crumbed steak sandwich with butter and black sauce; cooking smells in the vicinity are not helping; sense of smell is so keen I can identify what people are cooking miles away; I will not give in; slight improvement in my health.

12/04/03: Horrible ankle pain; have had this problem before; sends the leg into spasm.

13/04/03: Worked at the markets; ankle pain improved; will mention this to Elias next time I see him although I do not think he will be able to help. I have spent a lot of money on this pain but have not found anyone who could tell me what the problem is, let alone fix it.

The pain descends without warning and within a few minutes it is so bad I cannot put my foot to the floor. It remains for four days and disappears as quickly as it comes. It is so crazy, like a tidal wave, it hits with total devastation, renders me useless, then all is back to normal within a few days. I am not too concerned about it. My foot is the least of my problems.

15/04/03: The six weeks are up; viruses should start dying; I wonder if I am going to see any big improvement in my health; heat turns; sweats; skin is sore; ankle better.

I really need to get back to manufacturing my products because stocks are low.

16/04/03: Food cravings; I dream of bacon, eggs and toast.

17/04/03: Sinus really bad; phoned Elias; he said not to worry because it would clear with time; I wondered how long; hands are big with fluid; having huge working days; achieving heaps; start work at 5.30am; this is fantastic.

18/04/03: Heavy sinus; dry cough; chest tight; not much work done today; crave other foods, especially steak; I wonder if viruses get hungry; have lumps on right arm; glands must be draining; very sore.

22/04/03: Sinus wicked; must be patient as everything to do with the body takes time. Every problem I have seems to take forever to correct itself. I have always looked after myself, have never drank or smoked and I cannot believe I am in such poor condition. I can only but wonder what would have happened had I abused myself. And I wonder if I will ever be well and feel like an average person.

Must push such negative thoughts aside. I have forgotten what it feels like to be well and I still feel like a caged animal. But there is a person inside: the real me, trying to break out and be disease free. One must experience extreme ill health to fully understand the feelings of others who are sick.

It is 5am and would love a thick steak sandwich. The smell of brewed coffee and toast wafts through my windows. Food cravings are strong. Hope I have the strength to continue eating natural foods. My hands are big and I am coughing up continuously.

There is a strange trembling sensation in my chest. It feels as though I have had a shock. I do not know what is causing it. This is new. I feel so tired. My kidneys are struggling. It seems as though I have new problems every day. When will it end? Heaven help me!

I went to the library and felt so sick I had to sit on the floor so as not to faint. It is so different when I leave the security of my four walls. I do this occasionally to see if I can handle it and to gauge just how sick I really am. It was a shock because today's results prove I am not so flash. I can usually work at the markets because I sit in a very small and enclosed area. I have the need for walls to be close. I keep busy. Making products is proving a fantastic distraction. I must remain focused and concentrate on becoming well.

24/04/03: I am surviving on faith and discovering the truth about natural healing. It is slow because I have so many health problems. It is not easy to cook conventional meals for others; the aromas of searing beef almost bring me to my knees. I discovered I am mentally weak where food is concerned. Could it be simple greed?

I think of children who live in situations where they are victims and surrounded by squalor and without food. Some have to care for themselves. I, on the other hand, am surrounded by an abundance of gorgeous fruit. Wake up woman!

I must concentrate only on healing and I must be more appreciative of what I already have and what I have achieved so far. And I have a fantastic natural therapist who is looking after my health and guiding me every step of the way. What more could I ask for?

I need to make some serious mind adjustments because if I do not change my way of thinking, I will not survive. I must take control of my mind. There is a battle to be won and I am going to lose it if I continue thinking in this vein. My negative thoughts have created a serious problem. No one can do this for me. It is my fight and I must strengthen mentally.

25/04/03: I did some serious thinking last night; I have taken control of my mind and I will not allow negative thoughts to control me; in future I will tell my brain what to do; it will not control me.

In hindsight it is difficult to believe I allowed negative thoughts to do so much damage. I have wasted precious healing time through negativity. Even though food aromas are a force to be reckoned with, in future my force will be greater. I have started packing my products for the Cairns Expo.

01/05/03: Visiting Elias; told him about the sensation in my chest; he said a vertebra was out and he manoeuvred it into position; took him one second: I think I lifted a heavy box; diarrhoea has set in again because Elias is working on the kidneys and colon; not well at all.

03/05/03: Another massage; Elias said lemons were excellent for mouth ulcers; they balance stomach acid and clean teeth.

We discussed the difficulties of purchasing books on the healing properties of fruit. I told Elias I was having difficulty sleeping and he said to have more dates before bedtime because they helped settle the brain. I asked why supposedly healthy people suddenly become allergic to fruit and vegetables. He said it could be because they ate dairy products as well as meat and eggs and this disturbed the normal functions of the liver. This allergy reveals itself by its effects on the skin.

04/05/03: Massages are very deep and they hurt; as I listen to Elias speak it gives me confidence. What he has to say about nature is a breath of fresh air. I am so lucky to have met him and have his support.

05/05/03: During my massage, I asked Elias about the pain in my right ankle. He said there was a tiny bone out of place and pressing on a vein. He manoeuvred it back into position in a second. I have suffered with this problem for a number of years and he fixed it while I blinked. This man is just incredibly smart. How lucky I am to have met him.

06/05/03: We discussed soy products and the effect they may have on the body. He said when soy products were consumed, the body could manufacture mucus which interfered with the normal functions of the thyroid gland. This causes tremendous problems throughout the body. Bread, dairy products and pasta may also create these problems. He advised me not to eat honey because it was a substance manufactured by bees and contained animal DNA. He said over a period of time the effect it had on the body was similar to that of meat.

I asked why I was having so much trouble sleeping. He said sleep would come naturally as the body began to heal. I said I was losing weight and questioned him about the unwanted loose flab that was beginning to appear all over the place. He said the skin tightened with time. The need for patience is vital.

07/05/03: Elias pressed the sleep button yesterday because I had a beautiful sleep last night; sinus is nasty; coughing constantly; I asked if it could cause lasting damage; he said it would not.

09/05/03: Elias said not to flush sinuses with any substance because it destroyed delicate membranes and relief would be temporary. Instead, I am to make a tea using sage and inhale the vapour (sage infusion). Elias is happy with my progress.

My spleen, liver, and kidneys were no longer swollen and the viruses were dead. I asked if I could change my diet or add different types of food. He said: "But of course. You can eat whatever food you like, but if you are smart you will continue to eat nothing but fruit". No problem! No Problem?

10/05/03: A huge day; set up shop at the Cairns Expo; worked hard all day; feel tired but well; have a lot to be thankful for. Elias said after having massages, people sometimes got a red rash on their bottom. This is another way the body drains toxins.

My hands are still swollen and the arthritis in my right knee is making its presence felt, but it is a lot less painful.

17/05/03: A wonderful friend died at the age of 38. Like so many others I am in shock. This brought on the blindness of a migraine headache but without the usual pain; stomach swollen with much pain; went for a long walk but did not get relief.

21/05/03: A very sad day; hundreds of people at the funeral; kidneys sore; cannot quench thirst; blood pressure low; head spins; ate pears and watermelon and within a couple of hours the pain in my kidneys disappeared.

25/05/03: This is the last of another three-day craft expo 250km from home; food cravings are beginning to retreat; lots of ladies present; this has to be cheese cake heaven and chocolate bliss – but not for me!

29/05/03: Having rugged nightmares.

31/05/03: The back of my head is sore where I hurt it in a motor vehicle accident many years ago; maybe it is healing; low blood pressure 114/65; Elias said to eat more natural salt from tomatoes, zucchini and cucumbers. Should improve in one-and-a-half weeks.

10/06/03: The hundredth day of natural therapy; symptoms linger; I am sleeping much better; I see improvements.

17/06/03: Getting impatient; worked in the garden; thought I could do it; paying the price; need to start painting the house.

03/07/03: Having deep massages; breathing better; needling pain in my eyes; eye vessels cleansing with fruit and chilli.

05/07/03: Had the last treatment for this session; the mark on my back is smaller and lighter; Elias worked on my sinus and colon and said to handle the stress factor because it was dangerous if left unchecked; for my bladder pain I was to eat watermelon, pears and 2 tsp of crushed papaya seeds daily for three days.

10/07/03: Back home; really motivated; feel well; packing for another expo.

17/07/03: Stressed; chest pain; Elias advised chest x-rays; he said I still had bacteria in my blood; it will take up to one year to cleanse; to have three cups of sage tea a day.

18/07/03: X-ray clear; radiologist had problems understanding why the bronchiectasis and emphysema has disappeared. He said: "I am shocked to see the lung so clear". I asked: "Does this happen often?" He said: "It never happens. They all must have got it wrong in the first place". By all, he meant the CT scan and several other radiologist reports, general practitioners, chest physicians and a professor of medicine.

Elias's natural therapy has once again weaved its magic. How lovely. And it happened in a little over four months. I am over the moon. Again, thank you Elias and thank you Creator.

30/07/03: Sleeping well; sinus rampant but draining; sage tea is helping; less heat at night; mid-winter and I can wear socks to bed; making progress; small and subtle changes; not easy for me because I want big changes quickly; learning a lot about myself; need more patience; now 55kg; prepared for an expo; low blood pressure a nuisance; I wish it would go away because I have much to do!

04/08/03: Five months into my therapy; have came a long way; sleeping well; breathing improved; fewer sweats; planning ahead; another expo coming up; need lots of products. My health is improving and I am very grateful.

10/08/03: Expo went well; met a lady who is a client of Elias. She had suffered a cough for 10 years as the result of medication. It contained a heavy metal which caused the cough. Cleansing her body of this substance will be a long haul. But with Elias's natural therapy, positive thinking and hard work I am quietly confident she will do it because she wants to be well.

27/08/03: Natural therapy is working wonders; another big expo; lumps on my skin are appearing then disappearing; some have blisters; glands are cleansing; bowels active; low blood pressure a nuisance; learning about patience and listening to the body.

11/09/03: On this day one year ago after three months of continuous medical testing I was told I had six months to live; not so; thanks again Elias; I have come a long way and have a long way to go.

21/09/03: Even though most of my symptoms are still with me they are less ferocious but sinus is chronic. Lumps are over my entire body including face, scalp and in my mouth. They are ugly, uncomfortable and they itch. Even though the cleansing is nauseating it is excellent because the lymph system is draining.

After orbital sanding I have painted parts of the house, have gardened and sewed curtains and the products are turning out beautifully. When I overdo things I pay the price, but I just work through it.

If I were to give in and go to bed I would probably be a lot sicker because I would be guilty of wasting precious time and thinking of all the lovely things I could be doing. And I have wasted too much valuable time already through this illness.

I am experiencing needling pains in the head and entire body. This is the result of vessels cleansing and it is all good. Concentration levels are much improved and I can now carry out arduous tasks.

I tried to have my blood sugar level checked today. Three fingers were tried but the skin closed over that quick I could not have it done. The chilli is working its magic. My blood is of good quality and clotting quickly as nature intended.

The nurse said: "This has not happened to me before". I told her there was a good reason why it was happening but she was not interested.

26/09/03: Horrendous nightmares; dreamt I was locked in a room filled with giant snakes and as they opened their mouth others would slide out; my brain is going berserk; heart beat is erratic and I am as grey as a ghost with dark circles around my eyes. Last night I weakened and ate a piece of fish, it has made me feel so sick.

06/10/03: The weather is warming and my sinus is not so bad. Spoke to Elias about them, he said the sinuses were big and they took a long time to heal. Stress is creeping into my life; have a stress rash; low blood pressure; must concentrate on self and making products for an expo.

21/10/03: Behind the steering wheel on a trip to Brisbane; still not too flash with big crowds but that is fine; more patience is necessary. However, I wish I could breathe easier; no one knows how I feel.

But I am really excited about my business because it is all starting to fall into place; changing the presentation has been a big job; two years ago I would never have thought that my health would improve; even though it is mega slow it is happening but I must control stress; stress prevents healing and wastes necessary energy.

12/11/03: Having treatments; Elias is working on lungs and colon; having problems breathing but all will heal; I must tolerate this illness: there is a lot going on with my kidneys, bowels and lymph system; bacteria from chlamydia psittaci is still present in my blood but it will die within four months.

23/11/03: Struggling to breathe; swollen; skin sore; getting “fat” comments; feel afraid; sweating; illness full on; high blood pressure; must refocus; symptoms are the after effects of the therapy.

04/12/03: Nine months have passed since I began natural therapy; life is hard because I feel so ill; visited the dentist and had an injection and gas; not a good idea; blacked out from low blood pressure; after the treatments I had lung problems and had to take four teaspoons of crushed papaya seeds each day for seven days; getting comments on how sick I look; hair falling; illness places stress on the body.

10/01/04: Having more treatments; when I first met Elias he said on a scale from one to 10, my immune system was 2.5, now it is seven; he does not regard this as good but it is a lot better than it was; my lungs pain; he said the bacteria in my lung (pseudomonas aeruginosa) should be a thing of the past within three months; it takes 14 months to die; I will have lung scarring; must eat more chilli.

22/01/04: During the night Meniere's returned but quickly departed; I dream I am being eaten alive by bacteria.

I met a hospital superintendent who spoke about patients with pseudomonas aeruginosa.

She said: "Patients with this bacteria are put in a back room and forgotten about. They are on their own because there is nothing that can be done to help them". This was a sobering moment and I am more determined than ever to stay away from animal protein; in three months the bacteria will be dead.

24/02/04: Hair loss is so bad it trips me in the shower; blood pressure from stress is crazy; feel so ill; Elias said the kidneys were filtering dead bacteria and associated debris and this should continue for 10 weeks; excellent; making headway; body is swollen and face is as grey as a corpse; getting comments on how sick I look; I cannot say too much because people do not understand, but there is nothing to worry about; I know what is going on; having dizzy turns but still producing beautiful products. Very nice!

04/03/04: Lumps cover my body during the night and disappear as my feet touch the floor in the morning; mouth ulcers do the same; the body discharges toxins any way it can; I know what is going on and I am not concerned. Elias said my kidneys were not working properly because their load was heavy; must go on lemon and water only for five days to help unburden them.

This is my first anniversary of natural therapy. I am very pleased because in spite of the ups and downs I have made a lot of progress and continue to move forward. But this is also a day I will not forget because after my morning shower a memorable incident occured. An incident I was somewhat reluctunt to put into words. But this is my story and it should be told as it happened:

WHO? WHY?

I looked up and there they were – in my room.
They materialised from nothing and without a sound.

A tall, thin cadaverous figure stood motionless.
At its feet, a pathetic submissive creature sat prostrate.

It stood: the hooded thing in a black floor-length gown
that covered both hands and feet.

Ashen skinned,
its downcast stony eyes wedged in an emotionless face.

The grovelling ball at the tall figure's feet
wore black trousers and blue shirt. My clothes?

It looked like me.
My colouring, hair and style.

Could it be me?
Were they of this earth? I think not.

What was the agenda of this spineless pair?
Was this to be my fate?

"Be grateful for the gifts and your accomplishments thus far",
said a voice.

Oh but I am!
As I gave thanks they vanished ...

If that little encounter was another of life's valuable lessons then I am getting the message. It seems that while there is life it may be wise to expect the unexpected.

10/03/04: The lemon and water worked like a charm; painting around the house; walking on the beach; the mark on my back is beginning to fragment; red lumps over my body resemble hives.

20/03/04: The left side of my head is in chaos with pain accompanied by the sound of swarming bees; phoned Elias; he said not to fear because it was part of the healing process.

26/03/04: Had a wonderful day; feel as though I could fly; so this is what it feels like to be well; no two days are alike.

13/04/04: I felt so well I went to a doctor for a form to have my blood tested. He was surprised to see me because I had not visited in over a year. I asked if I could get rid of the lupus and he said that was not possible. I said I was feeling a lot better and told him what I was doing. In a stern tone he said: "If you are feeling better, enjoy it, because alternate healing is only temporary. The illness always comes back".

I said I wanted to have chemical levels checked as well. He said: "That is not possible because it is not necessary. You are not pregnant". I said I was a paying customer and I wanted chemical testing. Reluctantly, he signed the form and I had them done.

28/04/04: More treatments; Elias is very happy with the blood test results; he is working on my jaw because several decades ago while at boarding school, a dentist damaged it trying to extract a molar. I did not think it would be possible to fix it after all these years but he is working on it. The work he does is incredible.

He knows the problem of every client and what they have eaten well in advance of their visit when he begins to work on their nerve system. All he needs to know about his clients is in their nerve system. It even exposes the client's personality.

He can assess with 100 per cent accuracy whether or not the client will heal because success lies in the character of a person. He said the nerve system tells the whole story.

The lung bacteria are *DEAD AND GONE*. Excellent! And I

was told it was not possible! The healing process continues to inch forward ever so slowly. Thank you Elias and thank you universe!

20/05/04: Feel as though I am getting a handle on things; seem to have more control of the mind; maybe it is because my health is improving; need more products for an expo out west; love it; my business is a beautiful diversion from life's pressures; I only have heat problems if I eat something that is not raw fruit; even cooked fruit creates nausea; so much freedom without the perspiration and heat; severe needling within the vessels throughout the body and head; excellent, the chilli is working its magic.

02/06/04: Received news of an acquaintance whose breast was removed along with four glands from her armpit. Tests done after her surgery revealed cancer had not invaded these glands. She accepted both chemo and radium therapy. I feel so sad but remind myself we all have choices and she did not choose natural therapy and her vital healthy glands are lost forever.

30/06/04: Received terrible news; after having a Caesarean section a young friend died as the result of a misguided scalpel that perforated her bowel during the surgery. This is horrible.

03/07/04: Did a long bush walk effortlessly which included a set of 100 steps. Fantastic!

20/07/04: A fruitarian visited Elias with glaucoma and could no longer read fine print but after a few massages he regained his sight and will not require surgery or spectacles. I spoke with a lady who visited Elias suffering hay fever. He advised her to rinse her eyes with clear water and apply first cold pressed extra virgin olive oil to her nostrils with a cotton bud.

29/08/04: Having treatments; have bronchitis from sinus; severe headaches; after sinus massage I felt as though I have had surgery; ears, gums and teeth ache; Elias said this was normal.

24/09/04: Sinus draining like a waterfall; hearing in my right ear is improving. I visited an optometrist after two-and-a-half years. He was very surprised to discover the improvement in my eyesight and had difficulty believing what he saw. He asked me to revisit because he had a stronger machine that inspected all parts of the eye.

29/09/04: Had the second eye test and the results were excellent. The optometrist was baffled because he said there should be degeneration not regeneration. Thank you Elias! Thank you universe!

10/01/05: My mother is almost 91 and even though she is a fighter she has been extremely ill for quite some time. I am blacking out from low blood pressure.

06/02/05: My mother lost her biggest battle. Thankfully she had a beautiful death, painless and in her sleep after lying down after breakfast for a nap before attending Sunday worship.

21/02/05: Life goes on, way beyond our control. I have lost another friend who was very dear to me. This has been another difficult week.

06/03/05: Even though my mother was almost 91 she commanded a presence and retained it until the day she died. The stress of her death and that of my friend has been horrendous. Without a doubt I would not have coped had I not been having natural therapy.

20/03/05: Visited Elias; he said despite recent events, healing was progressing well. My lungs are slowly improving but there is damage caused by pseudomonas aeruginosa. He said in time it would heal itself.

21/04/05: Only one month has passed since the last entry but it seems like an eternity. Having sold our own house to move in with my mother before she died, I have now sold hers. The workload is heavy.

I went back to the same doctor I had visited a year ago to have another blood test. This time his attitude was somewhat different. He said: "Whatever you are doing is working. You are doing it right. You must know what you are doing".

He also said he was amazed to see me looking so well. I told him the path of natural healing was long and I had a long way to go. I pointed out the dark circles under my eyes were a good indication. He said: "I do not know anything about that". I told him the dark mark on my back was beginning to break up. He asked if he could have a look at it. After seeing it he said: "I have no explanation".

That doctor went away on vacation so I had to visit his colleague to get the results of the blood tests. After reading them he said: "You have a problem. It could be your asthma or your hay fever or you could have a belly full of worms".

I said I do not have asthma or hay fever and thought it could not be worms because of the amount of chilli, lemon and grapefruit I had daily. With a hearty laugh he replied: "I have no idea what is going on". I faxed the blood test results to Elias and he said they were all perfect.

Since my mother's death there has been a lot to cope with and I have put on 5kg. I have started power walking and eating lots of pineapple and citrus in an effort to lose the weight.

16/05/05: Having stomach problems as a result of stress; got immediate relief after Elias's massages.

13/06/05: Soon it will be time to leave my mother's house. I had a long settlement drawn up.

13/07/05: With mixed emotions I left my mother's house and moved away from the town where I was born and lived all my life. I made sure her gravesite was complete.

31/07/05: There are many changes afoot. My much-loved car that served me so well for the last 13 years has been replaced. Having turned my back on my former life I am on the cusp of another.

01/01/06: Settling into a new location; difficult to make new beginnings; so much happened during the last year; life is not easy.

01/03/06: No more ingrown toe nails, Morton's neuromas or tinea; hair rejuvenating but of a different texture; eyesight improving; hearing excellent; lung continues to improve; chronic sinus continues.

24/03/06: More treatments with Elias. In 1980 I fell on a wet surface and damaged my right knee. Surgeons recommended surgery but I was always too busy and did not want to be in a cast for six weeks. Arthritis had set in and the pain at night caused sleep loss. The knee was moving sideways, altering the position of my foot and wrecking my shoes.

Lifting was difficult and walking up steps a pain; Elias worked on the area twice daily. The pain was interesting to say the least, but the outcome was fantastic. He straightened the leg; absolutely marvellous. Should have mentioned it before.

04/05/06: Sore throat; heavy sinus problems during winter.

10/08/06: Winter is about to exit and I had sinus every day but not as severe as it used to be; after three years and five months down the healing track I finally got the opportunity to have eight days to myself; Elias said this was the first time he felt calm in my body.

24/09/06: It is five months since I had my leg straightened; I can walk and exercise without problems.

22/02/07: The months are flying by and my health continues to improve. The changes are so subtle I do not even notice them. I continue to wear glasses when I drive but there is little difference with or without them.

02/08/07: I had an altercation with a ladder and broke a foot bone. The pain is interesting.

05/09/07: Having treatments; my immune system was not strong enough to fight the influenza virus that struck Australia. I had chronic sinus and bronchitis as well but I am very lucky because I lived to tell the tale. There are those who did not survive.

I have noticed a big improvement in my lungs. Sinus is still a problem but not as savage as it once was. Elias said it may take a few more years for them to heal. I mentioned my broken bone to Elias and said the pain was still strong. He said I had seven bones out and he put them back in within seconds. No more pain. He is so amazing.

08/12/07: Have finished a week of therapy. Natural healing is going very well. On a scale of one to 10, my immune system is eight. That is very pleasing and a far cry from the 2.5 I started out at. All going well, Elias said I did not need any therapy for six months. That is so good.

05/05/08: I have influenza; very disappointed to say the least. However, after only four days the improvement is unbelievably rapid, but sinus prevails. I am having these problems because my gall bladder was removed and this affects the immune system.

16/06/08: I have just returned home after visiting Elias for a week. Over the last five-and-a-half years he has been working on my colon, lungs, liver, spleen etc., in order to compensate for the absence of my gall bladder. A surgeon removed it in 1993 after I had four painful attacks.

I was told by the surgeon before the operation that only the stones would be removed. But because I had hundreds of sand-like particles, he said it was easier to remove the entire organ. He said the gall bladder was not important.

21/12/08: Once again I am home after having two weeks of natural therapy with Elias. He had to drain my sinus again and I have not been well at all. I have learnt the hard way that the gall bladder is extremely important for daily body functions and that life without it is far from normal. The gall bladder is vital to the immune system and lymphatic drainage. One can expect anything when organs have been removed.

Elias explained that bile was produced in the liver. He said some went into the small intestine and some was released into the gall bladder. The gall bladder acts as a reservoir because it stores bile which is released into the small intestine which helps break down fats. If the body does not have adequate bile, it cannot break down fats. One may become deficient in vitamins A, D, E and K.

Vitamin A deficiency affects the eyes. The cornea can dry out, thereby damaging both the retina and cornea. Night blindness can occur and one may lose sight. A deficiency in vitamin A can result in a compromised immune system and infections may prevail. The skeletal system can also be affected.

If the body is deficient in vitamin D, it cannot properly synthesize the sun's rays on the skin. This vitamin is essential for healthy bones and it also helps to prevent the excretion of calcium and other minerals via the kidneys.

Vitamin E deficiency occurs to those who have diseases which prevent the absorption of fat-soluble nutrients and dietary fats. This vitamin is necessary for the nerve system and body tissue.

Vitamin K deficiency is rare in adults but it is associated with those who cannot absorb fats. If one is deficient in this vitamin, one may suffer blood-clotting problems. When I met Elias he said all the problems I had through a surgeon removing my gall bladder could have been avoided simply by eating as nature intended.

A piranha can replace its entire body even if 60 per cent has been bitten off. As long as its head, heart and lungs are intact, the fish will grow a new body. In recent years most of us have heard about genetic engineering and through the media we witnessed scientists grow a human ear on the back of a rat.

With correct intervention the human body is capable of rejuvenation. I am more fortunate than the laboratory rat and the feisty piranha because in a little over five years of natural therapy with Elias, my gall bladder began showing signs of regeneration.

The tube that led to the original gall bladder is still there as are the ends of two severed nerves that were attached to it. Now there is a small flow of bile coming from the opening and the nerve to what was once a gall bladder is beginning to grow ever so slowly.

I know this to be a fact because I am experiencing subtle changes to my digestive system. When I first met Elias he said growing a gall bladder was possible if I practised discipline, patience and if I ate correctly. He said I was not to become impatient because growing an organ took many, many years and discipline was the key.

If the surgeon had removed any other part of my digestive system it would be impossible to grow an organ. The body needs every part of the digestive system to extract nutrients from natural fructose which is found in abundance in fruit.

Even though this may sound remarkable, I am not surprised because Elias has many more clients who, through their discipline, patience and dedication, are achieving fantastic goals – many of which are much more exciting and significant than the regeneration of my gall bladder.

That leaves me questioning: "What more is possible"?

04/03/09: I first saw Elias on this day six years ago. In that time I made many lifesaving changes. Some of the important things I have learnt are: The more I learn the less I know; the benefits of keeping an open mind are enormous and the willingness to learn can either make or break a person. The most memorable issue that stood head and shoulders above all else seems to have been the chaos that stemmed from over inflated egos. Commonsense was over-ruled and the psychological barriers that were created prevented good health. In certain cases it impacted heavily on families and it was the children who suffered.

Sadly, during this time I also witnessed people with cancers who chose chemo and radium over natural therapy, and some lost their life within a brief period. I have reached the conclusion that many people would sooner die than try something other than drugs.

The grim reality is that many people are reluctant to surrender archaic methods of disease management. They do not have patience, and they do not have the will to work with nature because they simply do not believe in it. Many will not accept that natural therapy could save their life. Many will not admit they lack the confidence to think for themselves because more often than not, when we do, we find ourselves unsupported by a "dollar-orientated system".

Another grim factor seems to be the enormity of misinformation and the impenetrable barriers it creates. The "belief factor" is almost as extinct as the dodo.

We need to stop and take a good look at the manner in which we have been indoctrinated: meat and three veg; if it moves, kill it; the need to cook food; the new buzz phrase of "two and five" (two pieces of fruit and five of vegetables which will no doubt be cooked). And finally, the old saying: "We all have to die of something".

Are these not classic examples of why we must not follow the herd? It seems there has never been a better time to think for ourselves and live uncomplicated lives as nature intended.

But mankind takes great pride in complicating just about everything it touches. The question is: is eating raw, natural fruit all that difficult? Could it be no thought is required and that makes life too simple? Of course there are always the good old standby clichés for those who do not wish to make changes. Clichés such as: we eat what we like in moderation, and we eat a good balanced diet. But that could be a moderate balance of toxic acids that produce a list of deadly diseases as long as one's arm?

And are all the old clichés working? No. There are now more people suffering infections, obesity, viruses and terminal diseases than ever before. When people dispute this statement, they seem to have to fall back on statistics. But if one needs statistics, one can read independent information titled "Massaging Statistics" in Walter Last's web site: www.health-science-spirit.com/cancerscience.html

During a recent conversation, a fruitarian said she had been to three funerals in the last three weeks. The deceased were not related but had much in common. They were all cancer victims; each had accepted chemotherapy; and each suffered horrendous deaths.

She also said she knew another cancer victim who was going through the same "process" as the previous three before they died. Bewildered, she added: "I cannot understand why this cancer patient is so happy. Her family is stressed to the max, showering her with loving care and attention 24/7. She cannot see beyond herself. Would it not have been kinder to her family to choose natural therapy and heal herself?"

She said: "Why do so many people say they love their family but they do not show them how and why the body can heal itself? Why would anyone shun information on natural healing, is this not the best gift we could share?"

She added: "Sooner or later people were going to have to learn to say no to drugs and realise what chemicals and acids produced by animal DNA and processed foods were doing to us".

“

the illiterate of
the 21st century will not be
those who cannot read and write,
but those who cannot learn,
unlearn and relearn

”

– alvin toffler

"

the human
body is a laboratory
in which absolute miracles
of chemistry are
performed

"

– f.l.a. freytag

Chapter 4

THE BODY, FOOD AND DISEASE CONNECTION

Topics were briefly covered because space was limited.

It is difficult to have a healthy immune system when we live in a polluted world and especially when we are surrounded by killer diseases. Very few of us have not been affected by this disaster, whether it is ourselves, a loved one or a friend.

Our country is affluent and most have access to medical facilities. We have state-of-the-art drugs, alternative medicines and one would assume the mortality rate would be on the decline. But the number of people contracting diseases continues to grow. Our hospitals are bursting at the seams with patients and some have long waiting lists. Many doctors and hospital staff are overtired and overworked. Until the age of 21, I had only known of one person who had died from cancer. Now it is rampant.

We are all searching for good health, but it seems the highway we are travelling is taking us in the opposite direction. Every few years it seems viruses mutate and threaten civilisation. It is obvious the current methods of health management could be more efficient.

Nature created the world simplistically but we have unwittingly allowed our lives to become complicated. The key factor behind many diseases and unnecessary early deaths is misinformation.

Current methods used for disease management are based on "after the fact", not prevention as nature intended. We have the right and the brain power to think for ourselves and manage our own health.

If we get sick we have the power to find the cause, eliminate the source and prevent other illness from occurring. And we can do it ourselves with correct information. We must also remember *only the body can heal itself.* Many diseases and afflictions lead to others because they weaken the immune system. But most diseases are avoidable and can be healed naturally. Society is also facing the dilemma of excess weight and obesity. In most cases, like many diseases it is "a disease of the mind" – the end result of the way the individual thinks. There are thousands of diets, dependencies on the quick fix and man-made substances. But are they working?

We are encouraged to work hard and smart and plan for future prosperity and independence. To act "before the event" is forward thinking. But when it comes to health, it seems we put more thought into buying a television set.

So why do we not plan a lifetime of good health and why do we not manage our own body? The answer is simple: most people do not know how. There is little information on self-healing and that leaves no alternative but to continue the decades of drug taking. During my illness I discovered prescription drugs only masked my health problems, wreaked havoc and weakened my immune system, caused side effects and triggered other diseases.

ABSOLUTE FRUIT NUTRITION – THE ROAD TO GOOD HEALTH

Nature has its own checks and balances. They work perfectly until man intervenes. The human body was not created to become ill and diseased and to prevent this it was given an immune system. The immune system must be correctly nourished in order to function at its peak.

Nature created a complete food that is totally compatible to the body. This food is "fruit, nectar of the Gods". Fruit nutrients sustain human life which cleans and heals the body. Fruit nutrients are the only substances that repair and strengthen the immune system.

The human body is composed of 92 natural chemical elements internationally know as:

Group 1 – Rare gases and hydrogen: Argon (Ar 18). Helium (He 2). Hydrogen (H 1). Krypton (Kr 36). Neon (Ne 10). Radon (Rn 86). Xenon (Xe 54).

Group 2 – Base building/alkaline elements: Actinium (Ac 89). Barium (Ba 56). Bismuth (Bi 83). Cadmium (Cd 48). Caesium. Calcium (Ca 20). Cerium (Ce 58). Copper (Cu 29). Dysprosium (Dy 66). Erbium (Er 68). Europium (Eu 63). Francium (Fr 87). Gadolinium (Gd 64). Gold (Au 79). Holmium (Ho 67). Iridium (Ir 77). Lanthanum (La 57). Lithium (Li 3). Lutetium (Lu 71). Magnesium (Mg 12). Mercury (Hg 80). Neodymium (Nd 60). Nickel (Ni 28). Palladium (Pd 46). Platinum (Pt 78). Potassium (K 19). Praseodymium (Pr 59). Promethium (Pm 61). Protactinium (Pa 91). Radium (Ra 88). Rhodium (Rh 45). Rubidium (Rb 37). Samarium (Sm 62). Scandium (Sc 21). Silver (Ag 47). Sodium (Na 11). Strontium (Sr 38). Terbium (Tb 65). Thorium (Th 90). Thulium (Tm 69). Uranium (U 92). Ytterbium (Yb 70). Yttrium (Y 39).

Group 3 – Base elements: Aluminium (Al 13). Antimony (Sb 51). Arsenic (As 33). Beryllium (Be 4). Chromium (Cr 24). Cobalt (Co 27). Iron (Fe 26). Gallium (Ga 31). Germanium (Ge 32). Hafnium (Hf 72). Indium (In 49). Lead (Pb 82). Manganese (Mn 25). Molybdenum (Mo 42). Niobium (Nb 41). Osmium (Os 76). Polonium (Po 84). Rhenium (Re 75). Ruthenium (Ru 44). Tantalum (Ta 73). Technetium (Tc 43). Tellurium (Te 52). Thallium (Tl 81). Tin (Sn 50). Titanium (Ti 22). Tungsten (W 74). Vanadium (V 23). Zirconium (Zr 40). Zinc (Zn 30).

Group 4 – Acid building elements: Astatine (At 85). Boron (B 5). Bromine (Br 35). Carbon (C 6). Chlorine (Cl 17). Fluorine (F 9). Iodine (I 53). Nitrogen (N 7). Oxygen (O 8). Phosphorus (P 15). Selenium (Se 34). Silicon (Si 14). Sulphur (S 16).

Fruit is also composed of the 92 chemical elements listed above and this is the reason it is the only food that is 100 per cent identical and compatible to the human body. And nature in its infinite wisdom crowned the human body with a brain, and a nerve system that is an extension of the brain throughout the body. When we eat and live as nature intended, the nerve system functions correctly. It sends and receives correct messages to and from the brain connecting all parts of the body.

This protects the body from diseases because it strengthens the immune system. If the diet consists of processed foods, dead animals in the state of rigor mortis and their by-products, dairy, along with grains, vegetables, seeds, legumes and certain nuts, the body develops harmful acids.

These acids cause the nerve system to malfunction and as a result incorrect messages are sent and received by the brain, thus creating the perfect environment for viruses and disease. Viruses and diseases live on animal protein (animal DNA) within the human body. If the body is healthy and free of animal protein, the food sources of diseases and viruses are non existent.

Fruit, a healthy immune system and a stress-free life are ideal partners to maintain perfect health. However, there is always the flip side. Those who eat fruit only (fruitarians) can still become ill if they suffer the following:

- uncontrolled stress.
- sleep deprivation.
- working long hours.
- hunger and dehydration.
- a weak immune system etc.

And cancers may occur if they:

- use some mobile phones excessively.
- eat food cooked in microwave ovens.
- have excessive contact with electrical equipment and radar.
- use magnetic gadgets excessively.
- have x-rays and imaging excessively.
- have excessive contact with electromagnetic radiation etc.

Elias stresses the following: anything that works against nature and that which is unnatural weakens the immune system. Once again, problems start when man intervenes.

ABSOLUTE FRUIT PROTEIN

There are those who believe that the only source of protein

comes from animal DNA. But this information is incorrect and it is for this reason why the incidence of deadly diseases is increasing. And contrary to popular belief, the body requires only very small amounts of protein. The brain requires 90 per cent while the body receives the remaining 10 per cent. Protein is a molecule that creates cells.

Many have asked: "But how is it possible for the body to manufacture protein from fruit?" We must understand the human body was created by nature and it is a powerhouse in its own right: a living factory that sustains life by way of the nutrients it extracts from fruit in the precise amounts it requires to maintain and repair itself.

There are fruits that contain active protein, including avocado, passion fruit and pineapple. But the protein in most fruit is neutral and the body must activate it in order to function normally and have a healthy immune system.

The body manufactures protein the instant fruit's amino acids enter the system via glands at the back of the tongue. These amino acids stimulate both the brain and body, while the tongue's fluid extracts fruit enzymes. Then the body's natural hydrochloric acid, in conjunction with citric acid, fructose, and oxygen, and information received from the pancreas via the nerve system, create protein on a cellular level.

But the body does much more: it creates different types of protein for different parts of the body: the brain, heart, lungs, muscles, liver, kidneys, blood, pancreas, the nerve system etc., all require different types of protein. The body also manufactures energy from fructose which it converts into glucose then into energy.

All fruit is excellent. Every variety has cleansing and healing properties. In order to heal and cleanse the body and maintain a healthy immune system, fruit must not be processed, it must not be heated and it must not be cooked. Fruit must be eaten raw and fruit juices fresh – as nature intended.

Animal DNA pollutes the body and sabotages vital information that is sent and received by the brain via the nerve system. Animal

DNA also sabotages the normal functions of the pancreas which is just one reason why the human body becomes a receptacle for disease.

When the human body is "clean", it works in harmony with the brain. If the body and brain become deficient in a certain nutrient, the brain sends a message to the body in the form of a craving – it will require a certain fruit. That fruit will be laden with abundant nutrients for the "quick fix". If the brain sends these messages we must act upon them immediately.

There may be extreme situations when only one type of fruit or vegetable is available to keep us alive e.g. in times of war. The body recognises such situations and compensates by self-preservation. However, if the period of time extends to months, that food will build up toxin within the body and death from poisoning may occur. The more fruit one eats, the healthier one becomes.

ACID AND ALLERGY

It is not possible to be allergic to fruit. If a reaction occurs after eating fruit, it will probably be chemicals present on the skin of the fruit, e.g. copper spray on grapes or canker spray on oranges etc.

There are those who believe fruits such as tomato, cucumber, pineapple and citrus contain harmful acids and avoid eating them. This information is incorrect. Fruit acids are vital to good health and the body needs them for a multitude of reasons, one being to break down food.

When we begin to eat fruit only, the stomach may react within the first two weeks because of:

- pre-existing health problems or diseases.
- prior damage to the digestive system caused by stress or prescription drugs etc.
- fruit such as lemon might not have been tree ripened. Lemon juice can be diluted with water etc.

There are fruitarians who continue to suffer stomach pain caused by a build-up of acids in the stomach. This is usually the result of stress or stomach surgery e.g. Fruit acid is not the cause.

To help alleviate stomach acid pain:

- mash a banana and eat it very slowly before meals.
- dates calm and centre the brain. Eat five dates three times daily after meals and before bedtime. (Eat as many as necessary).
- drink diluted lemon juice.
- juice a potato, allow it to settle for two minutes then drink two teaspoons of the juice. Do this once a day for three days.

Despite the natural remedies, none can compare with the power of the mind. Solve your problems. Prevention is the best cure. We are the manifestation of our thoughts and many suffer unnecessarily through uncontrolled and negative thinking.

ACID OEDEMA

A skin complaint caused by food acids. The foods that contain harmful acids are meats, dairy, nuts (except brazil and coconut), grains, sprouts, legumes, pulses and some vegetables.

The skin is the first and fastest organ to repair when we eat natural food. But problems arise if scar tissue is present, especially if it is deep. The healing time depends on the length of time acid oedema has been present and its severity. Extreme cases may take 20 to 30 years. To assist healing, eat as nature intended.

ADDICTIONS

We may be oblivious to the fact that addictions are masked by disguises. We tend to think of the obvious: food, drugs, alcohol and cigarettes. But there are many others that cannot be seen, therefore we do not recognise them as destructive addictions.

Some people have a need to demoralise others. While there are those who give much of their time and self, trying to correct life's injustices in an effort to make the world a better place.

Some people appear unassuming and somewhat fragile, yet their selfish need to control and manipulate the lives and minds of others is strong. This negative, sinister and shrouded addiction has the capacity to wreck lives because manipulation is usually closely associated with lies. These people usually plan their moves well in advance and like thieves in the night, they may strike without warning. This character will usually take a bitter dislike to those they think are stronger than themselves and may embark on a path of destruction. Those associated with such a person must adopt a strong and positive attitude.

Regardless of what the problem is, all addictions are linked by common threads. For example: negative influences, the state of the mind, and the way one thinks etc.

Addictions prevent positive thoughts and negative thoughts prevent change. A change of character is the only way to conquer addictions or problems. In order to bring about change we must:

- acknowledge there is a problem.
- have the want and need to fix the problem.
- believe in change.
- not rely on others because only we can do it.
- acceptance plays an important role.
- we must realise a strong, negative ego will try to overrule.
- a strong, negative ego has the capacity to wreck one's life and the lives and welfare of others etc.

Will, belief, trust, faith, strength etc., are words that complement each other. Without them there is little hope. In order to bring about change, create a special space within your mind where only you can enter.

Surrender your problems to yourself. Nurture your brain as one would an infant. Be yourself, do not pretend. The worst disease is self-deceit. Lying to oneself becomes a habit and a character flaw. Look no further than yourself.

The body is altruistic, it obeys the brain. The brain is egotistical and will overrule if allowed. We must totally control our brain because if it is not properly managed it has the capacity to wreak havoc on the body. If the brain does as it wishes, it can send whatever message it pleases throughout the body. This is one of the reasons we remain ill and diseased.

Good health is a balance between mind and body. To accomplish total harmony the two must be as one. If we fail to connect, the mind will control and we could suffer many problems such as stress, diseases, chronic illness, addictions, phobias and obsessions etc., If we do not make vital changes, we will suffer the consequences of our thoughts until the day we die. Change is brought about through positive thoughts and a well programmed brain.

Give the brain clear instructions – tell it what is expected of it. Programme it with correct and reliable information. The brain is an instrument. It must be tuned with good information that enables it to perform with precision. Do not rely on willpower which plummets in moments of weakness.

Addictions rule because memories are strong. When the brain is well programmed it will over-rule negativity. Elias said smoking was high on the list of public health problems.

Death from cigarette smoking is preventable but unfortunately statistics show as many young adults smoke today as their predecessors did a decade ago. And it is a fashion statement in the eyes of teenagers. They do not think of death and they have very few fears, therefore warnings from adults about the dangers of smoking are of little relevance.

Long-term smokers with lung damage can heal themselves but they must stop smoking and they must have discipline. They must work with their mind and body because the body cannot do it alone. It takes many years for the lungs to heal, but it is possible. Alcoholics can also do much to help themselves and there are many wonderful organisations that help those with such addictions.

Junk and processed foods play a major role in the quality of health and weight gain. Many contain abundant amounts of grain products including inferior oils, processed cane sugar, processed salt, preservatives, colourants and additives, all of which pollute the lymph system and slow metabolism. Acids accumulate within the body, cementing a foundation for many life threatening diseases.

It is difficult to lose weight if such foods play a major part in one's daily diet. We must eat foods that do not contain these harmful acids and aim at making our bodies alkaline.

Many processed foods are nutrient deficient and their toxins accumulate in our tissues. As a result the quality of skin alters, and as cellulite and fat cells grow, health problems follow.

In order to lose weight, one must eat fat-free food daily. If one can achieve this, weight loss may be permanent. But we can take a further step and aim for good health as well, and to achieve this, one must eat as nature intended. When we work with nature we do not need to count calories.

A conventional meal consists of meat and three veg, bread, with a serving of pasta or rice. This is usually followed by a dessert which contains dairy or it may be a pie or a slice which also contains grain. But the digestive system has problems breaking down such foods because the protein in animal DNA is concentrated. And the starch in bread, rice, pasta, pie or slice is also concentrated.

Problems arise because it is difficult for the stomach to digest several concentrated substances at any one time. If this type of eating continues regularly, health problems and weight gain may occur.

When we look at meat from cattle that have been in food lots and the manner in which poultry is grown for slaughter, it is little wonder why so many people are suffering weight gain and obesity, while many suffer serious health issues such as various types of cancers. Many of these animals and birds are injected or fed with antibiotics and growth hormones regularly. These chemicals are consumed along with their flesh at the dining table.

When one is overweight and begins eating fruit, many changes will occur because fruit and water cleanse and heal the body. In the first few weeks one may experience joint pains. This is the result of the body cleansing uric acid crystals from joints.

When lemon juice is added to drinking water, blood circulation hastens and this may result in pain. In order to obtain relief from the pain, one must drink more water. Initially only small amounts of lemon should be added.

As the uric crystals leave the body, more (tree-ripened) lemon juice can be introduced. It may be wise to persevere in spite of the pain. The more water one drinks, the sooner the pain will go but not more than three litres should be consumed per day because the body will flush vital minerals. But there are no restrictions on pure fruit juice. When one eats naturally there is little need to think about weight loss because the body does it automatically.

However, for those who have had their gall bladder removed, the task is a little more difficult. Pineapple should become a best friend because its enzymes simulate those of the gall bladder. Indigenous Australians refer to pineapple as gall fruit. All citrus, including grapefruit, is excellent for weight loss especially when combined with sensible exercise.

When choosing an exercise, ensure it does not harm the skeletal system or place the body under pressure or stress. The aim is to strengthen and tone muscles. Preparing a meal of uncooked fruit is simple, there is little washing up, shopping is simple and it saves time and money.

Initially the body will lose weight rapidly, then settle for a period of time. One does not become obese over night, therefore one should not expect to lose weight quickly. When we eat as nature intended, the body dictates what weight it should be for its height and build. It is within the power of the individual to lose weight by thinking for oneself.

The body produces a blood supply but it only makes enough to compensate for the individual to be 10kg over the weight they are supposed to be for their height and build. Those who exceed this limit are in danger because they may not have enough blood to circulate throughout their body.

The body will only make one litre of blood more than it requires and it is not possible for the body to produce more than 10 litres of blood in total.

Remember: *aim to lose weight safely and slowly.*

It is wise to be in total control of one's weight loss and to do it naturally.

The following few steps may be of assistance:

- program the brain with logical information.
- eat lots of pineapple and citrus along with all other fruits, drink adequate water and do sensible and enjoyable exercise.

- eat only raw fruit. Cooked foods do not engender weight loss. They are hard on the colon and can remain in the stomach for several days. Raw fruit breaks down immediately it contacts the tongue's fluid and passes through the body in a matter of hours.
- chew slowly in order to obtain the most possible nutrients.
- eat small portions in order to allow the stomach to shrink.
- do not confuse hunger with thirst.

Elias said stomach banding or stomach reduction and the removal of parts of the digestive system should be avoided. He said every part of the digestive system performed vital functions throughout its entire length and if parts were removed or altered, many problems arise.

The colon extracts vital nutrients, vitamins and minerals from the food we eat in order to sustain life. But if the body does not obtain these nutrients, it cannot function normally. Every organ is affected because without the correct types and amounts of protein and other nutrients, it is impossible for them to function normally. The nerve system is also affected as is the brain and dementia may occur.

For example: if the body lacks fibrin, the blood will be thin, unable to clot and under certain circumstances one could bleed to death. Where calcium is in short supply, the skeletal system will become brittle. Elias said these scenarios were but the tip of the iceberg. He went on to say: "It is imperative to have a well disciplined mind. When we have discipline we also have the ability to do what is correct and the body will not suffer".

Elias said controlling hand actions was an imperative part of weight loss because it was the hand that picked up the food and placed it in the mouth.

ADRENAL GLANDS

The adrenal glands are located at the top of the kidneys and work with other glands. They produce a hormone that we know as adrenalin, stress hormones, cortisone and a special hormone for the nerve system etc.

The adrenal glands work with the liver and pancreas and they work with other organs including the ovaries in the regulation of monthly periods in females. The adrenal glands are the key point within the body because they support nerve system functions. Elias places great importance on these glands because they also produce nerve system hormones.

He said it was imperative that the body was free of all supplements, drugs and chemicals in order that these glands function efficiently. This rule also applies to every organ because every part of the body is connected by the nerve system.

Even if we eat a minute amount of processed cane sugar it sabotages the entire balance of the adrenal glands because they not only produce – they balance.

If we stress or become in a state of panic or fear, the adrenal glands produce stress hormones that reduce the size of the blood vessels, they increase the heart rate and prepare the body for fight and flight.

All organs must balance perfectly for the body to function normally. Chemicals and drugs are the enemies of the adrenal glands because these glands are intricate and become blocked very quickly. If this occurs, cancers can invade any part of the body and brain.

ADVERTISING

The following quote is from: *The Book of Remembrance – THE MESSAGE TO HUMANITY.* Author: F.L.A. Freytag.

Quote

Suggestion is a powerful influence capable of awakening in a person's mind the thoughts one intends to instil in him. Such thoughts are then imposed on the mind of the subject under the influence of suggestion. For this purpose willpower is brought into play. There are people amidst mankind who are able to wield this power.

A man with a powerful will imposes his own upon another man whose mind is weaker and who is unable to resist him. The weaker man feels his dependence and accepts the will of the man who wields the power of suggestion. This takes place almost without his realising it.

Unquote

Many industries concentrate heavily on advertising. Advertising directs the masses into spending their hard earned cash exactly where they want the revenue to go. Elias has taught me the benefits of natural eating and living simply, but this does not engender dollars for most companies. If we all began eating and healing as nature intended, many companies would not survive.

Bad eating habits and clever advertising campaigns make perfect partners. Most of us are aware of chemicals and their effect on the environment and the body. And we are also aware of the effects some advertising has on the minds of those who love to shop.

The strategies companies implement to market their wares are not accidental. Advertising works wonders on those who rely on the quick fix and those who do not engage change.

If we place our trust in nature, one automatically attempts to simplify other areas of daily life. When we experience the benefits, we usually have a fair idea of what is good for us and we need not rely on advertising to do our thinking for us.

One memorable advertised product was an avocado dip. It contained 1.5 per cent avocado. The remaining 98.5 per cent were chemical fillers, binders, colourants, animal fat, oils, enhancers and humectants. Clever advertising gave the impression that the product was natural.

I would love to see more advertising campaigns that encourage natural eating instead of processed foods. I would love to see people encouraged to live simply and think for themselves.

And it would be fantastic if we were made to feel good about ourselves, accept the way we are and to be content and grateful for what we already have. I feel sure it will be a long time before an advertising campaign tells me: "Do not purchase anything today because you have all you need and all the decisions you are making for yourself are fine".

ALTITUDE SICKNESS

Elias said changes in atmospheric pressure occurred at high altitudes resulting in altitude sickness. This can happen during mountain climbing or in non-pressurised aircraft. Atmospheric density is also a major factor. During ascent, air pressure falls and lungs take in less oxygen with each breath. As the climber struggles to inhale oxygen, breathing becomes rapid.

Elias's suggestion for climbers is not to ascend more than 300m a day. He suggested to wait for a period of two days, then climb down 100m and remain there for one day. He said by continuing to climb in this manner, the ascent would be achieved without causing brain damage as the climber acclimatised to the higher altitudes. Elias suggested caution when climbing over 2000m, or if one had a blood disease, middle ear problems, was taking drugs or if the ascent was vertical.

Neither physical fitness nor muscular strength is a match for altitude sickness. Guard against dehydration, avoid alcohol and eat frequent small meals. Symptoms associated with this illness are headache, rapid heartbeat, nausea, appetite loss, dizziness and breathing difficulty. Altitude sickness can result in an accumulation of fluid around the brain. Poor co-ordination, hallucination, coma and death can occur. The damage that altitude sickness does to the brain is irreversible. In order to fully understand this subject, one should research the bends because illness associated with altitude and depth, are closely related.

Remember: *prevention is the best cure and further in-depth research is vital.*

ALZHEIMER'S DISEASE

Aluminium is not regarded as a heavy metal but it is extremely toxic even in minute amounts because it settles in the brain. Elias said during World War II, soldiers used aluminium pots to cook their foods and they ate from the same pot. Water vessels were also made from aluminium.

Metal deposits found their way to the brain and Alzheimer's

followed. The number of sufferers dropped during the 1970s and 80s with the introduction of stainless steel cooking utensils.

Alzheimer's disease causes degeneration and loss of brain cells. Memory loss, confusion, irrationality, incoherence and emotional reactions follow. There are personality and behavioural changes, difficulty in thinking and speaking, and confusion with dates and time of day.

The sufferer has difficulty coping with personal hygiene as the disease progresses and must rely on others for help. The number of those suffering this disease is rising again because some popular carbonated beverages are packaged in aluminium cans and their acid content may leach aluminium from the metal. Elias said he was treating teenagers who had contracted Alzheimer's disease because some of these popular drinks, like cigarettes can be addictive.

He has helped many sufferers with this disease to heal themselves by first removing the source of the problem, placing them on natural food and massages to the nerve system. This problem is not easy to overcome and may take 10 years to heal.

Those who consume canned foods and beverages may suffer the same outcome because some of these foods have additives which leach aluminium from the container. These foods may also contain lead because some cans are soldered.

Underarm deodorants that contain aluminium should be avoided because they may damage the brain and nerve system.

ANTIBIOTIC – THE NATURAL ALTERNATIVE

Crushed papaya seeds are one of nature's antibiotics. Elias has advised his clients to use two teaspoons of crushed papaya seeds once a day for two to four days if they suffered chest infection.

APPENDIX AND GALL BLADDER FUNCTIONS

The appendix creates vital bacteria and produces a chemical that enables the colon to function correctly. This chemical ensures that the quality and texture of the stool are also correct. Without the appendix it is impossible for the bowel to function normally.

Those who have had their appendix removed may not notice the difference in their motions because they have become accustomed to the way in which their bowel performs. If one is pain free and if the stool is formed, one tends to think all is normal.

There are those who have had their gall bladder removed. One may be led to believe the body functions normally without this organ but this is not correct. To a certain degree the body is forgiving and it learns to compensate. However, it does not function as nature intended and this reduces one's lifespan and alters the quality of life.

The lymphatic system does not drain normally, the skin is affected as is the immune system and weight loss is difficult because the liver remains fatty. The gall bladder is an important organ and performs many functions such as regulating the hormonal system. It aids clear vision and among many other important functions it splits complex sugars.

ARTIFICIAL CHEMICALS – THE SILENT EPIDEMIC

One of the greatest problems the world faces is that of chemical contamination of all life forms. Synthetic chemicals pose the greatest threat because when two are combined, they can create a third and even stronger toxin.

The indiscriminate use of these products has created an imbalance in nature. These toxins ultimately find their way into the food chain, our water supply, oceans and atmosphere through rain and drifts.

The pharmaceutical industry uses vast amounts of synthetic chemicals. Australia is not a leader in the pharmaceutical industry but a follower and fast becoming a testing and dumping ground, and the home of chemicals. A television news report stated: Australians consume more prescription drugs than any other nation.

A news report in late 2007 stated a number of children from an Australian primary school were being used to test a mouth wash. In yet another news report, thousands of healthy Australians were called upon in early 2008 to test a new vaccine for an influenza virus.

The human body cannot cleanse itself of synthetic chemicals when it is on a diet that contains animal products. If a person is suffering chemical poisoning, they should enlist the help of a competent health professional familiar with this rapidly evolving problem.

Many poisonous agricultural sprays are banned in Australia. However, they are present in some imported foods because some countries allow their use.

In Australia one particular herbicide is widely used because it has been given the right of passage. We are led to believe it is safe on the environment because it is water soluble. But Elias regards it as another heavy poison that is detrimental to the body and brain. This substance is widely used by some farmers, horticulturists and gardeners. It has found its way into the food chain, and in mother's breast milk. He said this harmful chemical substance was detrimental to the nerve system and caused leukaemia.

It takes 20 years to rid the body of some substances injected during childhood vaccinations. Some of these formulas are made on a base of metals such as mercury and aluminium, and chemicals such as thimerosal and formaldehyde.

We are led to believe that throughout our lives we must have vaccinations to prevent diseases such as whooping cough, diphtheria, polio, measles and mumps etc. Some institutions even go as far as refusing a child entry if they have not had these vaccinations and their child allowance can be automatically withdrawn.

Healthy fruitarians can and do suffer from the common head cold occasionally, it seems air conditioning may be a contributing factor. (To obtain relief from head colds one may try two teaspoons of crushed papaya seeds each morning for two days to help relieve the symptoms. If the problem persists, repeat the process. Do not continue taking these seeds indiscriminately because they are natural antibiotic and the body will become immune to it).

Those on an animal protein diet should be aware of what affects them with regards to additives and chemicals. For example, asthma sufferers should be aware of substances such as MSG. This can cause anaphylactic shock – a severe reaction to an allergen which is an allergy producing substance or chemical. This reaction can be rapid and symptoms can be experienced in one to 15 minutes.

Symptoms can vary from uneasiness, palpations of the heart, tingling in the hands, feet and lips, itching, pulsations in the ears, coughing, hives, swelling and sneezing to heart failure and convulsions. Some may experience lung spasms resulting in breathing difficulties. After reading the menu when dining, communicate with the person who is cooking your food. (Bee, spider and other insect stings and bites can also cause anaphylactic shock).

Take precautions when handling chemicals. Wear protective clothing such as appropriate masks and attire. Follow the instructions on the label and do not inhale fumes. Prevent chemical accidents because their side effects can be unknown and each person reacts differently. Death from chemicals can be but a breath away. We are the market place of the chemical industry. Whether on not we buy chemicals is our choice.

ARTIFICIAL VITAMINS AND MINERALS

Elias has taught me that natural food cleanses the colon which allows the body to absorb nutrients, vitamins and minerals from fruit. When one's diet includes animal DNA, the stomach produces acids and chemicals in order to digest it. He said these reactions destroyed any nutritional value supplements may have.

Fruit contains vitamins, minerals and vital natural acid. Fruit's acid on the tongue, combined with the tongue's own fluid, absorbs fruit acid. This also improves the quality of the blood. Fruit contains all the vitamin and minerals necessary for normal body functions and growth.

ASTHMA AND SINUS

There are many who suffer asthma and chronic sinus. The length of time it takes the body to heal on natural fruit depends on the condition of the body, the immune system, the type of bacteria and the length of time this bacteria can survive without animal protein.

Many sufferers have healed in the first year of eating fruit, however the body will decide this. The following factors should also be taken into account:

- lifestyle of the sufferer.
- amount of water they drink.
- number of hours they sleep.
- their dedication to healthy eating.
- type of work they do.
- amount of exposure to pollens.
- their association with toxic chemicals and drugs.
- their ability to control anger and rage.
- stress level etc.

Asthma and sinus sufferers must have patience and discipline. A fruitarian must wait a period of at least three years before completely cleansing their body of animal residue. (This depends on discipline and dedication). This cleansing is also part of the healing process.

Asthmatics should not expose themselves to pollens and toxic chemicals because their airways and lungs are highly sensitive. During an asthma attack the airways tighten, swell and become red. Mucus forms within the air passages, which causes narrowing. The symptoms are: a high-pitched whistling sound from the lung whilst breathing, coughing, shortness of breath and a tightening of the chest.

A contributing factor to the ill health of an asthmatic is stress because it tightens the lung muscles and alters the breathing pattern. Where possible, during an asthma attack the sufferer should do all they can that works for them in order to de-stress. They must think positive and remain calm. Those around them also play an important role.

Asthmatics are advised to "manage their illness" but are prescribed chemicals. Many of these substances are toxic to the body, and may add to the problems that already exist. Is it not more sensible to manage one's healing process and become disease and drug free? It makes more sense to remove the source of the illness and allow the body to heal naturally. The source of the problem may be:

- animal DNA including dairy and eggs.

- pollen.
- chemicals.
- stress.
- anger and rage.
- lifestyle.
- drugs etc.

Asthmatics may suffer eczema because nature gives warnings. If we work with the body it will respond and heal. It is the ego, negativity and misinformation that let us down. These three factors govern the state of our health. As with all who suffer different illnesses, asthma and sinus sufferers should work with nature.

Life goes on whether we are well or otherwise. It makes sense to live each day with the knowledge that we are becoming healthier, and that one day in the near future, we will be disease free. Getting better slowly and living a life of not having to take prescriptions drugs and other chemical substances is very appealing and much easier on the wallet.

ATTENTION DEFICIT HYPERACTIVE DISORDER

Elias said the effect that processed sucrose (cane sugar) has on the body and brain of a child was no different to the trauma adults experienced when they become addicted to street drugs. He said processed sugar from sugar cane was a toxin to children because their brain was underdeveloped.

Processed sugar is addictive to children, it is a drug and a chemical, and it should be a banned substance in their diet. The underdeveloped brain of a child cannot process processed cane sugar because it contains many chemicals, therefore processed sugar is toxic to both body and brain.

But freshly squeezed juice from sugar cane stalks (pure sucrose) is highly beneficial and does not damage teeth. Problems arise when fresh sugar cane juice is heated, crystallized, bleached and when chemicals and additives are included.

There are addictive additives in many junk and processed foods. Addictions can occur at any age and whether it is caused from processed sugar in processed foods, junk food, some carbonated beverages, cigarettes, alcohol, some prescription drugs, cocaine or any other addictive substance, the result is the same. The more the body has, the more it wants.

Addictions do not discriminate. They have the same effect on children as they do on adults. Children suffer badly. They fight, kick, abuse, scream and cry from their processed sugar addiction just the same as the heroine addict does with theirs. But addictions are much worse in children because their brains and bodies are underdeveloped and they do not have the mentality to control behaviour. They are unaware of why they behave in this manner and unable to control their emotions. And they are totally dependent on adults who make decisions on their behalf and purchase their food.

Elias said the biggest problem was that processed sugar was not marketed as an addictive substance and Attention Deficit Hyperactive Disorder was classified as something some children acquired as they grew up. Children with ADHD may be ostracised, classified as naughty and adults classified as bad parents. Life for both parties is difficult to say the least and far from normal.

Processed sugar may be found in many carbonated (fizzy) drinks, imitation fruit drinks, chocolate, cakes, biscuits, potato crisps and confectionary etc. Processed sugar is also added to many processed French fries and breakfast cereals because it makes them crunchy. Many of these products are a major part in the average child's diet.

The number of children suffering ADHD is increasing. Many are placed on drugs which may only serve to mask the problem. Children who eat cereal and natural fruit for breakfast may have concentration difficulties mid-morning because it takes about two-and-a-half hours for the grain acids and vital pure fruit acids (necessary for good health, and body and brain regulation) to ferment and convert into alcohol in their stomach.

Children cannot cope with alcohol, therefore eliminating grain from their diet and supplementing it with pure fruit along with pure fruit juices easily prevents this problem. Pure fruit and pure fruit juices aid mental clarity. Adults should educate children to eat natural because they have the right to know why processed foods may make them ill and cause learning difficulties.

It is at this point that I must ask the all important question: who comes to the aid of the family who has a child suffering ADHD and who helps with the education of the child when they fall behind in their grades?

One cure for ADHD caused by a diet that is high in processed sugar cane is simple but it is not easy because discipline and change are essential. Those who care for children with this syndrome should change *their* way of thinking and *their* habits.

They must prepare healthy food and educate their children on why it is necessary to eat healthy. Adults must eliminate all foods that contain processed cane sugar, artificial sweeteners, additives, fillers and binders from the child's diet and out of their sight. Parents must work with and for their child. A child suffering from ADHD caused by processed sugar cane may be given an abundance of fresh fruit, fresh fruit juices and water. Parents should care for their children as nature intended. It is the right of the child to be healthy. They have the right to a healthy brain.

Children usually respond quickly to fruit. Elias said he has treated many children with ADHD and after placing them on natural foods, they were well on the road to recovery in just a few days.

Some students are taking prescribed drugs used to treat ADHD to school and overdosing during school hours, while others are selling and making a profit from these drugs. This practice is criminal and it may be setting a foundation for them to become the drug traffickers of the future.

Parents would be wise to view the welfare of the child and their future with loving care and caution. If the child's behaviour is adversely affected through their diet, this may come against them as adults. Bad behaviour can be controlled to a degree when they are children but the problem escalates as they grow into teenagers and finally adults. As parents lose control and discipline is almost a dirty word, the lifestyle of the adult of the future can be compromised beyond comprehension. Prevention is the best cure.

WARNING: *Self-diagnosis can be dangerous. We suggest that any person who suspects they may have ADHD should enlist the services of a qualified health care professional.*

BACTERIA

At least 7000 people contract bacterial infection from Australian hospitals yearly and figures are increasing. Bacteria live on surfaces, food, soil, water, the atmosphere and in and on our bodies.

After surgery or hospital visits, many face the problem of having contracted pseudomonas aeruginosa, golden staph or some other form of infectious bacteria that is capable of killing through complications. Drugs have no affect on some of these bacteria.

One devastated lady I met said she contracted golden staph during surgery for a hysterectomy. Her entire body, including her face, was badly scarred. A man said he had a "simple" procedure done in a hospital. He is now in danger of losing a limb because the bacteria he contracted during surgery may spread.

Another man in his late twenties said he had surgery on his hip after a motor vehicle accident. Golden staph entered the wound during surgery. He had further surgery to scrape the bones of the bacteria but it was unsuccessful. Surgeons later fused his thighbone to the hip joint.

He now suffers chronic pain and has a severe limp because the leg is shorter than the other. Elias said the methods he used to combat this problem were simple because this bacteria lived on animal DNA and must be starved until it died.

Option 1:

A. The sufferer must discontinue eating all animal protein including eggs, dairy, meats, chicken, fish, mushrooms and honey.

B. Eat fruit and chilli and drink three litres of lemon water daily until the bacteria is dead. The time it takes to heal depends on the type and strength of the bacteria, the length of the invasion, the severity of the bacteria and the condition of the immune system.

Option 2:

A. Drink three litres of lemon water daily.

B. Eat at least three birdseye chilli daily with pineapple and papaya. Pineapple cleans the lymphatic system and the papaya splits the protein.

Do this for at least three weeks. When the healing process has taken place, introduce soft fruits such as avocado, banana and citrus over a period of two weeks followed by all other types of fruit. Continue eating pineapple, papaya, chilli, lemon and three litres of water daily through every stage of the cleansing and healing.

Elias said that under normal circumstances a fruitarian would usually not contract MRSA (Methicillin-Resistant Staphylococcus Aureus), commonly known as "the killer bacteria" because it lived on animal DNA within the body.

MRSA has been known to kill its victims overnight. It is common in hospitals but has found its way into the general community. However, it can easily be eradicated if proper hygiene is carried out regularly.

An old fashioned scrubbing brush and good quality soap will soon put a stop to MRSA bacteria on surfaces. Are we using too many chemicals and not enough elbow grease? Maybe it is time to start cleaning the way our mothers and grandmothers did, without the harsh chemicals.

Elias said he has helped clients to help themselves overcome this disease but it was not easy. He said there were many factors that must be taken into account and each sufferer must be treated differently.

The treatment depends entirely on the condition of one's immune system regardless of age. He also said very little good and reliable information had been written about this subject.

WARNING: *Self diagnosis may be dangerous. If infection is suspected, seek advice from a qualified health care professional.*

BELL'S PALSY

This is a virus that may be caused by several factors. It could be the end result of stress or the forerunner to other diseases. It may be the result of other viruses already present in the body because viruses mutate and other viruses are born. When two mutate, the third is stronger than its parents.

Elias said it was difficult to predict how long it would take facial muscles to return to normal because that depended on a number of factors, such as:

- the strength and severity of the virus.
- the period of time they have been in the body.
- the physical strength of the sufferer and the state of their mind and health.
- the state and strength of their immune system.

Elias said those who ate animal DNA could kill the Bell's palsy virus by discontinuing eating all food and undertaking the following cleanse: drink the juice of three lemons in three litres of water each day for two days.

For the next two weeks continue drinking the lemon water and eat papaya, birdseye chilli, passion fruit and dates only. After the two weeks, introduce soft fruit such as banana, avocado, custard apple etc., in the following week.

He also said if a woman became pregnant while she was suffering from Bell's palsy, her baby may be born with a problematic nerve system and a weak immune system.

He said it was not possible for parents to have healthy children if they had health problems.

BIRD FLU – CHLAMYDIA PSITTACI

An infectious type of bacterial pneumonia transmitted to humans by birds: pigeons, poultry, canaries and some fulmar (certain oceanic birds of the petrel family). This disease is also carried by the psittacine bird family which consists of parrots, parakeets and lovebirds. Birds contract this disease by eating rotting meat and drinking stagnant water.

Chlamydia psittaci infects the lung and blood and can kill both birds and humans. Humans become infected with the psittacosis bacteria after inhaling small particles from the airway fluids (saliva) or dried faeces of infected birds. Other ways include mouth-to-beak contact, and handling feathers or tissue of an infected bird. The bacteria from this disease can also be spread from human-to-human contact, but this is uncommon.

The incubation period is about seven to 21 days after exposure to an infected bird. Early symptoms of this disease include severe muscle and joint soreness, difficulty standing and walking, loss of energy and appetite, severe headaches, chronic sinusitis, bleeding throat, fever and a productive cough.

As the fever rises the cough worsens. The patient may experience chills, shortness of breath, the chest may tighten as the bacteria infect the lungs and pneumonia may occur.

The severity of the disease depends on the patient's age, state of their immune system and disease strain. Those who may be at risk are vets, and staff of pet shops, avian quarantine stations, zoos and slaughter houses etc.

BIRTH DEFECTS

Birth defects are being discovered at an alarming rate within the womb. Elias said brains located outside the skull and intestines outside the body were not uncommon birth defects.

The unborn foetus is usually aborted because these complications cannot be surgically repaired. The blame for this horror may lie with genetically modified food, radiation from electrical powerlines and appliances, microwave ovens, microwave oven cookery, man-made chemicals, drugs, lifestyle, stress and processed food.

BLOOD, BLOOD DONATION AND BLOOD TRANSFUSION

Elias on blood transfusion and donation: as with DNA, every person's blood is different because it is genetic. All genetic problems are donated with the blood. The recipient of blood transfusions inherits the traits, diseases and viruses of the donor.

Donated blood is a foreign substance to the body of the recipient. Donated blood may be toxic and of poor quality which contaminates existing blood and adds to existing problems.

The blood of a person who drinks alcohol but has a quiet

disposition is of better quality than that of a healthy but aggressive person. If heavy metals are present, the recipient could become very ill.

Cloning can be created from one's blood. The donor gives away genetics and stored brain information when they donate. Donors give *themselves* away and the recipient takes pot luck as to what type of blood they receive. The result may be a totally different personality.

Donated blood and blood for testing is taken from the inner elbow. This blood is not pure because the body has used it and it is en route to cleansing. Therefore, like sputum and faeces, this blood is the body's excrement and contains toxins.

Elias said this was the reason why the results of blood tests were not always accurate.

He said he was not interested in "high levels" or "low levels" when he viewed blood test results, it must be a symphony between the two. If the two readings are in the "higher range" the person is sick. If they are in the "lower range" the person is also sick. The reading must balance between the upper and the lower range.

Healthy venous blood must have a pH between 7 and 7.3. Arterial blood must have a base reading of 8pH. If the level falls to five, varicose veins will occur.

Fruitarians who do not eat chilli can still enjoy good quality blood, however chilli thins the blood, lowers cholesterol, cleans the arteries and has a high level of natural antibiotic. Those who do not normally eat chilli should do so when they are ill.

Nature tells us how much fruit we should eat through its size. For example, watermelon is a large fruit and consists mainly of water. Our body is also composed mainly of water so we should have a lot of water and watermelon. Chilli is a tiny fruit, so the body only requires small amounts: at least three a day. Nature gives us clues.

BLOOD INFECTION

One day Elias accidentally stood on a rusty object that lay hidden under the surface of the ground. Within a short time, a vein quickly turned blue up the back of his leg.

He treated it naturally by eating 3kg of cherries each day for three days, after which the colour disappeared.

I asked if there was an alternative to cherries if they were out of season. He said 10 birdseye chilli per day would have helped cleanse the blood but cherries were more effective. When the immune system is poor, the quality of the blood is also poor and susceptible to infection. The blood is thick and dark in colour. Good quality blood is thin. To avoid blood infection, eating chilli daily may be the best medicine.

WARNING: *Self-diagnosis can be dangerous. Anyone who suspects blood infection or tetanus should seek advice from a qualified health care professional immediately.*

BLOOD PRESSURE

Many people suffer low blood pressure and it may be the end result of numerous factors. Walking up a flight of stairs is changing altitude and this can cause low blood pressure. Standing up quickly is also a change of altitude.

A fright, overwork, sudden shock, standing, tiredness, prolonged illness, stress, a weakened immune system, hunger, dehydration and poor quality blood etc., may also contribute to this problem.

Elias said to avoid low or high blood pressure, eat natural including tomato, cucumber and zucchini – they contain natural salt – and drink three litres of water daily. He said to eliminate stress, increase sleep hours, lose weight if necessary and exercise sensibly at least three times a week.

Eat three birdseye chilli daily to correct the blood. Deep, slow and calm breathing may help lower stress and lower high blood pressure.

In times of stress, blood rushes through the body and the pressure rises, the brain races and the heart palpitates. Corrective breathing helps to calm the body and increase oxygen in the blood stream. Slow deep breathing may also pacify the heart and aid blood pressure.

Five dates eaten three times daily after meals and at bedtime have a calming effect on the brain. Before retiring, avoid foods that contain processed cane sugar because it stresses the body and brain.

Grapes should not be eaten before bedtime because they are high in natural insulin. But if one needs a quick "pick me up", grapes are excellent because they are high in glucose.

Unless one suffers from kidney stones, do not eat watermelon or pear before bedtime. They encourage the kidneys to work harder. Do not eat bananas before bedtime because they contain high amounts of energy.

BODY ENERGY – POSITIVE AND NEGATIVE

Our electromagnetic field is laden with energy, both positive and negative. The body expels electric energy depending on the way we think and feel. We are unique, therefore some people's energies are stronger than others.

If one is kind, honest and leads a good life, their electromagnetic field is powerful and they will possess a presence. If this person walks into a room and even if they do not speak, their presence will be felt.

If a person is strong willed, entertains or harbours ill intent, their field will also create a strong presence, but it will be negative. A perfect example of presence was Gandhi. He maintained inner peace, calm and did not criticise others. This is the character of a powerful man. He was self-disciplined and lived life simply but did not expect the same of others.

Those with positive energy will attract likeminded people and may achieve much during their lives. But they may find they are unpopular because there will always be those who will try to bring them down to their level.

Those with traits of jealously, hate and disbelief etc., possess a strong, negative electromagnetic field. In some cases their face and mannerisms mirror their thoughts, while others may have mastered the art of masquerade.

Elias tells an interesting story about his magnetic field and its effect on others. While working in a German hospital, a visiting therapist gave a practical demonstration of hands-on-healing.

Elias said even though he did not believe in this practice, he was very attentive and actively participated. He believes only Jesus has healing powers and thought it strange that a mere mortal even thought he could do the same.

He thought about the laws of science, mathematics, physics and chemistry and knew it was impossible for any person to heal another. Elias said: "Only in my mind did I question what I witnessed, but continued to think of Jesus and the ego of the visiting therapist".

In the very next instance the teacher stopped the class and said: "Mr Schindelar, please go. We cannot accept people like you here. I do not like your way of thinking. I am stirred by the way you think".

Elias said this was the highest form of negativity. The lecturer was threatened by Elias's thoughts. He did not want the students to think anything other than what he was teaching. He had the need to control.

Elias said he knew he was in the wrong place from the beginning of the lecture. The lecturer was teaching opposite to the way Elias had been taught, and what he knew and experienced to be true. He felt Elias was a threat and mentally stronger than himself and this made him vulnerable.

When we are self-disciplined, strict and live life correctly, we grow stronger mentally and positively. Elias added: "When others come to us for help, we must have self-discipline and teach by example. If we do not have discipline and strength of character, it is difficult for others to have belief in us".

BREAST CANCER

Men and women of all ages can suffer breast cancer, including teenagers. As with most diseases the statistics are increasing. Elias said the major offenders that may cause cancer were:

- mammograms: breasts are highly sensitive glands, therefore they may not successfully absorb the radiation associated with this procedure because radiation destroys cells.
- oral contraceptives and HRT (Hormone Replacement Therapy):

these may contain a cocktail of chemicals, including artificial oestrogen. Elias said the level of artificial oestrogen may be so high it could be compared with the natural levels the female produced during pregnancy.

He said: "If a woman falls pregnant after she has taken oral contraceptives, these artificial chemicals may have the capacity to alter the structure of chromosomes in the early stages of pregnancy. It is for this reason we are witnessing a higher birth rate of females than males. These artificial hormones may also alter, damage and kill chromosomes and they can alter the hormones of babies."

Elias said artificial oestrogen may cause breast cancer in both men and women. It may also cause cancer of the hormonal glands, uterus, adrenal glands and the ovaries. Artificial oestrogen may also severely damage vessels throughout the body, including the brain which could lead to strokes.

Those who take oral contraceptives may also suffer severe bouts of depression and it could be for this reason that the incidence of suicide in young females is increasing. Men who consume oestrogen may experience breast and testicle enlargement.

Some dairy cows are given artificial oestrogen. They grow unusually large udders specifically to produce large amounts of milk. Many cows have to cope with udders that are so large the animal finds it difficult to walk. If beef cattle are given artificial oestrogen they also produce a higher yield of meat.

Many people are unwittingly consuming artificial oestrogen because it is eaten during meal time at the dining table. These chemicals may also be present in many lines of processed foods and beverages.

For example: certain beers contain this substance. It is added to the brew to hasten the fermentation process, enabling the manufacturers to produce their product quicker. The quicker the turnover – the more money they make.

HRT is used to alleviate the symptoms of menopause, a syndrome many middle age women tend to suffer. Menopause is the result of lifestyle and an improper diet. A healthy fruitarian with a strong immune system will not suffer these symptoms, nor do they suffer monthly periods. Their body is clean and their blood is of excellent quality, therefore they do not menstruate.

- smoking: cigarettes contain myriad chemicals, additives, humectants and addictive substances which pollute the body.
- dairy products: may pollute the lymphatic system, therefore it does not drain as it should. During cheese manufacturing, fats and casein are removed from milk resulting in a highly concentrated product.

Cheese contains many animal hormones, myriad allergens, herbicides, pesticides, dioxins and antibiotics, all of which are detrimental to the body because they are in a *concentrated* form. The process of turning milk into cheese does not eliminate toxins. Some pasteurised milk may now contain synthetic hormones.

- animal DNA such as meat, its by-products, poultry, fish and eggs: these foods may contain high levels of oestrogen, stress hormones, synthetic hormones that pollute the lymphatic system and produce harmful acids which prevent the natural functions of the nerve system.

BUY AUSTRALIAN

If we do not purchase home grown products we run the risk of consuming high levels of toxic chemicals that may be found in imported processed products, fruits and vegetables.

Many countries do not have the chemical restrictions we do in Australia. The following may be of interest:

- many of the canned products on supermarket shelves are not Australian.
- Australian farmers are throwing away high grade produce to animals as fodder because cheap imports are flooding our country.
- it is in our best interest to support Australian farmers because they have a much healthier product and they keep the prices down.
- fruit and vegetables (especially oranges) that are poor in quality are usually not grown in Australia.
- bananas not grown in Australia may have been sprayed with

toxins many times to control diseases in their country of origin.

CHILDHOOD LEUKAEMIA

Elias has treated many children with leukaemia and within weeks they are well on the road to recovery. He said: "When the source of the problem is removed, in conjunction with nerve massages, a calm environment, correct eating and total family commitment, the child heals quickly".

The most important factor in the healing process of this disease is complete discipline and honesty by those associated with the child. They must change current habits and trust Elias. Parents must change their environment because the electromagnetic field generated by electricity within homes is extremely detrimental to a child's body. Switch off all appliances when not in use.

The body of a child is underdeveloped, thus making it highly sensitive to the electrical frequencies that interfere with their body's own electromagnetic field. Radiation, chemical pollutants, processed food, microwave oven cookery and unsafe drinking water may all contribute to leukaemia.

Elias said heavy metals, chemical sprays and toxins such as mercury, thimerosal, aluminium and formaldehyde may be used in the manufacture of childhood vaccinations which could contribute heavily to this disease.

He said the underdeveloped bodies of babies and young children were incapable of handling metals and poisons. These substances weaken the body, brain and nerve system and many other diseases such as autism can occur.

The method he uses to help children and their families overcome leukaemia has not found favour within "the system" because he does not use drugs or surgery, and he is totally against radium and chemotherapy. On the contrary, he does not place children in stressful and painful situations. They eat natural foods and drink natural fruit juices that build their immune system which assures rapid healing.

Elias said the most important factor was the welfare and the noninvasive healing process of the child, and a comfortable and calm environment that would be conducive to their healing.

The death of a child can have a devastating effect on a family. One such case is that of a child who was born normal and healthy but after the 18-month vaccination, the child contracted leukaemia. Chemotherapy had no effect on the disease and the child lost its life. Unable to cope, the family fell apart through blame and guilt. The mother now carries the ashes of her child with her wherever she goes. Elias said childhood leukaemia was but one of many avoidable diseases.

COUGH MIXTURE

Elias's advice to his clients seeking cough relief has been to finely dice an onion and place in a glass jar. Add two dessertspoons of blossom honey and cap. Allow it to stand for at least two hours until a liquid has formed. Take two teaspoons of the liquid four times daily for two to four days. (This was suitable for both children and adults).

DAIRY – ITS ATTACK ON THE HUMAN BODY

Milk and dairy products may even be more damaging to the human body than beef and poultry because the toxic chemicals present in animal milk and dairy products such as cheese are highly concentrated. Elias places dairy higher than meats on the "food toxins list" and said it should be avoided.

Animals produce milk for *their* young. It contains nutrients designed by nature necessary for the health and growth of their offspring.

Humans should not consume milk that nature designed for animals because the human body requires nutrients suitable to itself and not that of a baby goat, sheep or calf etc. Milk from a cow was designed to set the foundation for its offspring which become beasts that can weigh more than a tonne.

Apart from breast milk for infants, nature provided humans with a source of fruit milk that is also 100 per cent compatible with the human body: coconut milk.

Elias said milk and all dairy products, especially cheese, may be termed as "cancer fuel". The hard cheeses may be extremely detrimental to the body. Some beef and dairy cattle may be vaccinated regularly with substances which contain growth hormones and antibiotics etc.

These may contaminate the human body through the milk and beef when consumed. This may be one of the many reasons we contract diseases such as breast, prostate and other forms of cancers.

Other illnesses including heart disease, diabetes (especially in children because it contains a protein called lactalbumin which has been linked to diabetes), malignancies, bronchitis, emphysema, asthma, influenza and pneumonia etc., are also linked to the consumption of animal DNA.

Dairy cows suffer many diseases and one may be Johne's disease. The animal is infected with bacteria and suffers diarrohea. The bacteria may find its way into the milk because it may not be eliminated during the pasteurisation process.

Sometimes, after consumption, the bacteria may begin to grow within the human body and the result can be severe. One may also suffer Crohn's disease, irritable bowel syndrome and other related problems. Milk decays rapidly. Bacteria multiply when it is allowed to stand at room temperature. Some milk may contain animal faeces and it may also contain pus because like humans, cows suffer from breast cancer, mastitis and other infections.

To learn more about such foods, one must research material that is independently written. There are many independent and free web sites, books, reports, journals and magazines that contain information that support Elias's theories on such topics. We should endeavour to make lifestyle changes while we are able because for some, change can come too late.

DEMENTIA

Elias said the lack of natural fructose was one of the main contributing factors to dementia. The brain requires fructose to function normally and it starves without it. If a diet does not contain satisfactory amounts of fructose, blood does not circulate correctly throughout the body and brain.

Alcohol must be removed from the diet of the dementia patient because it dehydrates and causes brain damage. The brain also dehydrates if not enough water is consumed. The person suffering from this disease must eat natural food.

The electromagnetic field generated by electricity and its frequency are detrimental to the brain and play a large part in this disease. Environmental toxins also contribute to what is fast becoming a common disease.

DETOXIFICATION

In order to heal, the body must be clean. Three litres of water and a combination of all fruits including three birdseye chilli daily are vital for the body to properly eliminate toxins. The body was made by nature, therefore it requires only natural foods to detoxify.

DIABETES

A healthy pancreas will create many types of hormones, including insulin in correct amounts for the body to function normally. If the pancreas is not functioning correctly – for example, an improper diet, stress, drugs or other influences – diabetes may occur. Elias said the pancreas should not be "pushed" into making extra insulin.

Glucagon is a hormone produced by the pancreas that increases the blood glucose concentration. It ensures self-regulation of the body.

Fluids made within the pancreas help the small intestines to break down food. Grapes contain glucose and natural insulin which is vital to a diabetic.

Diabetes is a disease in which the ability of the body to use complex sugars is impaired. Sugar levels appear abnormal in the urine. Elias said the problems that many diabetics have with their disease may stem from the lack of knowledge on this subject. Diabetics suffer from the complications caused by complex sugars that are incompatible to the body. Diabetics must have fructose in abundance in order to heal.

Diabetes is a complex subject and those who suffer it should educate themselves on their disease because correct information could save their life. It is difficult to get good information. Artificial insulin and other medication will not heal diabetes, but fruit sugar (fructose) *will.* Diabetics should learn about the healing properties that natural fruit sugars contain.

And they should be aware of the devastating and long-term effects artificial insulin may have on the body: blood circulation problems, loss of sight, gangrene in the lower limbs, heart and urinary tract disease, pancreatic problems, leg and foot ulcers, joint problems, fungi and bacterial infection etc.

Those with this disease who have not studied their illness and the affects that complex sugars have on their body are at the greatest risk if artificial insulin is administered. Elias said diabetics must be aware that the body produced a back-up supply of insulin in times of emergency.

If artificial insulin is administered, and if the body then releases the back-up supply some time later, the brain will become insulin saturated. The diabetic may lapse into a coma and death can occur.

An important fact that diabetics should remember is that, apart from fructose, the chemical structure of each type of complex sugar produces a different and adverse chemical reaction within the body and brain. Elias said diabetics should not eat foods that contained carbohydrates because the body converted it into complex sugar, causing severe and adverse reactions to blood sugar levels.

The more junk food, dairy and meat products people consume, the higher the risk of this disease. A diet rich in animal protein renders the pancreas highly sensitive. Diabetes can occur if one eats meat from an animal that has had a viral infection because it damages the human pancreas.

Elias has had many clients who have suffered diabetes who have healed themselves with correct information and natural therapy. He said the keys to healing diabetes were:

- the client must be totally honest and prepared to work with him 100 per cent.

- they must eat correctly at all times.
- a diabetic should not entertain negative thoughts.
- they must have total support from their family.

He said there have been several clients who have not healed but the problem lay within themselves. There are myriad reasons why people do not heal. Some lack self discipline and commitment, while others are negative and lack self-truth.

Elias said diabetes was sweeping modern society in almost epidemic proportions and it was a subject that most people did not understand because most of the information circulating was incorrect.

Diabetes may be the result of a number of issues, including a "fast" lifestyle, an inadequate diet, stress and incorrect information. Diabetes is an illness that is easily avoided and one that can be overcome with dedication and an open mind. Elias said he felt the public would have to wait a long time before educational programs were released on diabetes prevention.

Before 1940, the island of Tonga in the South Pacific did not have one person suffering from diabetes. Then meat, junk food and processed sugar, sweetened and addictive carbonated drinks were introduced to the island.

Unfortunately the Tongans succumbed to this easy style of eating and soon the first cases of diabetes were recorded. The incidence of the disease has now risen to one of the highest in the world.

Diabetes is on the increase in affluent countries. Their poorer counterparts cannot afford to eat meat, therefore the number of diabetes sufferers is lower. It seems diabetes is a disease of the rich. In America it is on the rise because of lifestyle and eating habits. It seems the trend in Australia is heading in the same direction. People are suffering this disease at a much younger age through lifestyle. In every country the number of people who have this disease is rising.

Diabetes and insulin are a huge industry. Insulin is derived from cultured bacteria from the pancreas of cattle and pigs, therefore the meat industry also benefits from this disease.

It takes a large amount of animal pancreas to produce insulin. This is ironic because the treatment for diabetes comes from the animal that caused the disease. And when meat is cheap, the number of people who contract diabetes increases.

Initially, artificial insulin is usually administered to diabetes sufferes in small doses. Within weeks, in many cases, this dosage is increased, then increased again. The more insulin a person has, the more they need. Artificial insulin does not heal diabetes.

Insulin is necessary to split complex sugar. If we eat meat, dairy, complex sugars and complex carbohydrates and other foods that are incompatible with the body, the pancreas is confronted with complex sugars, acids and toxin that create diabetes.

When we eat natural, the body does not require artificial insulin. If a diabetic suffers flu or viruses their blood sugar rises. Avocado is excellent for diabetes sufferers because it lowers blood sugar. Many other fruits do the same. Apple and fresh apple juice sipped slowly will also lower blood sugar. All types of fruit contain healing and cleansing properties.

Elias said when blood sugar was low with a reading of seven, the patient would become tired and lose concentration. If it falls below five the nerve cells die, the brain becomes "fuzzy" and perspiration is profuse. If blood sugar remains below five for a period of time, one can suffer brain damage and damage to the nerve centre.

He said if people have been insulin dependent, they have difficulty believing the body could heal itself with a little help. Not taking drugs to some may also be a problem because they may be addicted to the ritual or they may be too afraid to surrender them.

There are others who have started having natural therapy with Elias but when their healing was not as quick as they would have liked, they became impatient. Sometimes they may also have to deal with the disbelief of people they live or associate with.

If one has a health problem, their judgment or decision-making may become clouded. If a loved one speaks negatively on natural therapy the chances of healing will drop significantly.

Elias spoke about other dangers of artificial insulin and the effect it has on the body. He said during World War II, doses of insulin were injected into captured spies to kill them. But the cause of death often remained a mystery even after autopsies because all traces of insulin dissipate within the human body.

Whether the person is alive or dead, no trace of insulin is evident after two hours and the person who administered the drug has nothing to fear because their murderous act will remain undetected.

It seems artificial insulin may be a perfect killing potion ...

"Neurochemistry", an Introduction by Horst Jatzkewitz. Publisher: Georg Thieme Verlag Stuttgart 1978, may help diabetes sufferers understand the effects glucose has on the brain.

Quote

Even though glucose is under normal circumstances the main substrate for the maintenance of normal brain – and other organic functions, the glucose dependency of normal function is unusual: if fasting dogs are made hypoglycemic with insulin, then the arterial blood glucose level sinks simultaneously with the aterio-venereal difference.

While the arterial venous oxygen difference in the brain sinks parallel to this, it remains almost constant within the skeletal muscular system. This means that muscle tissue can oxidise other substances during episodes of glucose deficiency.

The brain has only limited capacity to do so. It therefore becomes clear, that brain functions fail initially during hypoglycaemic shock, while the heart keeps beating.

A hypoglycaemic episode is therefore very useful to examine whether the brain has alternate sources to draw upon glucose for energy delivery. Under normal circumstances this is not the case in-situ, because substances are delivered to the brain via blood.

During long lasting episodes of fasting or with diabetes, the body creates ketone particles and acetate. Both substances show huge arterial venous differences after passing through the brain.

To completely burn up the amount absorbed by the brain, it would require more than half the total oxygen usage of the brain. But ketone particles alone are not able to maintain normal brain function in the absence of glucose.

Because of the glucose dependency of the brain and the low blood volume in relationship to total brain mass (approx. 3-3.5 per cent), the blood flow in the brain and therefore the glucose supply are adapted to the oxygen supply: if the oxygen supply is increased during regular glucose supply, the speed of blood flow is decreased, if the oxygen supply is decreased, the speed of the blood flow is increased.

The speed of the blood flow is also increased if there is increased glucose supply, as during hypoglycaemia. These adjustments serve normal breathing (3.3ml oxygen/100g brain/min). A reduction in brain oxygen by 20-30 per cent already leads to interruptions in the electrical activity, which can be shown on the EEG and lead to unconsciousness.

On the other hand, physical changes such as seen with oxygen deprivation (altitude sickness and hallucinations) or with schizophrenia are not associated with changes in cerebral breathing.

Unquote

DRINKING RECYCLED SEWAGE AND FLUORIDE

According to the Gospel of St. John 2: 1-12, Jesus turned about 100 litres of water into wine during a wedding ceremony in the town of Canna at Galilee some two millennia ago.

More than 2000 years later, another phenomena is taking place in South East Queensland. The fruits of the sewers and toxic chemicals will be converted into a liquid that resembles water. This fluid is to be added to the existing water supply and people will have to drink it because they were not given a choice.

Fluoride is already being added to the water. But in 1930, it was used to kill rats. Elias said fluoride in drinking water was not acceptable because:

- it removes calcium from tissues.
- it tightens muscles.
- it thickens blood.
- it causes pain in bones.
- teeth become brittle.
- the roots of teeth decay.
- it affects the lymph system.
- it affects cartilage, hair and liver.

Fluoride is banned in many countries because of the risks to the brain, thyroid glands and kidneys and the high risk of bone cancer.

But fluoride is not just fluoride. When researching this chemical substance, it may be wise to investigate hexa flurosilicic, a compound that releases hydrogen fluoride which has been said to cause lung edema.

Other fluorides one can research are fluorosilicic acid, sodium silicofluoride and sodium fluoride, silicofluoride and hydrofluoric silicic acid. Also research the chemical N-nitrosodimethylamine (NDMA).

It is well worth noting that one of the fluorides – S6fluorosilicate – is used as a rat poison and contains heavy metals such as arsenic, mercury, lead, aluminium and cadmium. This cocktail of chemicals is toxic if ingested. Chemicals accumulate within the human body and they could have the same effect on our fragile environment.

The packaging of some toothpastes that contain fluoride warn that young children should be supervised while brushing their teeth because it should not be swallowed.

Many countries have discontinued using fluoride, while many health care professionals are calling for an end to water fluoridation and the ingestion of sewerage fluid. It seems such warnings are being ignored. Warnings about genital deformities, infertility, cancers, foetal deformities, genetic defects, mad cow disease, viruses, infections and hormone instability are also being ignored. Could it be that there is a fortune to be made in certain sectors from the on-going need to use chemicals during the conversion process of such fluids?

Billions of litres of healthy natural water flow into the oceans every year to the north of this state as a result of seasonal rains, storms and cyclones. Could some of this water not be piped to where it is needed? Why are people expected to drink a substance that looks like water which is manufactured from human faeces, body fluids, and which may contain the remnants of chemotherapy, radium, illicit and prescription drugs, abortion drugs, addictive substances, and fertilizers and pesticides etc?

Fluids and solids from hospital waste which contain a plethora of diseases, contaminated blood, bacteria and the spoils of mortuaries may all be collected. Then there could be the run-off from slaughter houses, heavy industry, and the list goes on.

This effluent will be passed through a treatment plant, irradiated and a concoction of chemicals added. Many people will have no alternative but to drink it. They will have to use it during food preparation.

They will have to bathe themselves, their newborn babies, their children and wash their clothes in it. It will be on scalps and in hair – there will be no escape. If there is a malfunction within the conversion of such fluids, the consequences could be catastrophic. One can only imagine what effect this nightmare will have on the human body and on the immature immune systems of babies and small children.

But sewage will always be sewage and chemicals will always be chemicals. And why some mere mortals think they can convert these substances into natural drinking water is beyond the realms of comprehension. People should not accept anything less than what nature planned for us.

For more information on this potential man-made disaster, please go to the following web sites:

- www.thehealthvine.net/
- www.ausiwakeup.webs.com
- www.loveforlife.com.au/book/exporthtml/5550
- www.dianabuckland.webs.com/peoplesalliancecouncil.htm
- www.fluoridealert.org/fluoridation.htm

- www.fluoride-journal/98-31-2/312103.htm
- www.fluoridealert.org/hp-epa.htp

DRUGS – THE CHEMICAL PROMISE

The history of penicillin harks back to the ancient cultures of China and Greece but it is only in modern times that the pharmaceutical industry has become one of the largest, richest and most powerful in the world.

Countries forged ahead after World War II – the timing was perfect. Woman's magazines became the order of the day. Advertising campaigns were cleverly orchestrated. Medicinal drugs were also new. They provided a quick fix and were embraced by the masses. These scientific discoveries gave birth to the pharmaceutical industry and companies have capitalised.

Experiments for new and improved antibiotics continued and then a major discovery was made: it was found there was little to fear from bacteria and viruses because in order for them to survive within the human body, there must be a continuous supply of animal DNA for them to feed on. But when animal DNA was eliminated from the diet of the bacteria and viruses, they died of starvation. It seems this discovery may be one of the world's best kept secrets of the last century.

Drugs, however, soon became widely accepted, embraced and part of a new lifestyle. An "untested over a lifetime" culture had evolved and to some this was seen as the beginning of the assault on the immune system. People no longer had to think for themselves as they had for centuries and in doing so, they surrendered the power to think for themselves. Home remedies were replaced with drugs and as a result the "healing" industry was born.

But despite all this we still have myriad viruses and diseases such as cancers, drug induced lupus, diabetes, stroke, high blood pressure, heart conditions – the list is long. Some diseases are growing stronger because they are becoming immune to drugs while mutating viruses have the potential to wipe out civilisation.

Sophisticated antibiotics have been with us for decades and many still regard them as wonder drugs and miracle cures. But drugs are becoming less effective in the fight against bacteria because as their strength increases, so does that of bacteria.

Chemicals create imbalance in the environment and drugs have the same effect on the human body because they may weaken the immune system, damage vital organs and other diseases may have a flow-on effect.

No one can deny some scientists have made wonderful discoveries and phenomenal contributions to mankind. However, the chemical fight against diseases and viruses is not being won because most of it is based on "after the fact" and not on prevention. Drugs are useless in the fight against viruses and when one links with another, a third is born that is stronger then its parents.

Elias said the pharmaceutical industry was presently using a chemical that he classified as "a very heavy poison". The problem is: industry is moving away from natural drugs and using the synthetic variety.

He said most times the body was capable of cleansing itself of the natural poisons that were used in the past. However, with the new synthetic type, his alarm bells were ringing because the body cannot eliminate these toxins. He said only time would tell as to how much they damaged the body, nerve system and ultimately the brain. He said people must be aware of what happened within their body after they had taken new drugs.

They must enlist the help of a natural therapist who can help them cleanse their body of these heavy chemicals and the therapist must know exactly what the problem is and how to handle it.

Recently, a medical practitioner spoke on a local radio station on the subject of children's drugs. He said no research has ever been carried out on children's medication and vaccinations. He said this should be a great cause of concern to parents because it was not possible to do this type of testing. Could this be one of the reasons why so many babies and small children are contracting serious illnesses?

More than 20,000 new words have been invented in the last 20 years to accommodate such a phenomenon. But despite the new drugs and some wonderful advancements in modern medicine, one would be hard pressed to find people who enjoy 100 per cent good health, especially in those over the age of 40.

It seems from time to time miracle cures come to our attention. For example, a fruit juice may be marketed on a promise that it will cure cancer and sells at about $70 a litre. If one has a loved one dying from cancer they will buy it in a desperate attempt to keep them alive, regardless of price. This is marketing.

But nature put healing qualities in every variety of fruit for a specific reason: to keep mankind healthy. It is up to the individual to accept the gifts and the powers that nature offers.

It seems diseases are invented from time to time and there are those who disease-monger in an effort to exaggerate mild conditions. For example, cholesterol, arthritis and osteoporosis etc., are depicted as diseases. But they are not diseases: they are the end result of one's eating habits.

We all know that those with power can take anything from those who do not. For example, female vanity: what a fantastic opportunity for those in the enhancement and beautification industry to make an absolute fortune. The vulnerability of men is also an easy target because it is a well known fact they do not speak openly about issues that concern them.

One such issue is balding, a natural and normal occurrence. Men and women experience thinning or loss of hair regardless of age but it is more prevalent as one grows older. There are those who have capitalised on what most of us accept as normal. Images at vantage points depicting balding is a ploy to make men feel bad about themselves. However, those with self esteem view this as manipulation of the mind.

Another issue that has been capitalised on is erectile dysfunction. Like so many other disorders this may well be the result of a number of factors such as an unhealthy lifestyle and poor eating habits.

Men and women can improve their health by purifying their blood and lowering cholesterol. Look at alcohol, nicotine and coffee intake, stress levels and relationships. Is weight a problem and is there a commitment to regular physical fitness? But some people do not have the capacity to address such issues and it is easier for them to adopt a cavalier attitude. It may also be even easier for them to lay the blame elsewhere.

The quick fix then becomes the remedy and one no longer needs to take responsibility. Some males are more than happy to take the risk and pay the price even though it is just to perform temporally. Here is another excellent market based on "after the fact".

If one is fit and healthy and feels good about themselves the body will usually function as nature intended. We should all look at the quality of our health and view it in the long term so as not to have to rely on a quick fix. When we look deep within our mind with honesty, most of us know where our short falls lie and whether or not we fix these problems is up to us.

How many times have we heard of a new miracle cure, food or preventive substances that work against obesity, cancer, diabetes, heart problems, hardening of the arteries, and stroke etc? But are they working? And no doubt many of them will be quietly ushered off the shelves because of their sinister side effects that we are not told about.

Parents are usually not encouraged to raise their children in harmony with nature. Instead, they are advised to feed them the flesh of dead animals in the state of rigor mortis and to give them processed foods laden with processed sugar, additives, colourants and addictive substances. Parents are not educated to take responsibility for the welfare of their health and that of their children. They are not told what substances are in medications and vaccinations and many of us have discovered their side effects by trial and error.

It may be difficult to monitor the side effects some drugs have on the body because it can be a slow process. This adds to the existing problem/problems because the sufferer becomes oblivious to the fact that something sinister may be happening within their body and assumes it is part of the illness.

It is up to the individual to think for themselves: remember, we do have alternatives. Do not allow yourself to become a statistic of the drug machine – let your food be your medicine. There certainly are many new and super drugs out there but we cannot fool nature and we cannot fool the body. Nature will always have the last say.

EATING DEAD ANIMALS

The nerve system is the life force of the body.

When a human body dies blood circulation ceases, every cell begins to break down, the protein alters and decay begins immediately. The same process occurs to dead animals. Whether or not the body is in cold storage, when life leaves the nerve system, the body is in a state of rigor mortis.

Animals are killed and their blood (which contains iron) is drained. The meat is processed and distributed for human consumption. Humans eat animals when they are in a state of rigor mortis. The problem is we have accepted this as a normal practice because this is the way it has always been. Many seem to accept what they do not know, without question.

Many meat processors also perform "gas flushing". It has been said this practice may add up to six weeks to the shelf life of beef.

Whether meat is cooked or raw, if it is allowed to stand at room temperature it discolours, breaks down and quickly rots, especially in hot weather.

A similar process occurs within the digestive system. But there it is much worse because the body generates heat and digestive acids perform similar to the decomposition process of a compost heap.

As meat cooks its temperature rises. At 42 degrees Celsius its protein goes into shock and its molecular structure alters, therefore it is no longer normal or natural. After the meat is consumed the digestive system begins the decomposition and elimination process. This takes place usually over a period of up to five days and it is during this time that severe damage occurs within the body.

The digestive system is forced into producing dozens of chemical substances in order to break down decaying meat within the colon. These substances are toxins and acids, while some may be bacteria.

They include ammonic, sulphuric, hydrochloric, hydrogen sulphide, serein, and botulinum bacteria (bacterium clostridium: .001mg can cause the nerve system to shut down causing death).

Cadaverin, putresein, exorphine, sulphate (sulphur hydrogen), primere amine and mercaptan, propionsure, decarboxylierung, lysine, ornithine, arginine and agmatine are also produced. Others include: phenylalanine, ptomaine, neurine, threonine, tryptophan and valine.

These toxic substances cause destructive reactions to the nerve system. Its malfunction results in the brain's inability to send and receive correct messages throughout the body. As a result, various types of brain cancers may occur as well as bowel and lung cancer, asthma and melanomas and many other diseases.

The chemical substances break down the putrefied meat within the colon. But other problems arise because the body must eliminate these toxins and it is forced to do so in various ways:

1. The body converts it into uric acid and filters it through the kidneys.

2. Through the lungs. Toxic acids produced by the decomposition of rotting meat cause intricate lung tissue to slowly break down and deteriorate.

Elias places the damaging effects that meat has on the lungs on the same level as smoking. But this destruction is much more dangerous because its effect is very subtle.

Most people do not associate eating meat and dairy with lung cancer, asthma and other related lung diseases. The condition of the lung and digestive tract is indicated by one's breath.

If a person eats fruit and if they are healthy, their breath is usually not strong (if one is under stress, the breath will be strong because stress causes acid). But if the breath of a meat eater is strong – like that of rotting meat – it is the body's warning that high levels of toxins and toxic acids are present. This is a warning from nature and it should not be ignored.

3. Toxic acids are released through the skin causing skin cancers.

4. Harmful chemicals and rotting animal DNA work their way

through the digestive tract over a period of up to five days before elimination via the bowel. These toxins may cause various types of cancers throughout the digestive tract.

If one suffers a skin condition, it is usually a sign from nature that there is a problem within the body or within the digestive system.

If an animal is sick from viruses or bacteria and if its meat is cooked thoroughly at a temperature of more than 50 degrees Celsius, all bacteria and viruses are killed and they do not affect the human body because heat destroys microbes.

But if an animal was sick from a chemical reaction – this may be because powdered animal DNA had been added to their food – and even though the meat was thoroughly cooked then eaten, the sickness is transmitted to the human and they will inherit the identical disease.

Other dangers can arise if meat is not cooked properly. If animals have had worm infestation (some are invisible to the naked eye), they transmit them to the muscles of the consumer because that is their habitat.

A mathematical equation of the effects that one prime piece of steak has on the human body is as follows: an average steak contains between 24mg and 28mg of uric acid. Kidneys flush acid slowly and they require between six and eight litres of water to flush one milligram of uric acid.

Therefore hypothetically, at least 160 litres would be necessary to completely cleanse them of the steak meal.

A clean lymphatic system is vital because it absorbs fats from the digestive system and cleans toxins and waste materials. Animal products contain saturated fats. The more animal fats and dairy we consume, the more pressure we place on the lymph system. It becomes congested and overburdened, it cannot function normally and cancer may occur. We must choose our foods wisely, correct our lifestyle, eliminate stress and microwave oven cookery, adjust alcohol levels and cease nicotine intake in order to prevent disease.

Bacteria can contaminate meat and small goods. Some bacteria are sinister because they are tasteless and the food looks normal.

There is no way of knowing if the meat is contaminated until it is too late. For example, if a woman eats contaminated pate, her body may harbour bacteria until it is properly diagnosed and eradicated. But if it is not diagnosed, there is a strong possibility that her future babies may be born blind.

Other problems may arise from eating dead animals because there is no way of knowing what the animal ate prior to slaughter. When humans consume by-products such as sausage, salami or other small goods – and especially those that contain ingredients such as liver and other offal and gelatine – infection and bacteria that are harboured within the animal's organs may be transmitted to the consumer.

The liver can harbour heavy metals, chemicals, bacteria, diseases and viruses such as hepatitis. The liver is an organ that secretes bile and performs various metabolic functions and should not be eaten.

Loss of life can also occur from meat contamination. Processed meats, in particular, may be dangerous to children because their body is underdeveloped, therefore their immune system may not cope as well as adults. Many deaths caused by meat contamination and foods that contain gelatine have been recorded.

The human body cannot neutralise animal DNA acids quickly, therefore they affect the skeletal system. As uric acid crystallises it settles within the joints. These crystals leach calcium from the skeleton, it becomes weak and fragile and bones are easily broken. In time bones may honeycomb and arthritis and gout may invade the joints. Uric crystals also attack nerve cells and cause severe pain.

Cattle, horses and other herbivores do not eat meat yet most have perfect bodies and powerful muscles. Their nutrients are derived from plants. Humans, on the other hand, kill and eat animals, then the dead animals kill them.

Meat from beef cattle and poultry contains a natural stress hormone that is released into their body during their dying process because animals "smell" death. This chemical is difficult for the human body to process because it is a toxin.

But chicken flesh is even more detrimental to the human body than beef because poultry also release a stress hormone daily during their entire life. It is this hormone that causes their flesh to rot even more rapidly than beef after slaughter.

After chicken is cooked and consumed, it begins to break down within the digestive system. The stress hormone causes further damage to the nerve system because it creates yet another chemical reaction when it connects with the other chemical toxins, acids and bacteria already present from the putrefaction process within the colon. As a result, many people have suffered paralyses while others have skin damage.

Animals only eat what they are supposed to unless man intervenes. Many humans are omnivores and they do not discriminate: they tend to eat just about everything as long as it tastes good and do so without question.

With time, animal protein, chemical substances and lifestyle choices can transform what was once a perfect and healthy human body at birth into one that is riddled with disease.

Throughout the centuries humans have become addicted to meat. The food industry is geared this way – this is what we know and this is what we accept.

No matter where we go for a meal most of it revolves around animal flesh and dairy and much of our food is no longer pure.

One day before I met Elias I purchased an oxtail. On arriving home from the butcher I set about dismembering the tail to make soup. But between each joint lived a maggot colony.

Within a few seconds the kitchen bench and floor became "alive". There were thousands of them. This vivid image is one I recall with disgust when I crave animal protein.

ELECTROMAGNETIC FIELD AND ITS EFFECT ON THE HUMAN BODY

The nerve system generates the body's electromagnetic field and it is as unique as our DNA. The external field is commonly known as the aura. Magnetic fields are powerful and should not be interfered with by other fields, especially those generated by electricity because they generate radiation (electric smoke) and cause cancer.

Military personal, especially those surrounded by radar equipment or those who work on submarines and warships, may be at high risk. Fishermen who have sophisticated equipment on their vessels may also be at risk. The electromagnetic field generated by some radar systems may cause cancer and blindness. Electromagnetic fields generated by electric smoke interfere with the brain and nerve system and may manifest in the form of explosive sounds within the brain.

The earth has its own extremely powerful magnetic force. For example, rivers flow and join beneath the earth's surface, creating power. When molecules of two bodies of water rub together, they create energy. This movement of quartz and water creates an electromagnetic force/field.

In earlier centuries, clever architects incorporated this energy into the design of significant buildings such as churches where magnetic fields were used to advantage. Some churches were built over river junctions and lecterns were strategically placed where the field was the strongest. Speakers stood long hours without rest or sustenance and it appeared they possessed supernatural powers. They were held in high esteem and shrewdly took advantage of nature's creation. They accumulated personal wealth and became influential. Today, magnets can be used for their pain killing qualities and like the body they have a magnetic field. They kill pain because their magnetic energy is transmitted throughout the body via the nerve system. When magnets are within close proximity to the body, they intercept messages to and from the brain causing transmission malfunction – the brain ceases to function correctly.

Elias said magnets were a quick fix for pain relief. He has treated clients who have suffered nerve damage caused by magnets. One particular client had worn a magnetic waist belt for back pain. Elias said the client would not believe that magnets could be dangerous and he continued to wear the belt. Unfortunately he lost his life to cancer to his midsection.

Elias said babies and young children were at particularly "high risk" with regards to electromagnetic radiation. He said their vulnerable and underdeveloped body, brain and nerve systems could not cope with the invisible killer.

Cooking food in microwave ovens may be harmful and may cause leukaemia, brain tumours and colon cancer etc. Food and beverages should not be cooked or heated in these appliances because it may interfere with the electromagnetic field of the body, causing it to short circuit. Correct messages are then not transmitted and received from and by the brain.

Elias said microwave oven cookery changed the polarity and chemical structure of food and beverages. For example, the chemical structure of calcium in food = Ca++. But when it is cooked or heated – for example, milk for babies – in a microwave oven, it changes to: Ca– – . The ions also alter and become a toxin. The body no longer recognises it as food: it recognises it as *a toxin*. This toxic food then creates a chain of events within the body and sinister diseases such as leukaemia and other cancers may occur.

Food cooked in microwave ovens may also alter the chemical structure of the blood and as a result it thickens and ages prematurely.

Food cooked in a microwave oven may be especially detrimental to babies and children because their brain, nerve system and immune system are underdeveloped, making them highly susceptible to sinister diseases.

During the 1900s, the first warnings were broadcast about damage to the ozone layer by negative electrical power generated by electronic machines. Damage to the ozone layer is well documented yet the problem continues to escalate.

To ensure good health and a good night's sleep, do not place beds against walls that house electrical cables. Beds should be situated five metres away from such cables and appliances should be switched off when they are not being used.

Elias said the electromagnetic field which radiated from television sets could make children aggressive. Radiation shoots from their screens in the form of electrons and damages the brain, nerve systems and eyes. LCD television and computer screens are safer and much safer for the eyes of both children and adults.

Elias said there was a very strong connection between brain tumours and the use of some mobile telephones. He said to cut down calls on mobile telephones from minutes to seconds. He said to hold the mobile telephone away from the head, particularly while it was ringing. Cordless telephones could have similar effects.

Lyn McLean is the author of the informative book titled *Watt's the Buzz?* (Scribe Publications, 2003) and Director of EMR Australia PL. Her web site is: www.emraustralia.com.au

She kindly wrote the following article specifically for this book:

Quote

It's with us at home and at work. It's with us as we drive along the freeway or recline at the local beach. It's in our children's schools and kindergartens, our hospitals and universities. It touches every person alive and every place on this planet. It's invisible; it's odorless; it's ubiquitous. It's electromagnetic radiation.

Electromagnetic radiation, or more simply EMR (**1**), is the companion of modern technology. It's emitted from all power lines, wiring, appliances, computers, TV, mobile phones and communications antennas (or phone towers).

As this technology gains an ever-increasing foothold in our lives, we need to ask the question: "Is this radiation safe?" Despite several decades of research, there is still no conclusive answer.

There is general agreement that high levels of exposure represent a health hazard and national and international standards have been designed to protect against these. However, there is still no consensus on whether everyday levels of exposure, not covered by existing standards, are a problem.

Some studies have failed to find health problems from the types of exposure we would expect to encounter in everyday life – but many have. Among the problems that have been linked with exposure to EMR are cancer, leukaemia, brain tumours, heart problems, reproductive problems, neurodegenerative diseases, suicide and depression. Scientists have also connected EMR with adverse effects on hormones, genes, immunity, sleep, memory, skin – and a host of other unpleasant symptoms.

The strongest evidence of risk is for childhood leukaemia and emissions from the electrical system. Since 1979 many studies have found that children living in higher-than-average fields from the power sources have an increased risk of the disease. In late 2000, Dr Anders Ahlbom (**2**) published the results of a study which had examined the data of nine previous studies of over 3247 children. He found that children exposed to a magnetic field of 4milliGaus [mG] – i.e. 250 times less than the draft Australian standard – had double the normal risk of leukaemia.

In 2001, a report by eminent UK scientist Sir Richard Doll (the man who had made the connection between smoking and lung cancer) reviewed a number of studies on the EMR-leukaemia connection. His report stated that "taken in conjunction they suggest that relatively average exposures of 0.4uT [4mG] or more are associated with a doubling of the risk of leukaemia in children under 15 years of age". (**3**)

As a result of studies such as these, in 2002 the International Agency for Research on Cancer (IARC) classified magnetic fields of more than 4mG from the power system as possibly carcinogenic. At the higher frequencies used by mobile phone and other communications networks, EMR has also been associated with unpleasant and potentially dangerous effects. Much of the scientific research in this area has focused on the effects of radiation from mobile phones.

It is well known that mobile phone radiation is absorbed by the user's head and that it does have an impact on the body, resulting in changes to genes and hormones and electrical activity of the brain.

Some studies have found breaches of the blood-brain barrier (which protects the brain against the incursion of harmful chemicals) and activation of stress response in cells.

In addition, many mobile phone users have reported unpleasant symptoms such as unusual and severe headaches, tightness in the head, disorientation, memory problems, warmth, tingling and sometimes burning in the scalp.

A key focus for researchers has been the possible connection between mobile phone use and brain tumours. While several studies have found no effect, others have found a definite connection. Swedish oncologist Dr Lennart Hardell has conducted six studies on the connection between mobile phone use and brain tumours, salivary gland tumours, non-Hodgkinson lymphoma and testicular cancer.

He and his team found that analogue mobile phone users had 2.9 times the normal risk of developing acoustic neuroma and 1.7 times the risk of developing astrocytoma types III and IV. Users of digital mobile phones had 1.5 times the risk of developing acoustic neuromas and astrocytomas types III and IV.

Cordless phone users had 1.5 times the risk of developing acoustic neuromas or astrocytomas III and IV. The risk of brain tumours increased with duration of mobile phone use especially with over 10 years of use. However, the researchers saw no consistently increased risk of salivary gland tumours, non-Hodgkinson lymphoma or testicular cancer with phone use. **(4)**

While scientists debate the risks of mobile phone use in adults, there is disturbing evidence that children users may be more at risk. Firstly, cells are thought to be more vulnerable to radiation during the process of mitosis, or growth.

Moreover, children's skulls are thinner and they have a long life expectancy over which to accumulate radiation damage.

In view of this and much other evidence associating EMR from a variety of sources with negative outcomes for health, some national and international authorities have recommended precautionary measures to reduce public exposure.

Sensible precautions that you can take include:

- have the fields in your home and workplace measured.
- ensure you and your family do not spend long periods of time (such as while sleeping) in high exposure locations.

- reduce unnecessary use of computers, video games and gadgets.
- use mobile phones only for emergencies and then only with hands-free kits.
- always use wired rather that wireless connections.
- keep a distance from high exposure sources.
- build immunity and reduce exposures to chemicals.

(1) The term EMR is used here to include fields from the 50/60Hz power system (also known as ELF or EMF) and higher radiofrequency radiation (RFR) of the communications networks.

(2) Ahlbom et al, Br J Cancer 83 (5):692-98, 2000.

(3) NRPB, "ELF Electromagnetic Fields and the Risk of Cancer", Documents of the NRPB, 12(1), 2001. (4) Hardell, L et al, World J Surg Oncol 4:74, 2006

Unquote

FOOD ADDITIVES

Much of the information in this section on food additives comes from the book titled: *The Additive Code Breaker*. Authors: Maurice Hanssen with Jill Marsden and revised for Australia by Betty Norris.

The book was printed in Australia by McPherson's and published by Lothian Books. 1991.

Quote

In 1987, a system of labelling for additives in packaged foods was approved in Australia. A code was set and food manufacturers must adhere to this code. All food must be correctly labelled and packaged to meet the set standards. An International Numbering System for Food Additives was adopted in 1989.

Many of the labels now have included numbers that signify the names and numbers of ingredients. For example, a certain type of edible oil blend that is 100 per cent Australian made and packaged. It contains several ingredients including the antioxidant 319. The label states it is excellent for frying, grilling, salad dressings, baking, marinades and mayonnaise.

When we check this number in the Additive Code Breaker book we discover this chemical is tert-Butylhydroquinone (TBHQ) which is derived from petroleum and is often used with other antioxidants such as BHA(320), BHT(321) and propyl gallate(310). The effect that TBHQ can have on the body is nausea, vomiting, ringing in the ears, delirium, feelings of suffocation, and collapse. A fatal dose of TBHQ is 5g. This additive is found in dairy blends, edible fats, edible oils, reduced fat spreads, lard, dripping, margarine and salad oils.

Unquote

The safe oils to use when cooking or in salad dressings are first cold pressed extra virgin olive oil, pure coconut oil and pure avocado oil. These oils are derived from fruit and should not contain chemical additives. Many oils such as soy, flax, cottonseed, sunflower and canola may also be genetically engineered.

It is wise to shop Australian because we have a higher standard in food manufacture than some other countries. A processed product that comes to mind is noodles.

One ingredient may be 920 L-cysteine hydrochloride and L-cysteine hydrochloride monohydrate. The origin is a naturally occurring amino acid, and manufactured from animal hair and chicken feathers. Chicken feathers add flavour.

Tartrazine is a food additive (E102). It gives foods a yellow colour. Tartrazine can cause a toxic response in the immune system and is banned in some countries. It is used widely as a food colouring.

The additive 932 Nitrous oxide (laughing gas) is used as a whipping agent in whipped cream. This substance may also be found in aerosol cans, desserts, sauces and toppings. One particular incident is that of a child who suffered an uncontrollable laughter spasm that lasted four hours. The child had eaten cake topped with cream which had been sprayed on the cake from an aerosol can. Parents must be aware of what affects their child.

The additive 310 propyl gallate (propyl 3,4,5-trihydroxybenzoate) is another antioxidant found in inferior oils and fats often in combination with 321 and 320. All alkyl gallates may cause gastric or skin irritation in some people, including those who suffer from asthma or are sensitive to aspirin. It is not permitted in foods intended specifically for infants or young children.

Propyl gallate is sometimes added to inner packaging of foods such as breakfast cereals and potato flakes, so it is possible that its vapour could contaminate the food it contains. This ingredient is found in dairy blends, edible fats, edible oils, reduced fat spreads, lard, dripping, margarine and salad oils.

A food additive is any substance not normally consumed as a food by itself and not normally used as a typical ingredient of food, whether or not it has nutritive value, the intentional addition of which to food for a technological (including *organoleptic) purpose in the manufacture, processing, preparation, treatment, packaging, packing, transport or holding of such food results in, or may be reasonably expected to result (directly or indirectly) in it or its by-products becoming a component of or otherwise affecting the characteristics of such.

The term does not include "contaminants" or substances added to food for maintaining or improving nutritional qualities.

*Organoleptic: sight, taste, smell and texture as perceived by the senses.

The approved class names and the functions they perform are:

anti-caking agents: ensure that products such as salt flow freely and that the particles do not stick together.

antioxidants: prevent foods that contain fats and oils from becoming rancid and other foods such as cut fruit from discolouring on exposure to the air.

artificial sweetening substances: are used to sweeten low-joule foods and brewed soft drinks.

bleaching agents: whiten foods e.g. colours, flour.

colours: restore colour lost during processing and storage and ensure a uniform colour in the finished product.

emulsifiers: ensure that oil and water mixtures do not separate into layers.

enzyme: break down foods e.g. milk into curds and whey.

flavour enhancers: bring out the flavour of the food without imparting a flavour of their own.

flavours: restore flavour lost during processing and maintain uniformity.

flour treatment agents: improve flour performance in bread making.

food acids: maintain a constant acid level in food despite variations in the acid level of the ingredients.

minerals: added to certain foods to supplement dietary intake.

mineral salts: enhance the texture of foods such as processed meats which might lose fats and meat juices.

preservatives: prolong the shelf-life of food.

propellants: used in aerosol containers.

thickeners: ensure content consistency.

vegetable gums: ensure content consistency.

vitamins: are added to foods to make up for losses in processing and storage.

FOOD COLOURINGS

100. Curcumin (C.I. 75300).

101. Riboflavin (lactoflavin; vitamin B2).

101. Riboflavin-5`-phosphate-sodium.

102. Tartrazine (C.I. 19140; FD and C yellow 5) a very commonly used colour.

E104. Quinoline yellow (C.I. 47005).

Not permitted in the production of Australian-made foods.

107. Yellow 2G (C.I. 18965).

110. Sunset yellow FCF (C.I. 15985; FD and C yellow 6).
120. Cochineal; (carmines; carminic acid; C.I. 75470).
122. Azorubine (carmoisine; C.I. 14720).
123. Amaranth (C.I. 16185; FD and C red 2).
124. Ponceau 4R (brilliant scarlet 4R C.I. 16255).
127. Erythrosine (C.I. 45430; FD and C Red 3).
E128. Red 2G (C.I. 18050).
129. Allura red AC (C.I. 16035; food red 17; FD and C red 40).
E131. Patent Blue V (C.I. 42051).
Not permitted in the production of Australian-made foods.
132. Indigotine (indigo carmine; C.I. 73015; FD and C Blue 2).
133. Brilliant blue FCF (C.I. 42090; FD and C Blue 1).
140. Chlorophyll (C.I. 75810).
141. Copper complexes of chlorophyll and chlorophyllins (C.I. 75810; copper phaeophytins).
142. Green S (acid brilliant green BS; food green S; lissamine green; C.I. 44090).
150. Caramel.
151. Brilliant black BN (brilliant black PN; C.I. 28440).
153. Vegetable carbon (carbon black).
E154. Brown FK (kipper brown; food brown). Not permitted in the production of Australian-made foods.
155. Brown HT (chocolate brown HT; C.I. 20285).
160(a). Alpha-Carotene, beta-Carotene, gamma-Carotene (C.I. 75130).
160(b). Annatto extracts (annatto; bixin; norbixin; C.I. 75120).
E160(c). Capsanthin (capsorubin). Not permitted in the production of Australian-made foods.
E160(d). Lycopene (C.I. 75125). Not permitted in the production of Australian-made foods.
160(e). Beta-Apo-8`-carotenal (Beta-8`-apocarotenal).
160(f). Beta-Apo-8`-carotenoic acid ethyl ester.
161. Xanthophylls-flavoxanthin.
161. Xanthophylls-lutein.
161. Xanthophylls-cryptoxanthin.

161. Xanthophylls-rubixanthin.
161. Xanthophylls-violaxanthin.
161. Xanthophylls-rhodoxanthin.
161(g). Xanthophylls-canthaxanthin (C.I. 40850).
162. Beet red (betanin).
163. Anthocyanins.
170. Calcium carbonate (chalk; C.I. 77220).
171. Titanium dioxide (C.I. 77891).
172. Iron oxides (yellow: C.I. 77492; red: 77491; black: 77499).
E173. Aluminium (C.I. 77000). Not permitted in the production of Australian-made foods.
E174. Silver (C.I. 77820).
Not permitted in the production of Australian-made foods.
E175. Gold (C.I. 77480). Not permitted in the production of Australian-made foods.
E180. Pigment rubine (Lithol rubine BK: C.I. 15850).
Not permitted in the production of Australian-made foods.
181. Tannic acid (tannins).

PRESERVATIVES AND SOME FOOD ACIDS

200. Sorbic acid.
201. Sodium sorbate.
202. Potassium sorbate.
203. Calcium sorbate.
210. Benzoic acid.
211. Sodium benzoate
212. Potassium Benzoate.
213. Calcium Benzoate.
E214. Ethyl 4-hydroxybenzoate (ethyl para-hydroxybenzoate).
Not permitted in the production of Australian-made foods.
E215. Ethyl 4-hydroxybenzoate, sodium salt (sodium ethyl para-hydroxybenzoate). Not permitted in the production of Australian-made foods.
216. Propylparaben (propyl 4-hydroxybenzoate; n-propyl phydroxybenzoate; propyl para-hydroxybenzoate).

E217. Propyl 4-hydroxybenzoate, sodium salt (sodium n-propyl p-hydroxybenzoate; sodium propyl para-hydroxybenzoate). Not permitted in the production of Australian-made foods.
218. Methylparaben (methyl 4-hydroxybenzoate, methylparahydro xybenzoate).
E219. Methyl 4-hydroxybenzoate, sodium salt (sodium methyl para-hydroxybenzoate; sodium methyl hydroxybenzoate). Not permitted in the production of Australian-made foods.
220. Sulphur dioxide.
221. Sodium sulphite.
222. Sodium bisulphate (sodium hydrogen sulphite; acid sodium sulphite).
223. Sodium metabisulphite (disodium pyrosulphite).
224. Potassium metabisulphite (potassium pyrosulphite).
225. Potassium sulphite.
E226. Calcium sulphite.
Not permitted in the production of Australian-made foods.
E227. Calcium hydrogen sulphite (calcium bisulphite). Not permitted in the production of Australian-made foods.
228. Potassium bisulphite (Potassium hydrogen sulphite).
E230. Biphenyl (diphenyl).
E231. 2-Hydroxybiphenyl (o-phenyl phenol; orthophenylphenol).
E238. Calcium formate. Not permitted in the production of Australian-made foods.
E239. Hexamine (hexamethylenetetramine).
249. Potassium nitrite.
250. Sodium nitrite.
251. Sodium nitrate (Chile saltpetre).
252. Potassium nitrate (saltpetre).
260. Acetic acid.
261. Potassium acetate.
260. Sodium hydrogen diacetate (sodium diacetate).
262. Sodium acetate (anhydrous) and sodium acetate.
261. Calcium acetate.
262. Ammonium acetate.

270. Lactic acid.
280. Propionic acid.
281. Sodium propionate.
282. Calcium propionate.
283. Potassium propionate.
290. Carbon dioxide.
296. DL-Malic acid.
297. Fumaric acid

ANTIOXIDANTS, SOME FOOD ACIDS AND MINERAL SALTS

300. Ascorbic acid (vitamin C; L ascorbic acid).
301. Sodium ascorbate (vitamin C; sodium L-ascorbate).
302. Calcium ascorbate (calcium L-ascorbate).
303. Potassium ascorbate.
304. Ascorbyl palmitate (palmitoyl-L-ascorbic acid).
306. Tocopherols concentrate, mixed (vitamin E).
307. Alpha-Tocopherol (vitamin E; DL-alpha- tocopherol).
308. Gamma-Tocopherol (vitamin E; DL-gamma-tocopherol).
309. Delta-Tocopherol (vitamin E; DL-delta-tocopherol).
310. Propyl gallate (propyl 3,4,5,-trihydroxybenzoate).
311. Octyl gallate.
312. Dodecyl gallate (dodecyl 3,4,5,-trihydroxybenzoate).
317. Erythorbic acid (iso-ascorbic acid).
318. Sodium erythorbate (sodium iso-ascorbate).
319. *tert*-Butylhydroquinone (TBHQ).
320. Butylated hydroxyanisole (BHA).
321. Butylated hydroxytoluene (BHT).
322. Lecithins.
325. Sodium lactate.
326. Potassium lactate.
325. Calcium lactate.
326. Ammonium lactate.
327. Magnesium lactate.
328. Citric acid.

329. Sodium citrates – sodium dihydrogen citrate (monosodium citrate).
331. Sodium citrates – disodium citrate.
331. Sodium citrates – trisodium citrate.
332. Potassium dihydrogen citrate (monopotassium citrate).
332. Potassium citrate (tripotassium citrate).
333. Mono-, di-, and tri-calcium citrates.
334. Tartaric acid (L-(+) tartaric acid).
335. Sodium tartrate (monosodium L-(+)-tartrate and disodium L (+)-tartrate.
336. Potassuim acid tartrate (monopotassium L-(+)-tartrate; potassium hydrogen tartrate; cream of tartar).
336. Potassium tartrate (dipotassium L-(+)-tartrate).
337. Potassium sodium tartrate (potassium sodium L-(+)-tartrate; sodium and potassium tartrate. Rochelle salt).
338. Phosphoric acid (orthophosporic acid).
339. Sodium phosphate, monobasic (sodium dihydrogen orthophosphate).
339. Sodium phosphate, dibasic (disodium hydrogen orthophosphate).
339. Sodium phosphate, tribasic (trisodium orthophosphate).
340. Potassium phosphate, monobasic (potassium dihydrogen orthophosphate).
340. Potassium phosphate, dibasic (dipotassium hydrogen orthophosphate).
340. Potassium phosphate, tribasic (tripotassium-orthophosphate).
341. Calcium phosphate, monobasic (monocalcium orthophosphate; acid calcium phosphate; ACP).
341. Calcium phosphate, dibasic (calcium hydrogen orthophosphate).
341. Calcium phosphate, tribasic (tricalcuim orthophosphate).
343. Magnesium phosphate, dibasic (magnesium hydrogen phosphate: magnesium hydrogen orthophosphate trihydrate).
343. Magnesium phosphate, tribasic ('neutral' magnesium phosphate).
350. DL-Sodium malate.
350. DL-Sodium hydrogen malate.
351. DL-Potassium malate.

352. DL-Calcium malate.
352. Calcium hydrogen malate.
353. Metatartaric acid.
355. Adipic acid (hexanedioic acid).
357. Potassium adipate.
E363. Succinic acid. This substance is not permitted in the production of Australian-made foods.
365. Sodium fumarate (monosodium fumarate).
366. Potassium fumarate.
367. Calcium fumarate.
E370. 1,4-Heptonolactone.
375. Niacin (nicotinic acid; nicotinamide).
380. Triammonium citrate.
381. Ammonium ferric citrate (ferric ammonium citrate).
381. Ammonium ferric citrate, green.
E385. Calcium disodium ethylenediamine-tetraacetate (calcium disodium EDTA).Not permitted in the production of Australian-made foods.

VEGETABLE GUMS, EMULSIFIERS, SOME ANTI-CAKING AGENTS, HUMECTANTS AND MINERAL SALTS

400. Alginic acid.
401. Sodium alginate.
402. Potassium alginate.
403. Ammonium alginate.
404. Calcium alginate.
405. Propylene glycol alginate (propane-1, 2-diol alginate).
406. Agar (agar-agar; Japanese isinglass).
407. Carrageenan (Irish moss).
410. Locust bean gum (carob bean gum).
412. Gur gum.
413. Tragacanth (gum tragacanth).
414. Acacia (gum Arabic).
415. Xanthan gum (corn sugar gum).

416. Karaya gum (Sterculia gum).
420. Sorbitol and sorbitol syrup.
421. Mannitol (manna sugar).
422. Glycerin (glycerol).
E432. Polysorbate 20 (polyoxyethylene (20) sorbitan monolaurate; Tween 20). Not permitted in the production of Australian-made foods.
E434. Polysorbate 40 (polyoxyethylene (20) sorbitan monopalmitate; Tween 40).
435. Polysorbate 60 (polyoxyethylene (20) sorbitan monostearate; Tween 60).
436. Polysorbate 65 (polyoxyethylene (20) sorbitan tristearate;Tween 65).
440(a). Pectin.
440(b). Amidated pectin.
441. Gelatine.
442. Ammonium salts of phosphatidic acid (ammonium phosphatides; emulsifier YN).
450. Sodium acid pyrophosphate (disodium dihydrogen diphosphate; disodium dihydrogen pyrophosphate).
450. Trisodium diphosphate.
450. Sodium pyrophosphate (tetrasodium diphosphate).
450. Potassium pyrophosphate (tetrapotassium diphosphate).
450. Sodium tripolyphosphate (pentasodium triphosphate).
450. Potassium tripolyphosphate (pentapotassium triphosphate).
450. Sodium polyphosphates.
450. Potassium polyphosphates.
450(a). Ammonium phosphate dibasic (secondary ammonium phosphate diammonium hydrogen phosphate).
450(a). Ammonium phosphate monobasic (ammonium dihydrogen phosphate; primary ammonium phosphate).
460. Microcrystalline cellulose.
460. Powdered cellulose.
461. Methylcellulose (methocel; cologel).
E463. Hydroxypropyl-cellulose.
464. Hydroxypropylmethylcellulose (hypromellose).
465. Methylethylcellulose (ethylmethylcellulose).
466. Sodium carboxymethylcellulose (carmellose sodium; CMC).

469. Sodium caseinate (casein-sodium).

E470. Sodium, potassium and calcium salts of fatty acids (soaps). Not permitted in the production of Australian-made foods.

471. Mono- and di-glycerides of fat-forming fatty acids.

472(a). Acetic and fatty acid esters of glycerol.

472(b). Lactic and fatty acid esters of glycerol (lacyoglycerides).

472(c). Citric and fatty acid esters of glycerol (citroglycerides).

472(d). Tartaric and fatty acid esters of glycerol.

472(e). Diacetyltartaric and fatty acid esters of glycerol.

473. Sucrose esters of fatty acids.

E474. Sucroglycerides.

Not permitted in the production of Australian-made foods.

475. Polyglycerol esters of fatty acids.

476. Polyglycerol esters of interesterified ricinoleic acid (polyglycerol polyricinoleate).

477. Propane- 1,2,-diol esters of fatty acids (propylene glycol esters of fatty acids).

480. Dioctyl sodium sulphosuccinate (docusate sodium).

481. Sodium stearoyl lactylate (sodium stearoyl-2-lactylate).

482. Calcium stearoyl lactylate (calcium stearoyl-2-lactylate).

E483. Stearyl tartrate.

Not permitted in the production of Australian-made foods.

491. Sorbitan monostearate.

492. Sorbitan tristearate (Span 65). Not permitted in the production of Australian-made foods.

E493. Sorbitan monolaurate (Span 20). Not permitted in the production of Australian-made foods.

E494. Sorbitan mono-oleate (Span 80). Not permitted in the production of Australian-made foods.

E495. Sorbitan monopalmitate (Span 40). Not permitted in the production of Australian-made foods.

MORE MINERAL SALTS AND ANTI-CAKING AGENTS

500. Sodium carbonate.

500. Sodium bicarbonate (sodium hydrogen carbonate; baking soda; bicarbonate of soda).
500. Sodium sesquicarbonate.
501. Potassium carbonate and potassium hydrogen carbonate.
503. Ammonium carbonate.
503. Ammonium bicarbonate (ammonium hydrogen carbonate).
504. Magnesium carbonate (magnesite).
507. Hydrochloric acid.
508. Potassium chloride.
509. Calcium chloride.
510. Ammonium chloride.
511. Magnesium chloride (magnesium chloride, hexahydrate).
E513. Sulphuric acid. Not permitted in the production of Australian-made foods.
514. Sodium sulphate.
515. Potassium sulphate.
516. Calcium sulphate.
518. Magnesium sulphate (Epsom salts, epsomite).
519. Cupric sulphate (copper sulphate).
E524. Sodium hydroxide.
Not permitted in the production of Australian-made foods.
E525. Potassium hydroxide.
Not permitted in the production of Australian-made foods.
526. Calcium hydroxide.
E527. Ammonium hydroxide.
E528. Magnesium hydroxide.
Not permitted in the production of Australian-made foods.
529. Calcium oxide.
E530. Magnesium oxide. Not permitted in the production of Australian-made foods.
535. Sodium ferrocyanide (sodium hexacyanoferrate II).
536. Potassium ferrocyanide (potassium hexacyanoferrate II).
E540. Dicalcium diphosphate (calcium hydrogen phosphate).
541. Sodium aluminium phosphate, acidic.
E541. Sodium aluminium phosphate, basic. Not permitted in the

production of Australian-made foods.
542. Bone phosphate (edible bone phosphate).
E544. Calcium polyphosphates. Not permitted in the production of Australian-made foods.
E545. Ammonium polyphosphates. Not permitted in the production of Australian-made foods.
551. Silicon dioxide (silica).
552. Calcium silicate.
E553(a). Magnesium silicate (synthetic) and magnesium trisilicate. Not permitted in the production of Australian-made foods.
553(b). Talc (French chalk).
554. Sodium aluminosilicate (aluminium sodium silicate).
556. Calcium aluminium silicate (aluminium calcium silicate).
558. Bentonite.
559. Kaolin (heavy) and kaolin (light).
570. Stearic acid.
572. Magnesium stearate.
575. Glucono delta-lactone (D-glucono-1,5-lactone).
E576. Sodium gluconate. Not permitted in the production of Australian-made foods.
577. Potassium gluconate.
578. Calcium gluconate.
579. Ferrous gluconate (iron gluconate).

FLAVOUR ENHANCERS

620. L-Glutamic acid.
621. Monosodium glutamate (sodium hydrogen L-glutamate; Aji-no-moto; MSG).
622. Monopotassium glutamate (potassium hydrogen L-glutamate).
623. Calcium dihydrogen di-L-glutamate (calcium glutamate).
624. Monoammonium L-glutamate.
625. Magnesium di-L-glutamate.
627. Disodium guanylate (guanosine 5`-(disodium phosphate)).
631. Disodium inosinate (inosine 5`-(disodium phosphate)).
E635. Sodium 5`ribonucleotide. Not permitted in the production of

Australian-made foods.
636. Maltol.
637. Ethyl maltol.

MISCELLANEOUS ADDITIVES INCLUDING BLEACHING AGENTS, FLOUR TREATMENT AGENTS AND PROPELLANTS

900. Dimethylpolysiloxane (dimethicone).
901. Bees wax (white) and bees wax (yellow).
903. Carnauba wax.
904. Shellac.
905. Mineral oil, white (petrolatum).
E907. Refined microcrystalline wax.
Not permitted in the production of Australian-made foods.
920. L-cysteine hydrochloride and L-cysteine hydrochloride monohydrate.
924. Potassium bromate.
925. Chlorine.
926. Chlorine dioxide.
E927. Azodicarbonamide (azoformamide).
Not permitted in the production of Australian-made foods.
928. Benzoyl peroxide (dibenzoyl peroxide).
931. Nitrogen.
932. Nitrous oxide (Laughing gas).
950. Acesulphame potassium (Acesulphame K, Sunett).
951. Aspartame.
952. Cyclamic acid (Cyclohexylsulphamic acid; Hexamic acid).
952. Calcium cyclamate (Calcium cyclohexylsulphamate).
952. Sodium cyclamate (Sodium cyclohexylsulphamate).
954. Saccharin.
954. Calcium saccharin.
954. Sodium saccharin.
957. Thaumatin (Katemfe).
965. Hydrogenated glucose syrup.
967. Xylitol.

1200. Polydextrose.
1201. Polyvinylpyrrolidone (povidone).
1202. Polyvinyl polypyrrolidone (Insoluble polyvinylpyrrolidone).

THICKENERS (MODIFIED STARCHES)

1400. Dextrins.
1403. Bleached starch.
1404. Oxidised starch.
1405. Enzyme-treated starches.
1410. Monostarch phosphate.
1412. Distarch phosphate esterified with sodium trimetaphosphate.
1412. Distarch phosphate esterified with phosphorus oxychloride.
1413. Phosphated distarch phosphate.
1414. Acetylated distarch phosphate.
1420. Starch acetate esterified with acetic anhydride.
1421. Starch acetate esterified with vinyl acetate.
1422. Acetylated distarch adipate.
1440. Hydroxypropyl starch.
1442. Hydroxypropyl distarch phosphate.
1450. Starch, sodium octenylsuccinate.

MORE MISCELLANEOUS ADDITIVES

1505. Triethyl citrate (ethyl citrate).
1510. Ethyl alcohol (ethanol).
1517. Glycerol diacetate (diacetin).
1518. Triacetin (glycerol triacetate).
1520. Propylene glycol.

Experiments to test the effects these additives have on the body were carried out on animals such as, rats, mice, dogs, cats, guinea pigs, monkeys, miniature pigs, hamsters and pigs.

Some of the possible side effects to humans and animals are: migraines; nettle rash; itching; slow digestion; flushing; mental excitement; depression; drowsiness; stupor; coma; kidney failure;

tooth erosion; thirst; kidney stones; senile dementia; rhinitis; blurred vision; blotchy skin and asthma attacks.

The list includes: gastric upset; flatulence; fluid retention; dermatitis; constipation; anaemia; shock; convulsions; tremors; possible cancers; skin allergies; gastric irritation; eye and nose irritation and urine disorders.

There was also gene mutation; mouth ulcers; kidney disease; delirium; vomiting; kidney inflammation; breathing problems; low blood pressure; neurological disorders; mouth numbness; ringing in the ears; feeling of suffocation; swelling of the skin; abdominal cramps; high blood sugar levels; foetal malformation; hyperactivity in children and skeletal abnormalities.

Also on the list were: heart palpitations; brain cell damage; anal seepage; anal irritation; respiratory irritations; nausea; brain dysfunction in children; tightening of jaw muscles; vaginal secretion in female beagle dogs; embarrassing behaviour in male dogs; depression of the central nervous system; impaired co-ordination and perception.

And finally: numbness of the neck; chest and hands; sleep deprivation in children; degeneration of the skeleton; degeneration of the heart muscles; cold sweats to face and armpits and increased liver cholesterol. Consumers of processed food should check the country of origin of the ingredients.

Flour produced in certain countries may contain human hair and when a packet of biscuits for example, is opened, the smell can mimic that of having been freshly oven baked. Human hair in flour produces an identical aroma to that of being freshly baked. Some flour may contain chalk which may be used as an extender. Many preservatives and additives are a major threat to good health because the human body cannot break them down and they may remain in the system causing deadly disease.

Even though Australia bans the use of certain chemical additives, they may still be present in imported foods.

It may also be wise to research the term "added fibre" on processed food wrappers because it may be bird feathers.

Before meeting Elias I baked regularly. The seven simple ingredients for a frosted sponge cake were: castor and icing sugar, eggs, vanilla, flour, jam and cream. While visiting a supermarket recently I read the packaging on a mass produced sponge cake. There were 72 ingredients and many were represented by a number which may indicate a chemical.

FOOD – ITS EFFECTS ON THE BODY

Foods that are most harmful to the body are listed from the highest to the lowest:

Eggs: the highest form of animal protein because it is concentrated. Eggs may cause rashes, stomach upset and swelling, vomiting and eczema.

Dairy: may cause constipation, breast cancer, diarrohea, stomach gas, migraine, colic, catarrh, sinus, asthma, eczema, hay fever and allergies. Dairy products may dry the fluid in the lymphatic system causing the throat to dry and the result is a chronic dry cough. This has been known to cause deafness in children. *Toxins in cheeses are concentrated.* Hard cheeses may cause the most damage because the artificial hormones, antibiotics and chemicals are concentrated even further.

Poultry: contains a natural stress hormone and sometimes artificial growth hormones which are detrimental to the human body. This meat takes five days to break down in the digestive system while creating dangerous toxins. May cause skin damage and many common life-threatening diseases, including cancers.

Meats: meat takes up to five days to break down under normal circumstances in the digestive system, while creating dangerous toxins. May cause many common diseases such as: asthma, cancers of the bowel, colon, pancreas and cancers within the digestive system, lung and brain, rheumatoid arthritis and arthritis.

Chemicals, drugs and diseases are stored throughout the body of the animal. But these toxins and diseases are more prevalent in offal such as the liver and kidneys because they are the filters of the body. And it is these that decay faster than other parts of the animal.

Shellfish: crustaceans such as mussels, clams, oysters and scallops have been known to ingest dinoflagellate (a single-celled planktonic animal of the class Dinoflagellata), which produces toxins capable of causing fish kills and severe illness. Death in humans may occur because of respiratory complications. Some shellfish may scavenge the ocean floor and may have contaminants such as chemicals and heavy metals. Other problems may result in swelling of the lips and tongue, stomach upset and nerve damage, hallucinations, nausea and hives. This allergy may be a life-long affliction.

Fish: ciguatera poisoning may occur after eating fish. The flavour of fish that harbours ciguatera is unaffected. Ciguatera cannot be removed from the fish before its consumption. The pain from this poisoning has been described as horrendous because it attacks the nerves. After fish is eaten it takes two days for the elimination process to take place within the digestive system. Fish does create dangerous acids but they are not as harmful as beef and poultry.

Some fish may contain toxins and chemicals capable of killing humans because they paralyse the nerve system. Fresh water fish may be infected with tapeworm. Like shellfish, fish also ingest dinoflagellate. Puffer fish have been known to cause death from respiratory paralysis because tetrodotoxin poisoning may occur. Scombroid poisoning may occur after eating tuna, mahimahi, mackerel, bonito and skipjack. Symptoms are: facial flushing, stomach pain, nausea, vomiting and skin irritation.

Grains, nuts, pulses, seeds, sprouts: contain acids that are harmful to the body. Some nuts, including peanuts, can cause anaphylactic shock and hives. Those who eat grain products (cereals, breads and pasta etc.,) regularly, followed by fruit, are at risk of suffering alcoholism. The natural acids which occur in grains when combined with the natural and vitally essential fruit acids, create alcohol.

Alcohol prevents the absorption of food nutrients by the digestive system, leading to nutrient deprivation. Many other problems may also eventuate, including alcoholism.

Vegetables: contain alkoide and eaten over a period of time, vegetables are almost as harmful as animal DNA because alkoide is a natural insect repellent. This chemical creates acid in the stomach that attacks the nerve system. Vegetables also absorb toxic sprays.

Fruit: a complete food necessary for the body to function normally. Fruit has the least amount of toxin. Unripened fruit also contains alkoide but the fruit emits it as it ripens. Chemical-free fruit is ideal but it is not always available. However, nature compensates sprayed fruit by neutralising the toxins. But some nutrients are lost. To compensate, eat extra fruit.

Peel or wash all fruit well because some sprays may contain metals such as copper. This is harmful to the nerve system and brain, and can cause cancer.

FRUITARIAN, VEGETARIAN OR VEGAN

1. A fruitarian is one who only eats fruit.
2. Vegetarians live on fruit, vegetables, eggs, dairy, grain, nuts, seeds and pulses.
3. A vegan eats fruit, vegetables, seeds, nuts, grain and pulses.

Vegetarians and vegans may not always enjoy good health because vegetables contain the natural toxin alkoide (Latin). It is one of a class of basic nitrogenous organic compounds occurring in plants, such as nicotine, atropine, morphine or quinine. Alkoide helps plants ward off insects.

Over time alkoide accumulates in the human body, entering the spinal cavity where it may cause nerve damage. With time, the chemical reaction it has on the body can almost be compared to decaying meat in the digestive system. Dairy, grains, pulses, seeds and nuts (except brazil nuts and coconuts) also contain acids that are detrimental to the body, brain and nerve system.

There are times when vegetarians and vegans may simply forget to eat fruit because they are busy preparing and cooking grains and legumes. However, vegans who do not consume animal products may not suffer from bowel cancer unless they:

- use microwave ovens and mobile phones.
- eat charred barbecued food.

- eat vegetables sprayed with poison.
- have uncontrolled stress levels etc.

Raw fruit contains natural enzymes that break down immediately on contact with the tongue's natural fluids. However, when cooked food enters the digestive system, it requires an enormous amount of energy to digest. This may leave one feeling tired and lethargic. Raw fruit has no ill effect and it does not place the digestive system under stress.

Raw fruit cleanses the body and the lymphatic system. A clean body strengthens the immune system and prevents disease. Our health depends entirely on the way we think and the way we choose to live. But the environment also dictates the health outcomes of the individual.

FRUIT PROPERTIES

All fruit contains 92 chemical elements but some are more abundant than others while some have special qualities e.g. grapes, dates, coconut and pineapple etc.

- IU: international units.
- RDI: recommended daily intake.

Apples: high in fructose, vitamin B and C and contain magnesium, iron, chromium, manganese and soluble fibre. Good for constipation and relieve diarrohea when grated. Grated apple can be used as a poultice. The core of the apple should be eaten because it contains vitamin B12. Discard the seeds because they contain harmful acid.

Elias said pure apple juice would bring down high blood sugar levels. Sip slowly to ensure complete absorption by the tongue's fluids or use a teaspoon. Green apples are a hybrid species. Elias said we should not eat them. The acid in some are so strong they may erode tooth enamel.

Apricots: contain vitamin C, iron, fibre and potassium. One 35 gram apricot has 914 IU of vitamin A.

Avocado: excellent for diabetes because it contains vitamins A, B (thiamine), B2 (riboflavin – half an avocado provides about 6 per cent of the RDI, 10 per cent minimum of B3 (niacin) and 15 per cent (pantothenic acid) B5 and (pyridoxine) B6). Avocado contains vitamin E and insoluble fibre.

It contains potassium and folate, monounsaturated fat and 18 to 26 per cent oil content, and is good for blood pressure, heart and nerve system. The subtropical variety of avocado has a higher content of monounsaturated oil and 124 calories per 100 grams. Contains one-eighth of the RDI of folate, has up to 4 per cent active protein. Half an avocado yields about 600 IU of vitamin A.

Avocados have the highest potassium content of all regular fruits – 600mg to 100 grams. Avocado is a excellent first solid food for babies because it contains necessary nutrients and consistency. Excellent also for those suffering diabetes because it lowers blood sugar. Be aware of overripe avocado because its rich oil content can turn rancid.

Bananas: have the second highest potassium content of our regular fruit. One banana contains one-sixteenth the RDI of riboflavin (B2). Banana contains iron, folic acid, fruit acid, fructose, glucose, calcium, carbohydrate, copper, magnesium, manganese, niacin, phosphate, phosphorus, pro vitamin A, tryptophan, vitamin A, B1, B3, B6, B7, B12, C, E and 70 per cent water. Bananas are energy food, high in carbohydrate, low in calories, high in protein, zinc, retinol, thiamine, riboflavin and ascorbic acid.

It is safe to steam food in banana leaves Asian style provided they have not been chemically sprayed. Bananas grown in some commercial plantations may have been sprayed up to 30 times. Wash the leaves well before using.

Blueberry: rich in antioxidants.

Brazil nuts: contain albumin, calcium, iron, magnesium, Vitamin B1, E, phosphorus. They are 14 per cent protein. Do not eat more than eight per week because they stimulate the nerve system.

Carob: a fruit tree from Mediterranean regions. Its long, dry pod contains hard seeds in a sweet pulp and is used as animal fodder and sometimes as a chocolate substitute.

Cherries: cherries purify and condition blood. They contain 10mg of vitamin C per 100 grams and 1000 IU per 100 grams of vitamin A. An effective antioxidant and anti-inflammatory, they reduce cholesterol, lower the risk of heart disease, stroke and arteriosclerosis. Excellent for the relief of constipation but it may be wise not to drink water half-an-hour before and after eating them. This may help prevent colic.

WARNING: *Self-diagnosis can be dangerous. Seek advice from a qualified health care professional before undertaking any cleanse.*

Chilli: three birdseye chilli a day are sufficient to cleanse and purify the blood. Chilli removes plaque from arteries, lowering the risk of heart attack and stroke.

Chocolate: was used in the Miera culture. Addictive, nerve stimulant, diuretic, contains theobromine. A purine alkaloid in the form of microscopic crystals, has alkaline properties. Obtained from the seeds and leaves of the cacao tree. Contains caffeine.

A few small segments of dark Swiss chocolate may help alleviate the symptoms of diarrohea. Chocolate should not be eaten (especially by children) because it closes off the colon and alters the natural process of food digestion. Therefore, chocolate is likely to cause constipation.

Citrus: vitamin C and antioxidants are found in citrus and tomatoes. Excellent for fighting cancer. Citrus skin is safe to eat if the fruit is tree ripened. Wash properly.

Coconut: highly nutritious. Essential for the healthy growth of babies and children. Contains myriad nutrients especially beneficial to the brain. Coconut has a high energy level, its fibre content is high, sodium is low and it contains protein. It does not contain harmful cholesterol.

Coconut contains vitamins B1, B2 and C. The minerals it contains are: iron, potassium, phosphorus, magnesium, copper, zinc and calcium. It is excellent for rehydrating the body and its organic compounds promote growth. Coconut milk and cream are excellent for skin rashes, especially prickly heat in babies. Coconut oil contains 9 per cent omega six.

Cucumber: contains potassium, magnesium, natural salt and iron. High amounts of silicon and fluorine. Excellent for the liver, kidneys and gall bladder. Strengthens nails, teeth and hair.

Dates: a most important fruit. Contains vitamin B12 and iron. A nutritious food source for children. Nutrients in dates help the brain to develop during vital growing years. Good for lowering blood pressure, headache relief, induces sleep. Dates are excellent for those suffering anaemia because they contain a high amount of natural iron. Dates help to strengthen the body. Unless Elias says otherwise, seven to 10 dates daily is ample.

Dragon fruit: excellent for colon cleansing. Elias said two dragon fruit daily for two months may cure colon cancer. Excellent for red blood cells and the immune system.

Figs: excellent for colon cleansing, they fight against prostate cancer and lower cholesterol. Figs have the highest amount of calcium of any of the common fruit, 35mg per 100 grams.

Fruit iron: fruits that contain extra iron are those that darken – or "rust" – when exposed to the atmosphere. Some are: banana, pears, custard apple, apple, eggplant, cherries, plums, dates, apricots, peaches, avocado, sour sop and figs. Excellent for anaemia and lack of energy.

Fruit (sometimes referred to as vegetables): capsicum, chilli, eggplant, cucumber, tomato, choko, pumpkin and any member of the squash family etc.

Grapefruit: cleans the colon and aids weight loss. Good source of vitamin C. Contains a citrus flavonoid compound which is not found in other citrus, the most prevalent is naringin. Flavonoids present in grapefruit may have protective biochemical effects.

Grapes – nature's wonder drug: unlike most other fruits, nature has processed its fructose into glucose. Grapes contain large amount of natural insulin. This insulin, along with vitamins and minerals, are absorbed in the mouth then transmitted directly to the brain.

Grapes are a quick fix for those who suffer low blood sugar or loss of energy. 100 grams will yield 18 per cent RDI of vitamin C. Grapes contain 20 types of antioxidants, calcium, iron, protein, oleic acid, enzymes, fluoride, copper and magnesium. They are high in grape sugar, phosphorus, chlorine, pro-vitamin A, vitamin B1, B2, B6, E, wine acid (tannin acid), fluoride, protective and natural plant chemicals. Resveratrol – a phenolic compound – is the best-known protective compound in red wine.

Grapes contain an anti-cancer chemical in their skin. They help repair wall cell tissues and contain a natural chemical that cleanses body tissue of unwanted fluid. Grapes are excellent for those who suffer from arteriosclerosis (an arterial disease which occurs especially in the elderly. It is characterised by inelasticity and thickening of the vessel walls, with lessened blood flow).

Excellent for those suffering excessive uric acid because they help break up the crystals. Excellent for gout, bladder stones, and their natural steroid helps to kill the smallest of parasites in viruses. Grapes help to stimulate the immune system and are exceptionally good for those who have suffered over exposure to the sun's rays because resveratrol repairs skin. Good for those who have lost a lot of weight and wish to gain. Lowers cholesterol. Kills the herpes virus. Cut a grape in half and rub it over herpes blisters. Grapes kill mouth bacteria. Chewing grapes is nature's mouthwash.

Guava: has the largest amount of vitamin C of all common fruit, 165mg of vitamin C per fruit and twice the amount of kiwifruit. One guava supplies 5 per cent of the recommended RDI of niacin (B3), 800 IU of vitamin A. High in potassium and dietary fibre. Elias says to chew guava leaf for toothache and discard the fibre.

Kiwifruit: extremely high in vitamin C and improves the body's ability to absorb and use iron. Has higher concentrations of vitamins and minerals per calorie than most other fruits. Contains iron. Has 14 per cent folate (B complex, folic acid) requirement. Potassium content = 330mg per 100 grams. Calcium is 2.25 per cent recommended daily intake. It has .1mg of chromium, that is 35 per cent of the daily need. Vitamin E is found in the seeds but they pass through the bowel undigested. High in fibre.

Lemon: Elias recommends three lemons daily. Lemons neutralise stomach acids. They contain natural enzymes that break down food.

Their potassium is essential to the skeletal system. After rain, there is usually a residue of mud in town water supplies and this may cause diarrhoea.

Elias said the juice of one lemon to one litre of water killed the bacteria after it has stood for 20 minutes before drinking. Lemon does not remove the dirt or heavy metals. Do not add hot water to lemon juice because it destroys nutrients.

Lychees: 10 will yield 100 per cent of the RDI of vitamin C.

Mandarin: two pieces will provide the daily RDI of vitamin C. Has vitamin A – 900 IU per 100 grams.

Mango: heart shaped – exceptionally good for that organ. One gives the daily intake of vitamin C. Has the highest concentration of vitamin A of all common fruits – 3890 IU per 100 grams.

Melon: high in potassium, rich source of vitamin A. One serve will yield half the RDI of vitamin C.

Olives: this fruit produces oil that is high in nutrients. The tree usually fruits between April and June.

Olive oil: pure virgin first cold pressed olive oil is monounsaturated – beneficial to the body because it does not oxidise in the arteries. Has a wide variety of anti-oxidants that protect against heart disease. Breast cancer is less in women from Greece and Spain than in most other parts of the world because in those countries olive oil is widely used. Purchase olive oil in amber or green bottles because it protects it from ultraviolet light.

Orange: abundant in vitamin C and folate.

Papaya: abundant in vitamin C and folate. A highly cleansing fruit that makes an excellent accompaniment to chilli. This fruit adds to the pigmentation of our skin.

Passion fruit: the purple variety contains 348mg per 100 grams of potassium and 700 IU of vitamin A per 100 grams.

Peach: one equals 5 per cent of the daily need of niacin (B3) and 530 IU of vitamin A.

Pear: a high quality cleansing fruit for those suffering from kidney stones. This fruit is imperative for those suffering from Parkinson's disease because it absorbs lead. Pears are excellent for those who suffer from stale phlegm in the lung from prior illness. They have a specific action that provides the lung with slightly heavy moisture that clears unhealthy fluid.

Persimmon: Japanese and Chinese have enjoyed eating persimmon for centuries and it is now grown under natural conditions in Australia. Its vitamin A content is 30 times greater than that of an apple while the vitamin C content is as high as citrus. Carotene level is 80 times higher than that of an apple. Concentrations of ascorbic acid are high in the skin. Some varieties have protective elements that guard against prostate cancer.

Plums: good for nausea, stomach upsets and constipation. Useful levels of calcium, riboflavin (B2) and vitamin C, rich in antioxidants which help prevent cell oxidation.

Pineapple: essential in our diet because the enzymes in its bromelain activate neutral fruit protein. Bromelain aids digestion, removes excess fluid and is excellent for those who wish to lose weight because it breaks down fats within the liver. Good for catarrh, arthritis, bronchitis, indigestion, blood clots, heart disease, sinus congestion and urinary tract infection. Slices of pineapple on the skin can be used as an anti-inflammatory and as a poultice. The flesh is rich in nutrients such as xanthophylls, zinc and fructose.

Vitamin B12 is a trace element and only very little is required by the body. There is enough vitamin B12 in one pineapple to last one person many years. However, it is not possible to preserve this vitamin without preservatives and additives. When such chemicals are incorporated with a natural substance its value is destroyed.

Excellent for those with thyroid problems because it contains iodine. The core of the pineapple is laden with nutrients such as calcium, copper, magnesium, mangan, iron, chloride, fruit acid, vitamin C and should be eaten.

To counteract the drugs that dentists inject into gums to deaden pain before procedures: drink freshly pressed pineapple juice slowly for two days after the visit along with the usual fruits and three litres of water daily. This will help hasten toxin elimination.

Pineapple helps the body to function normally, aids blood

circulation and activates the immune system. Pineapple is an excellent fruit for those who suffer rheumatic and arthritis problems because it flushes uric acid from the system. If one suffers stomach discomfort from over indulgence, a few slices of fresh, ripe pineapple will soon bring relief. One hundred and fifty grams of pineapple flesh eaten very slowly daily for one week will help cure inflamed gums.

Pomegranate: contains more oestrogen than any other fruit which is why it is called the love apple.

Pumpkin: its properties are similar to squash. Water content is about 90 per cent. Low in carbohydrate, rich in sodium, potassium, iron, phosphorus and chlorine. A natural laxative and diuretic but does not irritate the kidneys. Best when grated and eaten raw because cooking destroys the valuable water content, reducing it by 75 per cent. Cooking increases the carbohydrates by 50 per cent, converting its natural fructose into starchy carbohydrates.

Raspberries: reduce cholesterol. Excellent for those suffering heart disease, stroke and arteriosclerosis.

Stone fruit: contain iron.

Strawberries: kidney shaped and good for kidney stones, arthritis, gout, prostate cancer, rheumatism and lowers cholesterol. Eighteen will provide the RDI of vitamin B and 10 will cover vitamin C requirement.

Watermelon: the juice of watermelon and pear are excellent kidney cleansers with high amounts of vitamin C. The white rind should not be eaten because it contains alkoide which is a natural insecticide.

GENETIC ENGINEERING

It seems that what was once science fiction may be the destruction of the future. Elias fears genetically engineered food. He said genetic engineering had already infiltrated the food chain in a big way and even some varieties of bananas had a hepatitis B inhibitor. He added: "We need not fear hepatitis B if we eat correctly".

Do we know what is occurring in these laboratories? Can we see the difference in genetically engineered food? Can we taste the difference? What can we do about it? Nothing it seems. We have no control whatsoever over the food we eat because much of the seed stock is already genetically engineered.

Does genetic engineering have the capacity to destroy our health because the 92 natural chemical elements that nature has provided in fruit may have already been altered? Will our food be as nature intended: 100 per cent compatible with our body?

It seems that one cannot say how genetically engineered food is going to affect our body, the nerve system and brain in the future because it has not been tested over a long period of time. The genetic engineering of food is silent and effective.

The force and motives behind this tampering are known only to the select few. Does their creation have the potential to become a monster? Are we guinea pigs? Could genetic engineering be a weapon of mass destruction?

Jeffrey M. Smith is the independent author of a well researched bood titled: *Seeds of Deception.* It is printed in Canada and distributed by Chelsea Green Publishing. The ISBN: 0-9729665-8-7. In his book he exposed industry and government lies about the safety of genetically engineered foods we are eating.

Amongst a wealth of information, he documents the fate of rats that were used for testing after eating genetically engineered food. He also writes about supplements, canola oil and soy.

For more information go to the web sites:

- www.seedsofdeception.com
- www.chelseagreen.com

GROWING PAINS

Some children and adolescents suffer growing pains. This syndrome is the result of a poor diet that contains processed cane sugar (sucrose). Excess processed cane sugar in a child's diet activates the skeletal system into growth.

Processed cane sugar causes bones to grow more rapidly than ligaments so they develop at a different rate. The consequences are pain and muscles that do not develop as they should.

Teenagers suffer the most from growing pains because they are under stress from the pressures of part time jobs, peers, school and sometimes their home environments.

HAEMOPHILIA

Elias has treated this problem successfully and like so many other difficult issues he has dealt with, haemophilia is extremely complicated because the composition of blood is complex. He said because of this complexity, it was vital that sufferers sought competent advice. He added: "The medical professional who treats haemophilia must work with 100 per cent accuracy".

For those who wish to learn more about haemophilia, Australian author Bryce Courtney has written a book titled: *April Fool's Day*. It is an honest and vivid description of how haemophilia claimed the life of his son, its effects on their family and others who loved him.

WARNING: *Elias added: anything that is not normal or natural, e.g. microwave ovens, should not be used because the foods cooked in them alter the functions of vital organs. He said the problems become even more complex because it interfered with the structure of the blood.*

For example the blood may age at an alarming rate and it may thicken, causing problems within the arteries, brain, organs and the body. When the structure of the blood alters, many life threatening disease such as leukaemia, other cancers and diseases may occur.

HEAD COLDS

If a child has a head cold accompanied by a cough, Elias suggests his clients leave a very soft light on in their bedroom at night because it may give the child a better night's sleep. When the child is in the state of deep sleep their body relaxes, the bottom jaw falls and the mouth automatically opens.

If the nasal breathing passage is blocked with mucus, the child will breathe through their mouth, causing the airways to dry out and coughing will occur. A night light prevents children from going into deep slumber and their mouth will usually remain closed. They usually breathe correctly through their nose and may not cough as often.

HERBS AND SPICES

Many herbs and spices are drugs and natural antibiotics and they can be addictive. The more the body has, the more it wants and if we continue eating them, we will become immune to them. Herbs and spices should be used for medicinal purposes.

For example, sage tea is excellent for those suffering sinusitis because it breaks down mucus. Herbs and spices should be used with caution – women can die from excess haemorrhaging while menstruating during the saffron harvest. Herbs such as basil, rosemary and parsley are classified as a lower form of drugs, while pepper is higher.

HEREDITARY DISEASES

I asked Elias if bowel cancer, blood pressure, diabetes, coeliac, breast cancer, arthritis, gout etc., could be passed down to the next generation. I also asked if this chain of events could be broken.

He said it was impossible for a sick person to bring a healthy child into the world. If children are born with a disease, that disease is genetic. If a baby is born healthy then grows into an adult and becomes sick later in life, this illness is not genetic and parents should not be blamed. One should look at lifestyle, diet, or state of mind.

But the history of many families seems to follow familiar traits. For example, if a man of 70 years has a heart attack, his son will usually have one at 60 years and his son at 50 years. This is not genetic but the result of lifestyle.

If a woman eats dairy and other animal DNA, she can expect breast cancer. If her daughter eats the same food she also can expect breast cancer. This is lifestyle and the end result of poor choices.

If a man drinks coffee and alcohol and eats animal DNA and develops prostate cancer, it is usually not possible for his son to have the same disease if he eats healthy and lives stress free.

Eczema, asthma, croup, sinus and many others are normally labelled as diseases. They are not diseases but the end result of a diet high in dairy and animal protein. Remove the source, eat healthy and the symptoms will disappear as the body cleanses. Allergies are also symptoms of foods that are incompatible with the body and chemicals that may already be present in the system.

KIDNEY STONES

Stress can cause kidney stones. Stress alters the blood's chemicals, producing ammonic and uric acid which flood the kidneys. Pear, watermelon and water are excellent because they quickly cleanse the kidneys. Kidney stone sufferers should eat natural food only and avoid all animal DNA.

During an attack, warm beer at room temperature should be consumed. If the beer is cold the kidneys must work harder to bring it up to body temperature. When beer is consumed at room temperature it relaxes the body immediately because it contains hops which is a relaxant.

As muscles relax, so does the urethra. The beer encourages the kidneys to work harder which, in turn, flushes the stones through the relaxed urethra. Each person is different and one relaxes and sleeps in one's own time, therefore the body will dictate the amount of beer it requires to do the job. For example, there are those who do not consume any alcohol whatsoever and one glass may suffice. Others may require more.

LUPUS

Systemic Lupus Erythematosus (SLE) is an autoimmune disease. It is the inflammation in the small blood vessels in the connective tissue. This inflammation can cause problems within the structure of vital organs such as the heart, lungs, kidneys and brain etc. It is not infectious, therefore it is not contagious. SLE can affect the skin and joints.

There are various types of lupus. Discoid Lupus Erythematosus

(DLE) and Subacute Lupus Erythematosus (SCLE) are two that affect the skin. The result of DLE is raised reddish blotches on the upper body, face and scalp. The symptoms of SLE are much different and 90 per cent of those who contract this type of lupus are females. Symptoms may occur in the mid 30s and one can expect facial rash, flu symptoms, fatigue, lethargy, lack of energy, loss of appetite and weight, and joint pain. As time progresses, the sufferer may experience arthritic-like pain in the joints, loss of hair, swollen glands and fever.

Drug Induced Lupus: a perfect example of the dangers of drug use because they can cause lupus which compounds existing problems.

MELANOMAS

Elias believes the sun is not carcinogenic but the giver of life and a source of natural energy. He said the sun does not energise the body on the one hand and cause cancer on the other. Nature does not play games.

There is an unending trail of products marketed as skincare. But caring for the skin may not always be possible because some may contain chemicals that ensure a long shelf life. Soaps may contain wax which may clog the skin's pores and prevent it from breathing properly. Skincare should be natural and free from chemicals.

Adults have an external immune system that extends about 10cm beyond the body. This figure drops to about 1.5cm in babies. Harsh soaps, chlorine and other chemicals destroy this system.

There are many ways of bathing. A squeeze of lemon juice in warm water is just one way to help protect a newly-born baby's immune system. As they grow, one may graduate to any of the fruit oils: olive, coconut and avocado. Nature provided the external immune system for our protection.

Melanomas and skin cancers will always be a hot topic because Australians are notoriously outdoor individuals who take every opportunity to enjoy the beautiful climate.

Elias said we were led to believe melanomas and skin cancers were caused by exposure to the sun's rays and the damage to the ozone layer. He said this was not correct and we must expand on this subject because the problem was increasing. He said fluorescent lighting may cause cancers. There are those who suffer melanomas on their scalp.

Heavily twilled fabric and some other cotton garments may cause melanomas because the material is treated with formaldehyde and other potent chemicals and acids that are used to fasten colours. These chemicals are extremely toxic to the body. It may be wise to launder these clothes several times before they are worn because washing will help to remove the toxins.

Some garments are pre-shrunk. This gives a tighter weave, thus thickening the garment even further. The final product is dense and some garments fit the body tightly in order to accentuate the human form.

As they are worn the body can overheat, causing the skin to perspire. As a person walks, their harmful acid-laden perspiration – (these harmful acids are caused by food that consists of animal DNA) – activates the formaldehyde, other chemicals and acids in the fabric and it enters the skin through the pores, causing melanomas.

Foot melanomas: the colours used in some shoe dyes are intense. Most contain formaldehyde and chemical acids and some dyes are so potent they leave colour on the skin. Feet perspire as one walks. The acid-laden perspiration activates the chemicals in the shoes which enter the skin through the pores.

A large percentage of all melanomas occur under the feet. We cannot blame the sun for this because the soles of the feet are very rarely exposed to the sun. If one then enters a chlorinated swimming pool with formaldehyde and other harmful acids on the skin from either clothing or shoes, the chlorinated water activates the formaldehyde and other chemicals and causes melanomas.

Chlorine is an acid that damages the eyes and it causes emphysema because it damages lung tissue.

Swimming in chlorinated swimming pools also damages the internal and external immune systems and the natural chemicals in the skin. Children are particularly vulnerable. If we go into the sun with chlorine on our skin after swimming, cancer can occur. We must not blame the sun for this because it is the chlorine in the first instance that caused the damage.

Elias said chlorine was a toxic substance that caused cancer and it was easy to blame the sun for skin cancer problems. He also maintains swimming in chlorinated pools damages nerve endings which may take up to 40 years to repair.

Many fishermen do not suffer from skin cancer yet they are in the sun all day because they mainly eat fish which is not as harmful as eating meat, chicken, dairy and their by-products. Many also rub natural coconut oil into their skin to protect it from salt water spray, the sun and wind.

Indigenous Islanders eat mainly fruit and vegetables. They eat some fish and very little chicken and they are not badly affected by the sun. Westerners who live in the tropics usually eat a lot of meat and enormous amounts of dairy. Animal DNA produces high levels of acids which pollute the human system and kidneys are unable to detoxify effectively. These acids must then work their way through the body and a certain amount exit via the skin. As it does it causes tissue damage.

Those who eat animal DNA produce high and concentrated levels of perspiration. When their skin is exposed to the sun, the concentrated perspiration causes it to burn. People have the most amount of skin damage where there is a high number of lymph glands (at the tip of the chin, down the neck, across the chest and down to the waist). It can also occur on the arms and legs because they are further away from the kidneys, and where sweating is more profuse.

There are those who lie in the sun to tan but some go a step further and suffer severe burns. This may occur if the skin lacks pigment e.g. on the parts of the body that are normally shielded by clothing. Pigmentation is vital because the sun stimulates the body into producing vitamin D. If the skin lacks pigment, the body loses this essential vitamin that is also vital for healthy bones.

There are those who eat natural foods but lack skin pigmentation.

They will burn in the sun but this will usually not cause cancer because their body does not contain harmful animal DNA acids. It may be wise for them to cover up while outdoors.

Elias maintains if the skin has problems with the sun, the sun is not the problem. The problem lies within the body and the diet. He maintains the sun does not cause cancer. Skin cancers are caused by influences other than the sun. The body requires the sun's energy in order to maintain good health. To help eliminate the problems of skin cancer, eat natural and wear appropriate clothing if necessary.

MENOPAUSE

We are led to believe menopause is part of the ageing process. "Not so", says Elias. Menopause is the result of lifestyle. Healthy women who eat natural food and have healthy immune systems do not suffer this syndrome. After World War II, the average age of menopausal women was about 60 years. In the last 20 to 30 years, the age has lowered to 30-40 years. The more animal DNA, dairy, processed foods, cigarettes and alcohol a woman consumes, the quicker the onset of menopause.

Menopause can be life altering because women suffer profuse sweating which causes sleep deprivation, kidney disorder, dehydration and headaches etc. They may gain weight which has a devastating effect on their self-esteem. Natural food automatically cleanses the body daily and hormones self-regulate. This cleansing allows the body to function normally. A healthy woman who eats natural is capable of conceiving at a much older age.

Elias said there were two tribes in Africa where the adult females did not get monthly periods and they did not suffer menopause because they lived only on fruit. He said they also gave birth at a much older age.

MENTAL STATE AND THE HEALING PROCESS

We are the manifestation of our thoughts and our healing process depends entirely on the way we think – our mental state. The body is under the dictatorship of the mind, therefore all thoughts must be positive. The physical, spiritual, mental and emotional aspects of our being are governed by the brain and the way we think. Negative thoughts suppress healing while happiness and positive thoughts introduce calmness to the body which has a healing effect. Healing should lie between the mind and body excluding all external negative influences.

Living without doubts and fear is natural to many, but for others this is a mountain they must conquer. If they do not, it may become a stumbling block and it could interfere with their healing process.

The daily practice of meditation, yoga, tai chi and visualisation etc., may help relaxation on a deeper level. One can then go a step further and introduce the powers of positive thinking. And if one is housebound there are myriad DVDs and books that can be obtained. During my research I heard of several people who had been told they had terminal illness and could expect to die within months. But telling a sick person they are going to die can have a negative effect on some people. One can die quickly if they believe they are dying. When we believe in something we become that belief.

For some, this is a red rag to a bull and they fight to survive. But for others the issue becomes too difficult to conquer and it is easier for them to close down and accept death. Those who are ill may lack the energy and discipline required to think matters through in a logical sequence. They may be too ill to make sound decisions because illness and pain cloud judgment.

Those who are ill need positive people in their lives. They need reassurance that with a competent natural therapist and correct information their health may improve. But those who are strong and positive may encounter opposition from the weak and negative. The weak may feel threatened by change and by those they feel are mentally stronger than themselves. The mentally strong accept adversity as a challenge. But where there is illness nothing remains the same. Some may fear failure and this prevents them from working towards successful goals.

Elias said one particular client with diabetes had been recovering quickly but then discontinued the natural therapy and stopped eating natural foods. The reason given was a dislike of the taste of dates. The person went back to conventional medicine and injecting artificial insulin. With doctors doing all the thinking, that person will now remain dependant on others until death.

There are those who may enjoy their illness because they are showered with extra attention from family and friends. They become very good at being patients and the centre of attention. They may feel their life is worthwhile and fulfilled and they do not have the need to be well, therefore they do not fight.

Some people may say they wish to be well but they miss their ritual of sitting across a doctor's desk regularly and they may miss not having prescription drugs. For some, interaction with their doctor on such a personal level is a major part of their lives and they become accustomed to being ill.

Being healthy and independent would leave a gap in their lives that they are incapable of filling. For them it may be like a child losing their security blanket. When I was ill my belief was: one day I was going to meet someone who could help me overcome my illness. I could not accept the fact that I was a sick person and even though I was told I had a short shelf life, I could not comprehend my own death.

As far as I was concerned, being a sick person was demeaning. I needed to be well because I had lots to do. I concentrated heavily on finding a way out of my predicament as I had done on several occasions in the past.

I thought my problems were more of a pain in the proverbial and a huge waste of valuable time. Another thought was: It is a big world out there and there has to be someone who can help me. I was always looking. My beliefs and hopes, and faith in my Creator were powerful. Then one day it all happened. I am alive because of my beliefs.

MOSQUITOES

The female mosquito has two antennas and a proboscis. It requires blood from external sources for its larvae to survive and it is the female of the species that lays the egg. A female mosquito requires blood that is thick and travels slowly through the vein. She is capable of biting through the skin and into a vein and she will always find her target, even through clothing.

Blood contains iron and hydrochloric acid and as it flows within the vein it causes friction. Friction causes the vein to expand and it also creates an electromagnetic field that radiates from the vein. With the use of its antenna, the mosquito identifies and locates the pulses from the magnetic field and the vein becomes its target.

If human blood is good quality, between 7.3pH and 7.7pH, the mosquito may not bite because she cannot drink the blood. The blood is too thin and it is flowing too quickly for her to extract.

If the human diet consists of animal DNA, grains and processed cane sugar etc., the pH level of the blood lowers to about 4.5pH. At this level blood cells become less flexible, they gain in weight and the blood circulates at a slower rate that is conducive to the mosquito's needs.

The lower the pH level of the blood, the heavier and thicker it becomes. Even though blood of this quality travels through the veins at the correct pace for the mosquito, she cannot extract it in this condition because its thick consistency will encrust her proboscis.

The female mosquito efficiently rectifies this problem by injecting marcumar (blood thinner) into the vein, making it possible for her to withdraw the valuable fluid that will give life and sustain her young. It is for this reason that a lump develops on the skin and itches after a mosquito bites. Elias says to treat: rub lemon juice or oil of cloves into the skin. Fruitarians are usually not as badly affected by the female mosquito bites because their blood is of good quality and it is too thin for her needs.

NAILS

If a finger or toe nail is accidentally dislodged, Elias said not to remove it. Instead, press it into the nail bed and fasten it with tape. Clean regularly and secure it until the nail has fully grown out. This will prevent future disfigurement and protects the bed.

The body emits toxin when we begin to eat naturally. The elimination can be so rapid the body may even cleanse through the nails because the finger tips may pull away from beneath the nails. It then heals, creating unsightly cavities. Bacterial fungus may invade this cavity. If this occurs, Elias says to paint the nails with red nail polish, allow it to dry and coat with a favourite colour. The intensity of the colour prevents light from penetrating the cavity and fungi will not grow beneath it. Bacterial fungi require light to survive.

If a male suffers this problem, cover the affected nail with a plaster strip to keep out the light. Remove the strip during night hours and dress daily. Nail treatments must continue until the nails have healed. But this seldom occurs during cleansing.

Elias said we should grow nails to just beyond the tips of the fingers and toes – no longer or shorter. Nails are protective membranes that make our finger and toe tips more sensitive. If nails are cut too short, fingers and toes are not as sensitive as they should be. When nails are short and we press on a surface, the applied pressure will not be correct. This will affect the joints and they could become disfigured and pain may occur.

If nails are too short, we will not feel pain in our fingertips as we should and over the years we will become accustomed to what we do not know. If the toenails are cut too short, they may grow inwardly, causing infection. Short nails encourage short beds.

Elias said the correct length of his finger nails was imperative and an integral part of diagnosis and treatment. For example, when he corrects blood pressure, the length of his nails is vital because he must have 100 per cent accuracy in his finger tips.

In the last few years he has had problems with his hands and nails because some clients consume strong, toxic drugs which their body emits as acid through perspiration during massage therapy. These toxins eat their way through layers of the skin on his hands, causing it to weaken and his nails to split. He now takes protective measures.

In the past, some clients withheld information on previous chemo and radium therapy treatments. Within three minutes from the beginning of a massage, their body released toxic acids that were so strong they burnt though layers of the skin on his hands.

Elias said when he was working in Germany he had 250 clients a day and he did not encounter this problem. But he said people lived differently in Australia because they relied very heavily on toxic drugs and supplements as a quick fix. To gauge the body's toxicity one needs to look no further than the steering wheel of their car or inside the wristband of one's watch.

He said it was bad enough that people ate foods containing harmful acids but when combined with toxic drugs, the combination was lethal. Elias said horse's hooves should not be filed short because they would have difficulty galloping and walking on wet surfaces and they may slip and injure themselves. When hooves are the correct length, the animal has a sensitive connection with the earth.

NERVE DAMAGE

Nerves that are cut or damaged during surgery and accidents may cause pain to both ends. Elias said more information should be given to medical students during training about the importance of the nerve system because it was the life support of the body. He said it was imperative that nerves should not be cut or damaged during surgery. If a nerve has been cut it is possible for the ends to grow together but it depends on the severity of the cut. If the distance between the two ends is not greater than 0.3mm and if there is no scar tissue it is possible, especially with stimulation (nerve massage).

Elias describes nerves as cables that transmit electricity throughout the body but if they are severed, the electrical current cannot flow correctly. The current continues the flow to both ends of the severed nerve by jumping from one nerve end to the other but scare tissue forms at this point. Those who have this type of damage have described the pain as excruciating.

He said a client visited him after having had both breasts removed because of cancer and was badly scarred. She suffered severe nerve damage and had had previous doses of radiation. The pain caused by scar tissue was so great she was on heavy pain killing medication. To help her, Elias used a natural cream and added pure gold dust. He massaged her chest with the cream which enabled the gold (being a metal) to transfer electrical currents to each of the severed points and within 90 minutes the pain was gone.

Heavy gold neck chains have a calming effect on the brain. Gold lowers nerve frequency and heart stress. If the gold is of poor quality it will not perform as well. It was the culture in some countries for women to wear gold bands around their neck and they outlived their male counterparts by several years.

Copper has a similar reaction but it should not be worn because as skin perspires it turns green. Copper then enters the blood stream via the pores and damages the liver. Silver should not be used because it causes a similar problem.

PARKINSON'S DISEASE

Elias said Parkinson's was very difficult to diagnose because many illnesses have similar symptoms. Parkinson's disease is the result of lead poisoning. In years gone by, some people who worked in the printing industry contracted this disease because the inks contained lead. Those who drank water from lead pots or those who drank water that ran through lead pipes also suffered the disease.

Parkinson's is a chronic degenerative disease of the brain which affects voluntary body control. When certain brain cells die, muscle function and patterns of movements decrease. Symptoms are: tremor, stiffness, muscle rigidity and slow movements with occasional pain, energy loss and tiredness. The sufferer may display quick shuffling steps and daily activity is difficult.

Facial muscles grow rigid, causing a fixed expression and their eyes widen and blink less. Speech becomes impaired and swallowing becomes laboured along with loss of mental function and depression. Parkinson's disease may affect all parts of the body and as it worsens the sufferer should avoid stress.

Loss of dopamine may cause Parkinson's disease. Dopamine is a vital chemical hormone that is produced naturally within the brain if the body is functioning properly. Coffee, alcohol, medication, animal DNA and cigarettes cause the loss of this natural chemical. Street drugs are a minor contributing factor.

Elias said Parkinson's disease could be cured but recovery was slow. The source of the disease must be identified and eliminated. The sufferer must have patience and they must work with a patient therapist who understands the disease. Eating naturally is essential, especially pears because they eliminate heavy metals and absorb lead.

PREGNANCY, ULTRASOUNDS, CHILDBIRTH AND BABIES

Elias explained the dangerous effects that ultrasounds have on a pregnant woman and her foetus. We saw ultrasound images of the nerve cells of an expectant mother. In the first image her brain cells were normal, healthy and correct.

One hour later the nerve cells of mother and baby were damaged and within 24 hours some nerve cells of both mother and baby were dead. The reading of the ultrasound was 1.2MHz which is considered as "not very strong", yet it does this amount of damage.

Prior to the 1980s most women carried full term. If births were premature it was usually the result of an accident, illness, stress or shock. Since the inception of ultrasounds, premature births have become common. Elias said if abnormalities were detected it was too late because the foetus was already well developed.

He spoke of the dangers of amniocentesis and said this test could only be done after four months of pregnancy. He said nature provided the precise amount of fluid that surrounds the foetus which protects its body, especially the head.

During the procedure, fluid is removed for testing but this is dangerous because pressure is created within the womb. This pressure can damage the baby and its brain.

He said even if only three to 4mg were removed, it took more than two weeks for the mother's body to reproduce 1mg of this fluid. During this period the unborn baby is highly vulnerable.

The injection used to remove the fluid can also endanger the baby because it has been known to cause infection.

The unborn baby begins seeing whilst in the womb four months after conception. It reacts to the movement of light. At birth, babies cannot see clearly but they can see the reflection of light.

Many African women do not have ultrasound tests during pregnancy. In the main their babies are normal and healthy and do not die at birth. Those that do are usually the result of starvation or inadequate diets.

Elias emphasised: it is not wise for pregnant women to have contact with chemicals and electromagnetic fields such as ultrasounds and microwave ovens. He said it was also wise to avoid drugs and food cooked in microwave ovens. When these messages are ignored, deformities and short-term pregnancies may occur.

High blood pressure and stress must be avoided during pregnancy. Five dates three times a day and at bedtime may help calm the brain and lower stress. One cannot overdose on dates. Natural fruit and three birdseye chilli daily will help correct the blood and prevent clotting.

Elias said pregnant women suffering morning sickness and nausea could use fruit to help alleviate the symptoms. A little ginger may also help. Pineapple is excellent during and between meals. Mashed banana eaten slowly before meals may help settle stomach acids.

Many women have problems during childbirth. One may be the lack of expansion of the cervix. Elias said if the birthing mother was placed in a standing position, the cervix may expand the necessary extra centimetres for a natural birth.

If a woman stands during labour, it is beneficial for both she and the baby, and the birth could be quicker. He said immediately after the birth, the blood of both mother and baby should be allowed to settle within their vital organs before the umbilical cord was cut. Corrective breathing on the part of the mother will help both her and her baby's blood to settle. If it is cut too soon, the infant can have problems within its vital organs and its hair may be very fine.

After the umbilical cord is cut, the baby may suffer golden

staph infection in the navel because this bacteria is present in many hospitals. One method of treating it is to apply natural lemon juice to the affected area. Elias said sometimes after the navel healed, outbreaks could re-occur at various times and to continue treating the area with lemon juice until the infection disappeared.

Amalgam in tooth fillings of pregnant women and nursing mothers is dangerous. Mothers with these fillings who breast feed may be in danger of losing their child to Sudden Infant Death Syndrome because amalgam is also transmitted to the baby via breast milk.

Elias said amalgam in tooth fillings was but one factor of infant cot deaths. He said during autopsies, he has seen heavy metal deposits of amalgam, cadmium and mercury in the form of black spots scattered throughout the brains of babies. Some babies are born with a body rash which may be diagnosed as hormonal. But this may not be correct. It may be linked to the amalgam fillings in the mother's teeth.

Mother's milk is usually sterile but if a nursing mother suffers mastitis, she should not breast feed her infant until the infection has fully cleared. Breast glands become highly toxic and the chemical structure of the milk alters.

It becomes toxic and infection is transferred to the infant who also suffers the identical symptoms. The immune system of the baby is immature and underdeveloped, it does not protect the baby who could die as a result. Many mothers breastfeed but this can be detrimental to the baby if their milk is of poor quality. It will lack essential nutrients and may contain chemicals. A breastfeeding mother should eat only fruit and three litres of water daily because fruit's nutrients strengthen the infant's immune system.

Elias said: if a mother was unable to breastfeed, it was imperative they made a nutritious formula for the infant in order for its body, brain and immune system to develop and function normally. The ingredients include: banana, avocado, water and coconut milk. After a period of four months, dates may be added. Dates, coconut and avocado are brain food.

Babies dehydrate rapidly and require water as do adults.

Parents should research widely and choose wisely before giving infants processed artificial formulas. Elias said some could contain preservatives, additives and vegetable oils which may harbour harmful acids. Some may also contain soy and other grains which could be genetically engineered. Grains are detrimental to the infant's stomach because they produce harmful stomach acids which create gas.

Elias said mothers should stop breastfeeding and stop giving the child all other forms of milk (except coconut milk) when the baby cuts its first teeth. Babies can eat the same fruit as adults to strengthen their immune system and for vital brain development. The most valuable gift parents can give a baby is a healthy start to life. He also said that women should wait for two years after the birth of a baby before they become pregnant with another because the human body needs time to settle.

SALT

Processed salt may be detrimental to the kidneys because like processed cane sugar, it contains chemical additives. This type of salt places pressure on the kidneys because they must expel the substances. This pressure causes perspiration.

Tomatoes, cucumber and zucchini contain natural fruit salts which have a different chemical structure to that of processed salt. Fruit salt is compatible to the body.

Nutrients present in pink salt from mountain water falls or rivers are not as abundant as salt that is found on rocks adjacent to the ocean. Pink salt crystals that build up on rocks are organic because ocean water filters through living plant matter and is safe to eat in moderation. Many people also use Celtic salt.

SCHIZOPHRENIA (briefly)

This can be any of various psychotic disorders. Sufferers of this disease experience the breakdown of integrated personality functioning. They withdraw from reality and suffer from emotional blunting and distortion. Their thought patterns are disturbed, therefore their behaviour alters. Elias said this disease was occurring too often in adults as well as teenagers.

A diet of animal DNA, stress, fear, a lack of fructose, medication and heroine are contributing factors. Those who do not drink enough water are in danger of contracting this disease. An adequate supply of water is necessary for the brain to function normally. Loss of body and brain fluid – for example 70 per cent dehydration over a period of time – may cause this disease.

SOY

This section is dedicated to the memory of Valerie James, who valiantly and persistently fought against soy foods, including infant formula.

Valerie was a lovely and very intelligent New Zealand lady who loved life and offered a passionate enthusiasm for whatever enterprise she undertook: school teacher, mother, real estate broker, aviculturalist and food researcher. When she realised what she had fed her children, she resolved to try to prevent other mothers doing the same thing.

Even though she died February 23, 2008, her valiant effort will continue for our benefit and for generations to come. Valerie was a gentle soul who made a huge difference.

Much has been written about soy, a substance that Elias regards as a toxin. Two independent internet web sites examine various issues, including:

- Designer foods: processed foods with added supplements which are far removed from what is required for natural healing.
- Phytic acid in soy.
- Trypsin inhibitors.
- Soy phytoestrogens and endocrine functions.
- Antithyroid agents and a possible link to thyroid cancer.
- Vitamin B12 analogs.
- Soy and vitamin D.
- Lysinoalanine.
- Highly carcinogenic nitrosamines.

- Free glutamic acid (MSG) neurotoxin and soy products.
- Oestrogen compounds.
- Testosterone surge.
- The physical delay of maturation.
- Puberty and soy.
- The ban of certain soy products in various countries.
- The recall of certain soy products.
- Infertility, breast cancer, hypothyroidism and thyroid cancer.
- Aluminum and manganese.
- ADD and ADHD.

The web sites are:
www.soyonlineservice.co.nz
www.thewholesoystory.com

SUGAR

There are 500 types of sugars, some are:

Fructose: simple fruit sugar also known as the absolute food. There are 13 types of fructose. Fructose should *not* be compared with other sugars, for example, maltose, sucrose, galactose, lactose, hexose and dextrose… even though these words end in "ose".

Elias said: "Fructose is very badly misunderstood and maligned. Fructose should *not* be regarded as a sugar and is inadequately named. Fructose is unique because it is a complete food and the only food that is completely compatible with the body."

Manufacturers process fructose into a fine powder where chemicals and preservatives are added. Elias said: "But manufactured (processed) sugar from fructose is detrimental to the body because it contains chemicals and should *not be consumed"*. He added: *"All processed sugars are toxic to the human body"*.

Galactose: a hexose sugar manufactured within the body. Glucose is converted into galactose within the liver enabling the mammary glands to secrete lactose. Also found in fruit pectin.

Glucose (dextrose; grape sugar): a white crystalline sugar occurring widely in nature. A sugar form of which (dextrose) occurs in many fruits, animal tissue, and fluids and has a sweetness about one-half that of ordinary sugar.

Glucose is the major source of energy for most cells. Glucose and its derivatives are crucially important in the energy metabolism of living organisms.

Glucose is also a constituent of many polysaccharides, most notably starch and cellulose. These yield glucose when broken down, for example by enzymes during digestion. Used in the manufacture of many types of processed foods including confectionary and medication.

Hexose: any of a class of sugars containing six carbon atoms such as glucose and fructose.

Lactose (milk sugar): sugar comprising one glucose molecule linked to a galactose molecule. Lactose is manufactured by the mammary gland and occurs only in milk. E.g. cows milk contains about 4.7 per cent lactose. It is less sweet than sucrose (cane sugar).

Maltose: malt sugar derived mainly from barley. Found in a variety of foods and beverages including ale and beer.

Pentose: a sugar that has five carbon atoms per molecule.

Sucrose (cane sugar; beet sugar; saccharose): A sugar comprising one molecule of glucose linked to a fructose molecule. It occurs widely in plants and is particularly abundant in sugar cane and sugar beet (15-20 per cent), from which it is extracted and refined for table sugar. If heated to 200 degrees Celsius, sucrose will caramelize.

Pure raw sugar cane juice is beneficial to health. But processed cane sugar is extremely detrimental to the body and brain. Elias said this should be a banned substance because much of it was bleached and many other harmful chemicals were added during manufacture. Processed cane sugar is complex sugar and has a toxic effect on the human brain.

Each of the 500 sugars, including the 13 fruit sugars (fructose), has an individual chemical structure. The chemical reaction of each is unique because each has a different reaction on the body and brain. Sugar is a complex subject and a science in its own right. Sugars are not "just sugar" and they should not fall under one category.

TINNITUS

Tinnitus and Meniere's syndrome are related. Tinnitus is not a disease but a syndrome. It is ringing in the ears which involves the auditory nerve. Sufferers may experience sounds such as buzzing, roaring, hissing or whistling. Medical manuals state the cause of this syndrome is obscure but Elias said it was the end result of dental procedures that had not worked in the patient's favour.

He said when we bite, we placed pressure on our teeth. The normal pressure on the back teeth is 428 kilo of quadrant mm. This amount of pressure is high. The bone between the jaw joint and the ear canal is extremely fine and if it is altered slightly the bone structure also alters. The crown and the bridge must align correctly. During a tooth extraction, the dentist applies pressure. The problem arises six months after dental procedures. Ringing in the ears can also occur with sudden sounds or loud music but mostly it is a dental problem. Those with tinnitus should revisit their dentist.

But problems may also arise if the dentist fails to recognise that prior work was not carried out properly and resulted in tinnitus. This work is highly technical and the dentist may not feel he/she is capable of rectifying the problem. One must then search for a dentist who identifies it as a dental problem and is able to fix it.

TONSILS

Tonsils are the defence mechanism of the human body.

Tonsils are lymphoid organs – defence organs that guard the body from infection, bacteria and viruses. Nature placed them strategically at the entrance to the nose and mouth to protect the respiratory system and the digestive tract. Tonsils guard, destroy and eliminate.

There are three sets which are situated under the uppermost fine lining of the nose, mouth and throat:

1. The lingual lies at the back of the tongue.
2. The palatine is at the back and to either side of the throat.
3. The pharyngeal or nasopharyngeal (adenoids) are at the back

of the nose.

Tonsils have many functions, some are:

- They detoxify the body by eliminating poisonous debris.
- They monitor the quality of food, water and air which enter the body.
- They play an important role in tissue change.
- They regulate the activity of the entire mucous membrane.
- They produce lymphocytes – a type of white blood cell which plays a central role in the body's immune system.

There are three types of lymphocytes:

1. NK cells (Natural Killer). These cells kill cancer cells.
2. B lymphocytes. These come from bone marrow and produce specific types of antibodies.
3. T lymphocytes. These are derived from the thymus and they stimulate antibody production.

TONSILLITIS

Elias said: "The best way of treating tonsillitis is to prevent it, and this is very simple". He said dairy products were one of the major reasons why children suffered from infected tonsils, childhood illnesses such as croup and other diseases.

He said the mouth and throat, including the three sets of tonsils, were covered with natural mucus which protected the respiratory system and digestive tract.

But many children are allowed to drink the milk from animals and to eat its by-products. They are also fed animal DNA such as beef and chicken. These foods are incompatible with the body and create a haven for disease.

Children are eating convenience and processed food in mammoth proportions. These foods are usually high in grains, processed sugar, carbohydrates, fillers, binders, colourants and chemicals.

And instead of fresh fruit juice and water, many are given drinks from a can, carton or plastic container. It appears where food is concerned, people are taking the easy way out, but it is the children who are paying the price.

Such foods play havoc with the nerve, immune and lymph systems, and ultimately the brain. This has a flow-on effect which results in diseases. Children also become accustomed to taking prescription drugs from an early age. These are not good examples of what children should be learning.

Children should be taught to eat properly and they should learn that only the body can heal itself. Many of the chemicals in drugs are toxic to the body, so how can they heal?

In order to have a healthy body, it must be cleansed daily and made alkaline. Diseases require acid to survive. When processed foods, drugs and animal DNA are consumed, the body becomes acidic. It then becomes a receptacle for disease, because the nerve and lymph systems cannot cope with the flow of toxic acids such substances produce. For example: dairy products contain large amounts of bacteria, artificial hormones, artificial antibiotics and chemicals – all of which are concentrated during their manufacture. The milk from animals and its by-products dehydrate the protective mucus coating of the mouth and throat. When the throat is in this "dry" state, disease, infection and viruses enter the body through the mouth and nose. The immune and lymph systems become stagnant, sluggish and inactive.

The health of the child or adult is then at great risk because their body has no protection against infection and diseases, including cancers. Infection is a good indication that the immune system is not functioning correctly.

Elias said children were at high risk of contracting infection because many were not being given a natural diet high in fructose. Only fructose cleans the lymph system. A clean lymph system produces a healthy immune system.

Children should also be given fresh fruit juice and ample water to drink to prevent dehydration.

Some children are contracting infections regularly, as often as every six weeks. In the main, this is the result of an inadequate diet. This can lead to many trips to a doctor's surgery, followed by the usual gamut of prescription drugs which weaken the immune system even further. Children who live on fruit are usually seldom ill.

Late last century, many vital body parts and organs were removed in an effort to combat disease, mainly through ignorance and misinformation. But it seems the penny has dropped and the important role tonsils play in the fight against bacteria and disease has finally been recognised.

Most babies are born perfect and healthy. But the health of a child is a product of their environment and as we all know, children quickly adapt because they do not know the difference. Children eat what adults provide.

Adults are in total control of the child's health. But many opt for the easy way out by saying: "My child will not eat fruit". It is easier for some not to persevere, because if they did, they would have to make changes. Some will take the easy way out because their lives are already complicated.

When a child is handed processed food in a wrapper, their immune system is at the mercy of the chemicals and additives of the contents.

But where childhood infections and diseases are concerned, it is the adult who makes the decisions on their behalf. Often it is the children who pay the price.

Elias said parents should keep children well away from hospitals. They should not allow the removal of the glands that protect their immune system. He said: "The immune system of a child was immature and they could easily contract deadly diseases such as MRSA, staphylococcal and pseudomonas aeruginosa present in some hospitals".

VARICOSE VEINS

A diet consisting of animal DNA including dairy products, grains, vegetables and other acid-laden food lowers the pH level in the blood.

Harmful plaque residue forms in veins, arteries and vessels, causing obstruction. Varicose veins are the result of a poor diet.

VIRUSES – THEIR HABITAT, SURVIVAL AND EXTERMINATION

Throughout our lives many of us have had viruses such as Ross River fever, Barmah Forest, dengue fever, flu virus, shingles, Bell's palsy, measles and mumps etc.

Symptoms may subside after several weeks or months. But while animal protein is part of the host's daily diet, viruses will remain in the human body because this form of DNA is its life support. Drugs will not kill viruses.

Different viruses live in different parts of the body and brain. For example, the HIV-AIDS virus lives in the killer cells – the white blood cells – in the immune system. It destroys these cells, resulting in reduced immunity therefore infections, disease and death may occur. Elias said of all the viruses, this one took the longest to kill. Others live in arteries and cause severe haemorrhaging. Ebola virus, often fatal, lives in vessel cells and causes internal haemorrhaging.

Our nerves have a "coat" and it is under this coat the herpes virus survives. Herpes are any of certain inflammatory viral infections of the skin or mucous membrane, characterised by clusters of vesicles that tend to spread.

Viruses require animal DNA to survive and each requires a special type of animal protein. To eradicate them, eliminate all animal DNA and their by-products from the diet. It takes at least three years to completely cleanse the human body of this residue.

To learn more about viruses read a book titled: *Neutralization of Animal Viruses* written by N.J. Dimmock © Springer – Verlag Berlin Heidelberg 1993. ISBN: 3540560300 and 0387560300 Another interesting book is titled: *Die Geplanten Seuchen. (The Planned Plague.) AIDS – SARS und die militaerische (and the military) Genforschung* by Wolfgang Eggert (Hrsg.) ISBN 3935845081. Web site: www.beimpropheten.com

This book is a compilation of works by various authors including:

- *Vaccines to Ruffle Flu's Feathers* by Julie Clayton.
- *Avian Influenza is a Killer.*

- *Is SARS Someone's Weapon of Mass Destruction?* by Earl Bousquet.
- *SARS – a Great Global Scam* by Dr. Leonard Horowitz.
- *Pathogenicity of Avian Influenza A H5N1 Viruses* by J.M. Katz, R.A. Bright, J. Hu-Primmer, H. Chen, Y. Matsuoka and K. Subbarao.
- *Development and Evaluation of Candidate Influenza A Vaccines for Pandemic Preparedness* by K. Subbarao. H. Chen. B. Murphy. J. Katz. N. Cox. D. Swayne and Y. Matsuoka.
- *SARS: Genetic Engineering/Coronavirus Bio Weapon.*(Third World Network Biosafety Information Service).
- *Switching Species Tropism: An Effective way to Manipulate the Feline Coronavirus Genome* by Bert Jan Haijema. Haukeliene Volders and Peter J.M. Rottier.
- *Genetically Engineered Coronavirus More Potent in Enteric and Respiratory Tracts of Swine* by Trevor G. Marshall.
- *Engineering the Largest RNA Virus Genome as an Infectious Bacterial Artificial Chromosome* by Fernando Almazan. Jose M. Gonzalez. Zoltan Penzes. Ander Izeta. Enrique Calvo. Juan Plana-Duran and Luis Enjuanes.
- *The Making of Infectious Viral RNA: No Size Limit in Sight* by Michael M.C. Lai.
- *SARS and Genetic Engineering?* By Dr. Mae-Wan Ho and Professor Joe Cummins.
- *Corona Virus Genetic Engineering and the Origin of SARS* by Professor Joe Cummins.
- *Bio-terrorism & SARS* by Dr. Mae-Wan Ho.
- *Genetic Engineering Super-viruses* by Dr. Mae-Wan Ho.
- *SARS as Economic Warfare* by Jon Rappoport.

VACCINATIONS

The damaging affects vaccinations may have on the human body is frightening and this small section cannot do justice to this subject.

Before a child is vaccinated it is vital parents read books titled:

(1). *Vaccinations – The Medical Assault on the Immune System* written by Viera Scheibner Ph. D. printed by the Australian Print Group in Victoria, Australia. ISBN 0646 15124 X.

(2). *Behavioural Problems in Childhood – The Link to Vaccinations* by Viera Scheibner.

To obtain this vital information, telephone Vera on 02 4787 8203 or 02 9327 8544.

Parents have a right to know exactly what ingredients are used in their child's vaccination. Pharmacies and medical practitioners may have a list. Ask for: The Australian Standard Vaccination Schedule by CMPMedica Australia (MIMS Reference).

Parents of infants and children should ask doctors and chemists for the list of ingredients that make up vaccinations, then research *each* individual ingredient in order to learn about the effects they have on a small child before vaccination takes place.

Comprehensive research may save the child's life and it may prevent a lifetime of heartache. When researching, it is vital to obtain information from independent sources that have nothing to gain through the sale of these chemicals.

Vaccinations of people of all ages adversely affect the nerve system and brain. But this is even more so in infants, babies and children because their body, brain and immune system are underdeveloped.

Elias said when vaccinations were first introduced, people were not as adversely affected as they were today. Only one disease was covered per injection and the chemicals used were not as toxic as they are now. Later, two diseases were covered by one injection. As science advanced, it went to three, then six and now the number has escalated to 22 diseases in one injection.

Vaccinations are severely and adversely affecting many children because we are witnessing those with Attention Deficit Disorder, leukaemia, brain disorders, motor neurone disease and other diseases and disorders. Elias is treating many children with disorders caused from the heavy metals and toxins that make up vaccinations. Children who were born normal and healthy.

The number of children who visit the Schindelar Natural Therapy Clinic is increasing. Elias said it was heartbreaking to see children in that condition as a result of vaccinations. And nothing is being done about it. He said there was a strong connection between cot deaths and vaccinations. He said some babies who were born normal and healthy have died within hours of having had vaccinations.

Many parents believe their child will die without vaccinations but they are not told of the dangers. Some children are not the same after vaccinations. They cannot enjoy their young lives and are prisoners within their own body. They become victims and they must remain in the care of parents who also suffer as a result.

Elias can provide shocking and first hand information on the suffering of tiny children as a result of vaccinations because he treats them regularly. He added: "It is now an epidemic because the chemicals are becoming stronger. Children should not endure this suffering. The only way it is going to stop is if people take back their powers. They must say 'no' to drugs".

Parents do have choices. They have rights and they can exercise those rights if they choose. An effective way to protect a child's health is to promote a healthy immune system. This can be done from the moment they are born. Elias has helped many parents of newly born babies with information on how to protect and strengthen their infant's immune system. Many of these children grow up without experiencing so much as a head cold. He added: most of them rarely miss a day of schooling.

VITAMINS AND MINERALS

Apart from a little salt daily, Elias maintains it is not necessary to consume supplements because fruit contains all the natural vitamins and minerals necessary for normal body functions and growth.

A newspaper article warned: some vitamins and minerals sold through the internet may contain crushed glass and bricks.

The sun is the giver of life and vitamin D is a gift of the sun. Vitamin D deficiency is the result of the lack of sunlight. This deficiency leads to loss of muscular strength and bone density.

Those with dark or olive skin require greater amounts of sunlight. Florescent light leaches vitamin D from the body.

The body creates this vitamin but it remains neutral because it requires activation by the sun. Those who work indoors during daylight hours and those confined to a bed are at the greatest risk. Sun screens that contain chemicals may prevent the sun's absorption into the skin.

The elderly are also at risk. Many suffer brittle bones because their diet may be high in harmful acids and they may be fructose deficient. Many consume prescription drugs and they may not drink enough water. The amount of broken bones caused by stumbling is alarming amongst our elderly.

VITAMIN FUNCTIONS (some):

- *Vitamin A* is essential for the eyes, skin, hair, cell protection, resistance to infection and protects against cancer.
- *B1* releases energy from carbohydrate. Aids the nerve system, heart muscles and memory.
- *B2* converts protein fats and carbohydrates into energy. Good for growth and resistance to infection.
- *B6* is important in protein metabolism, for growth, skin, hair, nerves and the production of red blood cells.
- B12 is essential for cell construction and protection, resistance, production of red blood cells and tissue growth.
- *C* protects the immune system, it aids iron absorption, connective tissues and skin cell maintenance and construction.
- *D* is necessary for bone density. It is created in the skin but activated by the sun.
- protects the cells and is an antioxidant. It detoxifies the liver and protects against cancer.
- *H (Biotin)* is involved in the metabolism of proteins and fats, carbohydrates, also for the blood, nerves, skin and hair.
- *K* coagulates blood. Found in berries and dates.
- *Folic acid* is essential for growth and cell production,

particularly red blood cells and it protects against heart attacks.

- *Niacin* is vital for energy release in tissues and cells, for skin, heart, nerves and growth.
- *Pantothenic acid* releases energy from foods and is necessary for bones, skin, hair and hormone protection.

"

the soul of
the flesh is in the blood

"

– lev. 17: 11 - 14

"

the way I work is not
a secret. with the same education,
anyone can work as I do

"

– elias ludwig schindelar

Chapter 5

FOETAL ALCOHOL SYNDROME (FAS)

This chapter is dedicated to Neroli Endacott.
The tireless work she does for children who
do not live in loving homes is inspirational.

Think about it ladies: would you buy your baby a pint at the pub? So why give it to your unborn child?

When young women go partying and looking for a good time, the last thing they think about is Foetal Alcohol Syndrome. What causes FAS and other foetal alcohol-related neurological disorders? Alcohol.

Women who drink alcohol daily during pregnancy may lack the vital nutrients of a good diet, and especially one that is high in fructose.

Some women who drink alcohol also smoke cigarettes, while some abuse drugs. But alcohol seems to be the worst of the worst. It seems to have a direct and toxic effect on the cells because it interferes with DNA synthesis. It interferes with cell migration and development, so it is not surprising that we see certain birth defects during critical periods of exposure.

The critical periods of cell exposure for facial features are during the first trimester. But most of the nerve system dysfunction that we see occurs probably between the second and third trimester exposures.

Initial studies from the University of Washington suggest that women who were alcoholics and have had heavy amounts of alcohol exposure were placing the brain of the unborn foetus in a high state of vulnerability. The study also showed that binge drinking can also be extremely harmful to the unborn.

If women drink heavily only on weekends – binge drinking – this can also affect the unborn child. Even though they are only drinking heavily for a "short" period of time, it is the level of alcohol concentration in the blood that does the damage. Episodic exposure to alcohol is harmful.

There does not seem to be any safe level of alcohol during pregnancy. University studies show that at the moment there is no data on how many children are affected. In Australia, very little has been done to even recognise that the problem exists. But this is not the case in the United Kingdom, United States, Canada, Russia, Europe and South Africa.

In some communities 10 per cent of children are affected. This syndrome is a worldwide problem: it is not isolated. It can affect anyone from any background. Alcohol does not discriminate.

This syndrome requires correct diagnosis because some of the symptoms are similar to other diseases.

Affected children sometimes display a lack of interest in food. They fail to thrive so they start off small and their growth is often below average. Their growth and nutrition should be monitored and they need to be checked for other birth defects, including their sight and hearing.

They may have social problems and some are placed in care because they are difficult to look after. There is also a risk if inadequate bonding has occurred and there may be incidences of neglect and even physical and sexual abuse.

As children grow a little older, developmental issues may become obvious. They can be slow to speak. Some at the extreme end may have mental retardation. They can have trouble reading and spelling, and mathematics can prove difficult. Their general level of adaptive functioning is poor.

They have difficulty understanding right from wrong and the consequences of their actions. Families often run into difficulties with discipline.

Attention Deficit Disorder is very common in children with Foetal Alcohol Syndrome. Sometimes it manifests as hyperactivity and sometimes just as an inability to concentrate.

The primary disabilities with Foetal Alcohol Syndrome are to the physical features and the abnormalities of mild mental handicap. Another primary defect is frontal lobe syndrome where children lack judgment.

They get into situations they are best to stay out of but they do not have the judgment to guide them. Foetal Alcohol Syndrome also effects speech and maturity.

The secondary disabilities include mental health problems, a low self-esteem and short attention spans. As adults, they suffer from depression. They have no true friendships because they are incapable of expressing themselves.

In school they are disruptive and often get into trouble with the law. They begin stealing and often engage in sexual promiscuity or assaults. This becomes a vicious circle because often they are very naive children.

Many end up in youth courts and in jail as adults. A recent study at the University of British Columbia by dedicated doctors interested in Foetal Alcohol Syndrome, discovered that 24 per cent of youths who are incarcerated have evidence of FAS or partial Foetal Alcohol Syndrome.

Alcohol Related Neurological Disorder is a major problem for the law and the justice system.

Many of these children get into trouble through alcohol and drug abuse.

As adolescents and adults there may be a high frequency of dependant living. Even if they have a normal IQ (Intelligence Quotient), they may not be able to budget or look after their money and they may not be able to plan ahead. Many require supervision well into adulthood. And they can have problems with fitting into a place of employment.

The secondary disabilities present major problems. Doctors at the University of Washington maintain that if a child is diagnosed before the age of six, more can be done to help them.

Some doctors in the United States are trying hard to work out exactly how to prevent these secondary disabilities. They say action should be taken immediately to prevent them.

A child born with Foetal Alcohol Syndrome can have very small eye slits. They may have a flattened upper lip and their philtrum may be thin and flat. They may also have cleft palates, renal abnormalities and hearing defects.

Children who do not display the full range of facial abnormalities may not be correctly diagnosed. They are not recognised as having this syndrome and they do not get the vital early interventions they need. Foetal Alcohol Effects or Alcohol Related Neurodevelopmental Disorder are sometimes incorrectly diagnosed.

US studies discovered that school teachers perceived more behavioural, discipline and activity-type problems in children who did not display the full range of facial abnormalities. This is called partial Foetal Alcohol Syndrome.

The children who present the most difficulties for both their parents and teachers are those who are not completely affected but have the more moderate form of the damage.

This is a shame because the expectations that are placed on them are the same as those of normal children. But they cannot perform like a normal child. Some are wrongly diagnosed as having hyperactivity disorder and placed on drugs, but drugs do not solve their problems.

This is a syndrome that can be overwhelming because it involves the child, the parents and family, the school, the community, the health care system and ultimately the justice system.

Some American doctors maintain they may not be able to solve the problems that already exist but more could be done to educate school children, adolescents and adults about the dangers of alcohol. This is a preventable situation but it is not easy to prevent because it takes discipline and a higher order of thinking. If we did not have alcohol we would not have Foetal Alcohol Syndrome. Women do not set out to have an abnormal child but these abnormalities occur through ignorance and lack of correct and vital information.

A young woman drank a bottle of liquor in a one-day binge

during her pregnancy. Her unborn baby paid the price. It was born with damage to the heart, lungs and other vital organs. Instead of having four heart chambers, the baby had three and by the age of 13, the child had three open heart surgeries.

Another woman said that when she was young and in her partying stage, weekend drinking was classed as normal. One day during her pregnancy she drank a bottle of spirits. She weighed only 45.5kg and as a result her baby was born with many complications including two right lungs.

She said: "Had I not drank that day my child would not have had birth defects".

She said she began recognising behavioural problems when the child was six. Her daughter was not the same as other children her own age with regards to social, emotional and developmental issues. At 13, the child was still playing with toddler toys. Her best friend is a dog.

The mother said when she took the doctor's report to the school explaining Foetal Alcohol Syndrome, the teacher said: "Oh, so you are an alcoholic". She had to explain she only drank one day during her pregnancy because the teacher had not heard of FAS.

She added: "We really need to be telling people that one binge or one night is enough to create physical and neurological damage to our unborn children. What I did that day will affect the rest of my life and the rest of my child's life".

Brain damage from alcohol is more common than most people realise. More children are born with Foetal Alcohol Syndrome than Down syndrome and spina bifida. Research in the UK, US, Russia, Canada, Europe and South Africa states that one in 100 babies are born with alcohol-related birth defects and Attention Deficit Disorder, heart problems, hyperactivity, nerve system damage and other disorders.

When a pregnant woman drinks she can alter and damage her baby's brain. The brain of a normal baby is well developed and detailed and it is larger. The brain of a baby born with FAS is less featured, smaller and it looks like an underdeveloped organ. The brain develops throughout pregnancy, not only in the first three months. It can actually be very vulnerable to the effects of alcohol in the latter months as well.

In one particular family, three out of the four children were born with Foetal Alcohol Syndrome. One had trouble walking and suffered autism. One does not speak and is hyperactive while the third also has problems. The oldest is 16, not affected and is doing very well at school. He detests alcohol because both his parents died from alcohol poisoning. The four children live with their grandmother who does all she can to care for them.

A young teenager born with Foetal Alcohol Syndrome spoke about the problems she encounters daily. She said: "I have a learning disability caused by my birth mum drinking alcohol. I have trouble with some stuff like maths, spelling and with my memory. I try to be smart because others in my class are smart. When I get things wrong I am called dumb. But when I get things right I am called a cheat. So now I have stopped trying."

She added: "I want to be like other adults but I cannot always be like them. So it's frustrating. I cannot take the bus to school and I cannot drive. I get worried a lot – more than other people do. Sometimes I wish I did not have Foetal Alcohol Syndrome."

Her foster mum said the girl joined the family when she was 14 months old. She was recognised almost immediately as having special needs. From the beginning she had difficulty with friendships and to this day she has very few friends. She makes social telephone calls daily but she has no understanding of what she does. Her anxiety level and depression are escalating as she grows older because she is not fitting into society.

Her foster mother said she tried to look like anyone else and to talk well, which was also true of the majority of children who have Foetal Alcohol Syndrome. But society also expects them to think well. Nothing could be further from the truth.

Where Foetal Alcohol Syndrome is concerned, talking well and thinking well do not equate. Society needs to see a disability before they can recognise it. For example: a white cane, a hearing aid, a wheelchair or maybe two heads. The majority of these children look normal but society does not accept them because they cannot see their brain.

She went on to say: "Foetal alcohol children are usually matured to only half their age during their teens in terms of their emotional and social development. If they are in a 16-year-old body, they are expected to act that way – not like an eight year old."

Another woman who spoke is the mother of a 30-year-old daughter. She lives in a daily state of self-torture because she drank wine when she was pregnant. She said she only ever drank it because she thought it was safe. Her daughter has the mentality of a six year old and plays with dolls all day, every day.

She concluded by saying: "It is a horrible cross to have to bear because of my irresponsible actions when I was 19. I did not think of the consequences." Foetal Alcohol Syndrome in a child just does not go away.

The question is always being asked: what is a safe amount of alcohol a woman can drink while she is pregnant?

The answer: No alcohol = no risk.

Elias Schindelar on Foetal Alcohol Syndrome

Elias said he had treated many children with this disorder. Foetal Alcohol Syndrome is a complex subject because every child is different and the state of their health, brain and immune system is different. Their previous diet plays a major role because they may also be malnourished.

He said the children were not the problem: the parents were the problem. A child with Foetal Alcohol Syndrome needs much love, support and a fruit diet because the healing brain requires a lot of fructose.

But if the mother is an alcoholic, or both parents are alcoholic it is very difficult to get their support because their first priority is to themselves and their addiction and not the welfare of their child.

Therefore, healing is not the issue. Much patience and many nerve massages are required and it takes about two years before there is any sign of improvement. They had a much better chance of healing if he could treat them when they were one or two years old.

As these boys and girls grow into adolescents, the more attractive they are, the more problems they seem to encounter. Some teenagers have the looks and body of supermodels but the mind of a child. And many are easily led.

Elias said this posed an even more sinister problem, especially if they harboured hidden anger and if they had psychological issues. They may blame their mother for all their problems.

He said another alarming problem is that it may not always be possible to supervise them 100 per cent of the time. It is imperative for those who care for these children to know they must always be propley supervised when they are in their care. If they are not supervised at all times, they can become extremely easy prey to sex predators and molesters.

Neroli Endacott

Neroli is a unique lady that society cannot do without. She lives on the Gold Coast in South East Queensland.

She has raised her own four children and cared for more than 100 disadvantaged, disabled and others in need. About 11 years ago she cared for one young boy who was diagnosed as having Foetal Alcohol Syndrome.

She said it became apparent how many other children displayed the same symptoms, yet were being diagnosed with Attention Deficit Disorder, Attention Deficit Hyperactive Disorder and autism.

Others were diagnosed as having Obessive Compulsive Disorder, Oppositional Defiant Disorder and more recently, bipolar – a mental disorder marked by alternating periods of excitement and depression. To Neroli, this was the missing link. It seemed drinking during pregnancy was an issue that was not being addressed.

She is now caring for two teenagers. She said it has been very difficult because she had to wait three years to have them diagnosed as having Foetal Alcohol Syndrome.

She is focused on coping from day to day with their medical, social, educational, financial, behavioural and emotional demands. And just when she thought she could not do more, she has found herself not being able to afford a house or car.

At the age of 63, when many of her contemporaries are out playing scrabble or bowls, she finds herself having to work a full week and she wonders how long she can keep up the hectic pace.

Neroli said she was very grateful for the help and support she has received from her family and caring friends. She said she could not have done her job without them.

In the past she had been chosen as Australia's Biggest Hero for her work as a foster mum and a regional finalist for Mother of the Year. She has received the Prime Minister's Award for being one of the top 100 volunteers of Australia.

Neroli has received a certificate for citizen of the year, and the Bernard certificate for Mother of the Year in 2005. In the same year she received the Queensland Premiers Award for Seniors for her outstanding service to the community. At the beginning of 2008 she became a finalist in the Australian of the Year awards.

She has received dozens of awards and is grateful for all the accolades and recognition that has been bestowed upon her. But the grim reality is that all the accolades in the world do not provide a roof over her head, neither do they put food on her table. Neroli has a golden heart and shoes very few could fill even for a single day.

Neroli Endacott has spent most of her life working for children who need care. Of late she has concentrated her efforts on Foetal Alcohol Syndrome.

Her contact e-mail address is: neroli@bigpond.net.au

Her caring nature inspired her to write the following poem to honour the lost children of New Guinea after the tsunami:

SOUNDS OF SILENCE

I hear the children weeping
and the night – 'tis a creeping
upon the little souls still unfound.

Now, I want to hear the laughter,
of the children, forever after.
But sadly – silence is the only sound.

Let us not suffer blindness,
but whisper words of kindness
knowing we have helped to ease their pain.

Take my hand – hold me tight
I will help you through the night,
picking up the little cherubs from where they have lain.

I still hear the children weeping – God
how I wish they were sleeping safely in their mother's arms,
dreaming peacefully beneath the quietly swaying palms.

Help me please – join my prayer,
the children need our care
for no longer will they weep if the promises we keep.

God, please help us make earth happy as heaven above,
knowing what we do
we do for love.

Chapter 6

GENERAL KNOWLEDGE

WARNING: Self diagnosis is dangerous.
Readers are urged to seek assistance from
qualified health care professionals on all health issues.

Absorption: If animal DNA acid is present in the colon, it prevents the absorption of valuable food nutrients. For example, if a meat eater eats 10 apples, their colon will absorb only one but if a fruitarian eats 10 apples their colon will absorb all 10.

Alkaloid: One of a group of nitrogenous organic compounds derived from plants and having diverse pharmacological properties. Alkaloids include morphine, cocaine, atropine, quinine and caffeine, most of which are used in medicine as analgesics (pain relievers) or anaesthetics.

Some alkaloids are poisonous, e.g. strychnine and coniine, and colchicine inhibits cell division.

Almond: The crushed bitter seed of the nut mixed with water is a swift acting poison and one spoonful will kill a human. But it loses potency when heated.

Aloe vera: Applying fresh aloe vera gel from the plant twice daily and allowing it to dry before dressing may help heal cuts and sores. It may help heal leg ulcers. Do not wet the area. If the dressing has stuck to the sore, saturate it in lemon juice for at least 10 minutes.

Aluminium: A silver-white metallic element, light in weight, ductile, malleable and not readily oxidised or tarnished. In nature it is found in igneous rocks, shales, clays and most soils. It is used extensively in alloys and for lightweight utensils, castings and aeroplane parts, etc.

Amalgam: An alloy of mercury with one or more other metals. A mixture or combination. A rare mineral, an alloy of silver and mercury occurring as silver-white crystals or grains.

Amino acids: Any of a group of water-soluble organic compounds that possess both a carboxyl and an amino group attached to the same carbon atom called alpha carbon. Amino acids are essential and must be present in the diet.

Amphetamine: A drug, that stimulates the nerve system by causing the release of the transmitters noradrenaline and dopamine from nerve endings. It inhibits sleep, suppresses the appetite and has variable effects on mood. Prolonged use can lead to addiction.

Animal diseases: Humans contract contagious animal diseases and vice versa. Toxoplasmosis (toxoplasma gondii) in birds and mammals affects the human nerve system. Infection may also occur by eating rare beef, lamb and pork. Diseases such as this may reoccur after 20 to 30 years, causing blindness.

Cat owners should not come into contact with soil, uneaten food or litter that has been infected. Pregnant women should avoid this disease. If the owner of a pet has gout or rheumatoid arthritis and if the animal lies at their feet, it may also suffer these diseases.

Animal residue: It takes at least three years of eating naturally for the human body to cleanse itself of animal residue. But one has a feeling of well-being after three months. For some, the process may take longer.

Antibiotic: Many people eat some form of animal DNA daily. It will take those that do 25yrs for their body to flush 1mg of antibiotic. For those who eat natural the process is much quicker.

Antioxidants: Substances that slow the rate of oxidation reactions. Naturally occurring antioxidants include vitamin E and beta-carotene. They limit the cell and tissue damage caused by foreign substances, such as toxins and pollutants, in the body. Chilli and capsicum are excellent anti-oxidants.

Arteries: Within the first few months of eating fruit only, the arteries begin to cleanse. Some may experience needling pains throughout the body and eyes. These sensations may be strong and painful. This pain indicates cleansing.

Aspergers syndrome: A developmental disorder that affects how the brain works. It shapes a child's social and communication skills, and behaviour and is rarely recognized before the child is aged three.

ATP/ADP: A nucleotide that is of fundamental importance as a carrier of chemical energy in all living organisms.

Autism: Fantasy; introverted thoughts; daydreaming; chiefly characterised by some degree of inability to comprehend or communicate; failure to relate emotionally; and inappropriate or obsessive behaviour.

Bacterium: A single cell organism that can cause disease in animals.

Barmah Forest virus: A mosquito-transmitted disease found widely throughout Australia. It can cause polyarthritis. Usually not fatal. Some people, especially children, may not show any symptoms. Many suffer lethargy, fever, arthritis, headaches and swollen ankles, knees, wrists and elbows. Others may have a mild skin rash from three to 11 days after infection.

Bed linen: The safest fabric is linen. Doonas should be filled with goat's fleece and covered with linen. Some doonas and pillows are filled with bird feathers which contain calcium. But if feathers are accidentally inhaled, they must be surgically removed.

Beta carotene: If the skin begins to turn orange, it could be the result of beta-carotene from fruit and a sign that the body is strengthening. If beta-carotene is in excess, the skin may be prone to sunburn.

Bladder infection: Watermelon, pears with 2 tsp of crushed papaya seeds once a day for three days may help a bladder infection.

Blockage of the bowel: A diet that includes seeds and grain may cause this problem. As faeces builds up in the bowel, it causes a blockage, and cramps and contractions may occur. It also releases chemical toxins and toxic shock may occur within a few hours. Death can also occur within hours as the result of toxic shock. Children are particularly vulnerable to this dietary problem. Popcorn may contribute to this problem.

Blood boil: We have all heard the term: "He/she makes my blood boil". This is true to a point. Anger and stress increase blood's temperature and places enormous stress on organs. They swell and release toxins into the blood stream. If the kidneys cannot cope with the added pressure, the body can shut down and death may occur. Anger and stress can cause seizures, brain tumours, aneurisms and stroke. Anger and stress create heat within the body and chest area, especially the lungs. Muscles contract causing heart attack.

Blood pressure: An ideal reading may be below 120/80 while 120/80 to 130/85 may be considered normal. 130/85 to 160/100 may be classified as high to normal. High blood pressure increases the possibility of cardio vascular disease, thus increasing the possibility of death. High blood pressure burdens blood vessels, causing kidney functions to slow down. As a result, kidneys do not flush and function as nature intended.

Blood vessels slacken, they become less resilient and atherosclerosis (hardening of the arteries) may occur. Plaque within artery walls causes narrowing of the arteries which interferes with the blood's ability to clot. These problems stem from lifestyle choices. The food one eats also dictates the state of one's health.

Body strength: The body strength of children will greatly increase if avocado, dates and coconut are consumed daily.

Body temperature: Creating an even body temperature (37.7 degrees Celsius) is important. On entering a cold air-conditioned room, body temperature falls. If we suddenly move outside without warm clothing where the atmosphere is hot, we may pop vertebrae and ribs. Allow the body time to adjust to temperature change.

Bulbs: Onions, shallots, spring onions and garlic help to break down rotting meat in the colon of those who choose to eat animal DNA. Bulbs contain acid that is harmful to the body.

Calcium: Calcium derived from natural foods is an essential element for the normal growth and development of living organisms. In animals it is an important constituent of bones and teeth and is present in the blood, being required for muscle contraction and other metabolic processes. In plants it is a constituent (in the form of calcium pectate) of the middle lamella.

Carbohydrate: Bread, pasta, grains, cereals and potato contain carbohydrates which the body converts into complex sugars. The result is poor quality blood with high acid levels, loss of calcium, adverse affects on the adrenal glands and lymphatic system.

Carbonated beverages: May damage gums and cause bleeding if consumed regularly.

Carcinogen: Any agent that produces cancer, e.g. tobacco smoke, certain industrial chemicals, and ionizing radiation (such as X-rays and ultraviolet rays).

Carotene: A member of a class of carotenoid pigments. Examples are beta-carotene and lycopene which colour carrot roots and ripe tomato fruits respectively. Alpha and beta-carotene yield vitamin A when they are broken down during animal digestion.

Cellulite: Fatty deposits resulting in dimpling of the skin.

Cellulitis: Inflammation of cellular tissue.

Cereal: Grasses grown for their seeds.

Chlorine: A greenish yellow gaseous element, incombustible and highly irritating to the organs of respiration. It is used as a powerful bleaching agent and in various industrial processes.

Chocolate: Children should not eat chocolate because it may cause constipation.

Cholesterol: A fatty substance produced by the body and found in the blood. It is a sterol occurring widely in animal tissues and also in some higher plants and algae. Cholesterol is absorbed through the intestine or manufactured in the liver. It serves principally as a constituent of blood plasma lipoproteins and of the lipid-protein complexes that form cell membranes.

Cholesterol has many good uses, but can become problematic where there is too much of it in the blood. There is a direct connection between cholesterol, fats, calories and cancer. Increased levels of dietary and blood cholesterol have been associated with atherosclerosis.

This is a disease in which fatty substances (lipids) deposit in and beneath the intima (the inner walls) of the arteries and harden to form plaque, thus immobilising the artery by obstructing the blood flow). Aortic aneurysm is also caused by arteriosclerosis (an arterial disease occurring especially in the elderly, characterised by inelasticity and thickening of the vessel walls, with lessened blood flow).

Chromosome: Any of the threadlike, rodlike or beadlike bodies which carry the genetic information in a cell.

Citric acid: A white crystalline hydroxycarboxylic acid. It is present in citrus fruit and animal cells.

Clove oil: Excellent for treating ticks because it is a natural anaesthetic. Saturate the tick with the oil for half an hour. As the tick relaxes it releases its grip and falls. Smear clove oil over bait before casting when fishing – it may increase the yield.

Colitis: Acute inflammation of the colon that may be caused by prescription antibiotics.

Collagen: An insoluble fibrous protein found extensively in the connective tissue of skin, tendons and bone. The polypeptide chains of collagen (containing the amino acids glycine and proline predominantly) form triple-stranded helical coils that are bound together to form fibrils, which have great strength and limited elasticity. Collagen accounts for more than 30 per cent of the total body protein of mammals.

Colloidal silver: A banned substance in Germany. Elias said the body could not expel colloidal silver. Ingesting this substance or rubbing it on the skin may result in a condition called argyria, a bluish-grey discoloration of the skin, other organs, nails, gums and deep tissues. Argyria cannot be treated or reversed and is permanent. Other side effects from using colloidal silver may include neurologic problems (such as seizures), kidney damage, headaches, stomach distress, skin irritation and fatigue.

Colon: A clean colon is essential for the multiplication of red blood cells.

Colon cancer: Elias says the consumption of animal DNA and microwave oven cookery contribute to colon cancer.

Cooked food: Of all life on earth, only humans eat cooked food. The longer food is cooked the more difficult it is for the stomach to digest. Therefore, of all the species on earth, humans suffer the most disease. Frying alters the sugar content in raw food. If potato is steamed then mashed, the diabetic index value is 60, but when it is fried the value is 95.

Cravings: Many people crave chocolates and sweets etc. This is not craving but an addiction. It has been said: if the body craves it – it needs it. This is incorrect. Cravings are governed by the memory sector of the brain. There are times when children in particular crave bitter fruit such as lemons and grapefruit. This is the brain sending a message to compensate for the excessive amounts of processed cane sugar in their diet.

However, if fruitarians crave a certain fruit, they should satisfy this craving immediately. This is the brain's method of telling the body it is deficient in a certain nutrient or nutrients. Ignoring such messages is dangerous.

Cyclamates: Sodium and calcium cyclamates were formerly used as sweetening agents in soft drinks etc. Their use was banned when they were suspected of causing cancer.

Deep Vein Thrombosis: The result of a high caffeine diet. Tea, coffee and alcohol dehydrate the body. Sit up straight, drink ample water and exercise while seated when travelling long distances.

Dementia: A term used to describe the symptoms of a group of illnesses that cause a progressive decline in one's functions. There are several causes and the most common is Alzheimer's disease. Dementia is not a normal part of ageing but it can happen to anybody, especially those aged over 40.

The signs: memory loss, confusion, personality and behavioural changes, apathy, withdrawal and loss of the ability to perform daily tasks.

The different types of dementia are:

- *Alzheimer's disease* – most common form. A progressive, degenerative illness that attacks the brain.
- *Vascular dementia* – associated with problems of circulation of blood to the brain.
- *Dementia with Lewy bodies* – abnormal structures called

Lewy bodies develop inside nerve cells within the brain.

- *Fronto Temporal Lobar Degeneration (FTLD)* – the name given to a group of dementias when there is degeneration in one or both of the frontal to temporal lobes of the brain.
- *Parkinson's disease* – a progressive disorder of the nerve system. Symptoms include tremors, speech impediments, limb and joint stiffness. Some may develop dementia in latter stages of the disease.
- *Alcohol-related dementia* – excess alcohol intake and a poor diet deficient in vitamin B1 (thiamine).
- *AIDS-related dementia* – caused by the HIV-AIDS virus. It may not affect all HIV-AIDS sufferers.
- *Huntington's disease* – an inherited degenerative brain disease that affects the mind and body. Causes dementia in the majority of cases.

Drinking tea in excess may hasten the onset of dementia. The body loses iron and the brain becomes dehydrated. The countries with the highest number of dementia sufferers are England, Australia, New Zealand, India, Japan and China.

Desiccant: A drying agent. There are many types, including anhydrous calcium chloride, anhydrous calcium sulphate, concentrated sulphuric acid, phosphorus(V) oxide, solid sodium hydroxide, lime, and silica gel.

Detergent: A substance added to water to improve its cleaning properties. Various synthetic and soapless detergents have been developed from petrochemicals (a chemical made from petroleum). Synthetic detergents are also used as wetting agents, emulsifiers and stabilisers for foam.

Dialysis: When kidneys fail, they stop removing waste products (such as urea) from the blood. These toxic waste products build up and will eventually cause death.

During dialysis, blood is passed through a dialysis machine. The machine takes over the functions of the kidneys by removing waste products from the blood.

A tube is connected to a vein, then to the dialysis machine. The blood is pumped through tubes made from dialysing membranes inside the machine. A dialysis solution is on the other side of the dialysing membrane and is kept fresh by a constant flow. The blood then returns to the patient's arm.

Dining: Speak with the cook when ordering at restaurants. Be aware of food colorants, enhancers, preservatives and additives such as MSG. An allergic reaction to MSG can be fatal. Benzoic acid (210 in food and drinks) can cause neurological disorders. Beware of animal stocks, cheese and eggs. Canola oil, soy products and other ingredients may have been genetically modified. Be aware of peanuts, they are integrated into many processed foods.

DNA (deoxyribonucleic acid): One of a class of large molecules which are found in the nuclei of cells and in viruses and which are responsible for the transference of genetic characteristics, usually consisting of two interwoven helical chains of polynucleotides.

DNA is often described as the blueprint of an organism because it enables various cells to develop and work together to form a fully functional body. It controls characteristics such as eye colour.

DNA can be modified to transfer from one organism to another. Genes are made up of short lengths of DNA. Modern gene technology is able to make changes at the level of individual genes.

Dopamine: A hormone and neurotransmitter occurring in a wide variety of animals, including both vertebrates and invertebrates. In the brain, this phenethylamine functions as a neurotransmitter, activating the five types of dopamine receptors – D1, D2, D3, D4 and D5, and their variants. Dopamine is produced in several areas of the brain, including the substantia nigra and the ventral tegmental area. Dopamine is also a neurohormone released by the hypothalamus. Its main function as a hormone is to inhibit the release of prolactin from the anterior lobe of the pituitary gland.

Dried fruit: Some may contain preservatives that inhibit mould and bacteria. The most common is sulphur dioxide. This is a gas that dissolves in water but it may yield potassium sulphide and other chemicals. Sulphur dioxide is burnt under drying racks during humid weather. Ethyl formate is another insecticide used in packed dried fruit. Methyl bromide is a fumigant chemical that is used as an insecticide for boxes of dried fruit stacked in packing sheds.

Fruit may also be soaked in a solution of sodium bisulphite. When mixed with water, it penetrates the surface of the fruit, slowing oxidation and enzymatic browning. These chemicals may cause adverse reactions, especially to asthmatics.

Dangers of sulphur dioxide:

- A gas found in crude oil, coal and iron ore.
- May cause severe airway obstruction.
- Hypoxemia (insufficient oxygenation of the blood).
- Pulmonary edema: a life threatening accumulation of fluid in the lungs. Can cause death within minutes. Coughing and shortness of breath may occur within hours or days and permanent lung damage may occur.

Potassium sulphide: highly flammable. If inhaled it can cause sore throat, cough, shortness of breath, headaches and dizziness. It can cause eye pain, redness and burns. The skin can blister and burn. If it is accidentally ingested, it may cause burning, sore throat, stomach cramps, nausea, diarrohea and vomiting.

Ethyl formate causes irritation to eyes, throat and upper respiratory system, short breath, drowsiness and headaches. The skin becomes red and dry. It can crack and burn. This chemical is dangerous to health and life.

Methyl bromide: used to control insects, rats and other rodents, and is used to kill weeds. Used as a methylating agent, a fire extinguisher, a solvent, refrigerant and degreaser. This chemical damages the ozone layer. It has a devastating effect on the nerve system, even in small amounts. A highly toxic chemical that can cause death and environmental issues.

Sodium bisulphite: another harmful chemical. Its adverse and harmful reactions to the body are horrendous and too numerous to mention. It is also harmful to the environment because it retains harmful residues. Research well before purchasing dried fruit.

Eating naturally: The body reacts instantly when we begin to eat as nature intended. It eliminates toxins from every source, including the skin. Pain may occur to any part of the body, especially the joints. Fruit cleans uric acid crystals from within the joints. For the first two weeks try: papaya, avocado, watermelon, pears, zucchini, squash, pumpkin, choko and cucumber. After this period, the acids settle and one may introduce all other fruits. All fruit acids are essential to the body and vital for normal body functions. As the body eliminates drugs and other chemicals, mouth ulcers may occur but this should settle.

Elderly: The elderly should have as much fresh fruit and fresh juice as possible in their diet. Many seniors consume large amounts of medication which results in bowel problems, loss of muscle elasticity, diseases, pain and discomfort. Fruit eaten before a meal will add to their wellbeing and stomach comfort.

Electric shock: Elias said it was imperative for those who have suffered electric shock to have their blood tested regularly because they may develop leukaemia or other cancers. Those who have had electric shock prior to having had children should have the children's blood tested regularly because they may also suffer these diseases. He said these cancers could take years to develop.

Energy loss: Many people tend to stress. This causes hormone imbalance and loss of energy. Stress hormones induce depression and weaken the immune system.

Enzyme: A protein (or protein-based molecule) that speeds up a chemical reaction in a living organism. An enzyme acts as a catalyst for specific chemical reactions, converting a specific set of reactants (called substrates) into specific products. Without enzymes, life as we know it would not exist.

Ethanol (ethyl alcohol): A colourless water-soluble alcohol. It is the active principle in intoxicating drinks, in which it is produced by fermentation of sugar, using yeast.

Eyes: Sleeping in an air conditioned room and with the fan on may cause blindness. The skin of our eye lids is very fine and they were designed by nature to protect the eyes. But nature did not take into account the interventions of man and inventions such as air conditioning and ceiling fans positioned directly over the bed.

As our body temperature lowers, eyes may also dry out. The unnatural atmosphere that air conditioning and fans create can adversely affect the eyes, sometimes causing immense pain. Elias said as the condition of the eye deteriorated, the function of the "skin" and its structure behind the eye began to alter. He said if it was not correctly diagnosed and treated immediately, the skin may collapse and blindness could occur. This damage is permanent and irreversible.

He said this problem may easily be mistakenly diagnosed as a virus or infection, and drugs may be administered. But drugs will usually not assist and may compound the problem.

Fats and cholesterol: Not all fat is bad. It is beneficial to good health to have a certain level of good fat. When we eat as nature intended, the body converts some fruit nutrients into good cholesterol which is found in the blood. The fats to avoid are found in some foods that are classified as junk. This fat is also in some processed foods. The type of animal fats and some vegetable oils used in cooking contribute to high cholesterol levels in the blood.

There are two types of cholesterol:

1. LDL (bad fats – low density lipoprotein) causes cholesterol to accumulate in vessels. This then causes narrowing of the vessels (atherosclerosis), after which heart attacks and stroke may occur.

2. HDL (good fats – high density lipoprotein) prevents plaque from building up in the vessels; removes cholesterol from the blood; transports it to the liver for disposal; lowers cholesterol. HDL cholesterol is found in first cold pressed extra virgin oils manufactured from olives, coconuts and avocados.

Fats in food are a mixture of polyunsaturated, monounsaturated, saturated and trans fats. The different types of fats have different effects on the cholesterol level.

- Polyunsaturated fats help lower blood cholesterol.
- Monounsaturated fats also help lower blood cholesterol.
- Saturated fats raise blood cholesterol. Found in animal DNA, greasy foods, cakes, potato chips, biscuits, pastries and dairy etc.

- Trans fats elevate LDL cholesterol (bad fat) levels and lower the level of HDL cholesterol (good fat) in the body. These fats are found in hydrogenated and partially hydrogenated vegetable fats and animal fats. Found in abundance in some pies, pastries, cakes, biscuits, some bread products and some foods.

Fibrin: Good quality blood is thin and should form tiny clots. When the body is working correctly, it produces a protein called fibrin. This is the substance that glues the clots together and prevents excessive bleeding. Cigarette smoke acts as an anticoagulant.

Fluid retention: Pure grape juice taken under direction from Elias may help eliminate excess fluid.

Folic acid: Found in most fruit.

Fungi and mildew: There is little way of knowing if food is fresh. Some can harbor bacteria. It is imperative to get rid of any food if fungi or mildew is present. We can see certain types of bacteria because they produce a skeleton that is better known as fungi: a group of thallophytes including mushrooms, moulds, mildews, rusts, and smuts etc. One particular fungi is called aspergillus flavus. It can be present in all types of food, including fruit. Aspergillus is an insidious killer. If it is present in the body, it will not allow the nerve system to feel pain, therefore the victim is unaware of its presence.

Aspergillus can live in the body for 20 years or more. Then, when the immune system is down or a major change has occurred in the body, it will strike in a form of cancer. It invades every part of the body and brain, including the blood and skeletal system. It can cause bones to crumble. This form of cancer can spread rapidly and it is usually identified when it is too late: during autopsies.

This fungi can invade all food including grains and their by-products. Think before eating peanuts because aspergillus also lives in the soil. One may be wise to wear a mask and gloves when working with soil in the garden. Aspergillus is notorious for dwelling in potting mix.

Mildew is a plant disease and is also a silent killer. It can live anywhere in the home and it can also be present in our bedding. If mildew is present in a mattress or pillow, it can enter the lungs while we breathe. It can then invade the heart valves, paralyse them and death can occur within hours. It may be wise to check pillows and bedding, even in five star hotels before the room is used. Prevention is paramount. If mildew is present in the home remove it. Some alcohols may kill mildew.

Glucagon: A hormone produced by the pancreas that increases the blood glucose concentration.

Glucuronic acid: A compound derived from the oxidation of glucose. It is an important constituent of gums and mucilages.

Glycine: A sweet-tasting, colourless, crystalline compound, it is the simplest amino acid occurring in proteins.

Hair: Dates, coconut and avocado eaten daily thicken hair.

Herbicide: Certain organic herbicides used to control broadleaf weeds and grasses may be poisonous to humans, having toxic effects on the liver, lungs and kidneys if ingested. They are not easily broken down and can persist in the environment.

HIV/AIDS: A virus of the blood which attacks and weakens the body's natural immune system.

Honey: Bees produce honey. It contains a protein similar to animal DNA, therefore fruitarians should not eat it.

Hops: Beer drinking promotes snoring. Hops weaken muscles to the back of the tongue. Hops may cause increased bleeding during menstruation and may cause abortion.

Hormone: A substance that is manufactured and secreted in very small quantities into the bloodstream by an endocrine gland or a specialised nerve cell and regulates the growth or functioning of a specific tissue or organ in a distinct part of the body. For example, the hormone insulin controls the rate and manner in which glucose is used by the body.

Implants: Elias warns that if something is not normal or unnatural, it will usually find a way of working against the body. And it seems as though for the many things we do to our body, there is a price that must be paid in one way or another. Like other implants, teeth and metal plates can also fall into this category.

It may be wise to research this topic thoroughly before following through with implants. Artificial teeth are usually made from porcelain or ceramic because these substances are dense and hard wearing. The artificial teeth are then placed on the jaw bone and screwed into position. These screws are about 1cm long and they may be made from titanium. Elias said there was a strong possibility of this metal leaching into the jaw bones and finding its way to the brain. A disease with similar symptoms to that of Alzheimer's may then occur. (In France for example, dentists use gold screws).

Elias maintains the following: before allowing the placement of any substance or object into the body, each ingredient of its composition should be well researched for adverse reactions and any side effects they may inflict.

Insect repellent: Natural insect deterrents are oil of clove mixed with water and neat lemon juice.

Irritable bowel syndrome: Many suffer pain after a bowel movement. An improper diet causes the colon to over-stretch, therefore it does not shrink to the correct size where it meets the bowel. This causes damage and pain. Eating natural may rectify the problem.

Junk food: Food that is high in processed salt and sugar, colourants, preservatives and additives contributes to the loss of calcium, which leads to a loss of bone density. Osteoporosis may be the result of a diet high in these foods.

Children are particularly vulnerable because they may suffer from bone density problems later in life. Food that is high in potassium may prevent brittle bones. A diet that is high in alcohol, carbonated drinks sweetened with processed cane sugar, animal DNA and high amounts of processed salt plays havoc with the skeletal system.

Kidney: Watermelon and water clean kidneys.

Lactalbumin: A protein found in cow's milk which should not be given to children and infants. It has been known to cause diabetes and may have damaging effects on the lymphatic and auto-immune systems.

Lactic acid: Lactic acid is produced from pyruvic acid in muscle tissue when oxygen is limited and subsequently removed for conversion to glucose by the liver. It may build up in the muscles during strenuous exercise, causing cramp-like pains. It is also produced by fermentation in certain bacteria and is a characteristic of sour milk.

Lectin: A lectin is a sugar-binding protein. Lectins can be used to identify mutant cells in cell cultures and to determine blood groups as they can cause the agglutination (gluing) of red blood cells. Lectins are found in seeds of legumes and in other tissues, in which they are thought to act as a toxin.

Legumes: A plant which has pods that contain seeds such as beans and peas.

Liver: The female liver is smaller than that of a male but it can clean the blood much quicker.

Magnetism: A group of phenomena associated with magnetic fields.

Mannitol: A polyhydric alcohol derived from mannose or fructose. A white sweetish crystalline, carbohydrate alcohol occurring in the manna of the ash and in other plants, used in medicine as a diuretic and to assess renal function.

Mannose: A monosaccharide. Obtained from the hydrolysis of the ivory nut and yielding mannitol on reduction.

Mercury: A heavy silvery liquid metallic element belonging to the zinc group. It is remarkable for its fluidity at ordinary temperature; quicksilver. It is used in medicine. Mercury is used in thermometers, barometers, and other scientific apparatus and in dental fillings. Also, any herb of the euphorbiaceous genus – a dangerous weed (dog's weed).

Microwaves: Electromagnetic wave of extremely high frequency. Their wavelength range is from 1mm to 50cm.

Milk of magnesia (magnesium hydroxide): A white solid compound. Magnesium hydroxide occurs naturally as the mineral *brucite* and can be prepared by reacting magnesium sulphate or chloride with sodium hydroxide solution. It is used in the refining of sugar and in the processing of uranium.

Medicinally, it is important as an antacid and as a laxative. Milk of magnesia is also used as a laxative for infants.

Monosaccharide: A simple sugar, such as glucose, fructose, arabinose and ribose, occurring in nature or obtained by the hydrolysis of glucosides or polysaccharides.

Monosodium glutamate (MSG): A natural sodium salt of glutamic acid used in cookery to enhance the natural flavour of food. MSG is Chinese salt, a powder that enhances taste and may be toxic.

Morphine: A bitter crystalline alkaloid, the most important narcotic principle of opium. It is used in medicine – usually in the form of a sulphate or other salt – to dull the pain, induce sleep. (Also, morphia, Morphin, from Morph(eus) the Greek god of sleep).

Mushrooms: Contain a protein similar to animal DNA. Fruitarians should not eat this fungi.

Myoglobin: Muscle protein that, like haemoglobin, can combine reversibly with oxygen.

Nicotine: A colourless poisonous alkaloid present in tobacco. Also used as an insecticide.

Nitrates: A group of chemicals that may be associated with gastric carcinoma.

Nitrogen: A colourless gaseous element. It occurs in air (about 78 per cent by volume) and is an essential constituent of proteins and nucleic acids in living organisms.

Omega 3: Abundant in fruit.

Organic: Is this word misused in Australia? Elias said in Germany, government officials took yearly soil samples from organic farms and tested them. If chemicals are detected, the owners lose their certification.

Osteoporosis: This disease can be caused by several factors, including acids found in foods such as animal DNA and hard cheeses. If there is a lack of fruit in an animal protein diet, the neutraliser for animal protein acids will be the human skeleton. The bones dissolve and release alkaline substances. Fruit neutralises harmful acids produced by animal DNA. In order for meat eaters to protect the density of their skeletal system, it is essential they eat a lot of fruit.

Oxalic acid: Strongly acidic and very poisonous. It occurs in certain plants, including sorrel and the leaf blades of rhubarb.

Papain: A protein-digesting enzyme occurring in the fruit of the West Indian Papaya tree (*Carica papaya*). It is used as a digestant and in the manufacture of meat tenderisers.

Pepsin: An enzyme that catalyses the breakdown of proteins to polypeptides in the vertebrate stomach. It is secreted as an inactive precursor, *pepsinogen*.

Pesticide: Any chemical compound used to kill pests that destroy agricultural production or are in some way harmful to humans. Pesticides include herbicides; which kill unwanted plants or weeds; insecticides which kill insect pests; fungicides, which kill fungi; and rodenticides which kill rodents.

The problems associated with pesticides are that they are very often non-specific and may be toxic to organisms that are not pests. They may also be non-biodegradable, so that they persist in the environment and may accumulate in living organisms (bioaccumulation).

Some insecticides are biodegradable but can also damage the respiratory and nerve systems in humans as well as killing useful insects, such as bees. They act by inhibiting the action of the enzyme cholinesterase. Organochlorine insecticides are very persistent and not easily biodegradable.

Phosphagen: A compound found in animal tissues that provides a reserve of chemical energy in the form of high-energy phosphate bonds. The most common phosphagens are creatine phosphate, occurring in vertebrate muscle and nerves, and arginine phosphate, found in most invertebrates.

Phosphorus: Found in apple, sweetsop and banana. Excellent for bone density.

Polio: It is difficult to believe that polio still exists in this country. A brilliant child of primary school age was born prematurely. He was supposed to have been placed in an incubator for 100 days but he advanced so well he was discharged from hospital after 89 days.

As his parents were leaving the hospital with him, they were told by a staff member that he had been given an anti-polio vaccination that morning. This was done without their consent or knowledge.

But instead of the vaccination protecting the child, he contracted the disease.

Health care professionals at the hospital had made a mathematical error. They should have waited until three months after the baby's proper birth date or until his immune system was strong enough.

The infant's immune system was immature and totally vulnerable. And one can only imagine the trauma his parents suffered.

In the years that followed, the family has experienced many challenges and the monetary cost has been astronomical. Calipers have to be specially designed and renewed regularly and each one costs thousands of dollars.

Elias is working towards getting the child out of his wheelchair and capable of standing unaided and walking by the age of 14.

Another family welcomed the arrival of their new infant. The baby was vaccinated against polio when it was three months old.

The following day all the family members were home. The baby was suffering the after-effects of the immunisation and soiled its nappy a number of times. The nappies were not properly disposed of and other family members became infected with polio.

Polyrheumatoid arthritis: Caused by a diet high in animal DNA and not drinking enough water.

Polysaccharide: Any of a group of carbohydrates comprising long chains of monosaccharide (simple-sugar) molecules. Homopolysaccharides consist of only one type of monosaccharide; heteropolysaccharides contain two or more different types. Polysaccharides may have molecular weights of up to several million and are often highly branched. Some important examples are starch, glycogen and cellulose.

Potassium: A chemical element abundant in bananas, apples and lemons. High in potassium helps to lower blood pressure.

Potassium sulphate: A white crystalline powder, soluble in water and insoluble in ethanol. In the laboratory it may be obtained by the reaction of either potassium hydroxide or potassium carbonate with sulphuric acid. Potassium sulphate is used in cements, in glass manufacture, as a food additive, and as a fertilizer for chloride-sensitive plants, such as tobacco and citrus.

Processed products: The more affluent society grows, the more animal DNA, refined and processed foods they eat and the sicker they become.

Progesterone: A hormone, produced primarily by the corpus luteum of the ovary but also by the placenta, that prepares the inner lining of the uterus for implantation of a fertilized egg cell. If implantation fails, the corpus luteum degenerates and progesterone production ceases accordingly.

If implantation occurs, the corpus luteum continues to secrete progesterone, under the influence of luteinizing hormone and prolactin, for several months of pregnancy, by which time the placenta has taken over this function. During pregnancy, progesterone maintains the constitution of the uterus and prevents further release of eggs from the ovary. Small amounts of progesterone are produced by the testes.

Prolactin (lactogenic hormone; luteotrophic hormone; luteotrophin): A hormone produced by the anterior pituitary gland. In mammals it stimulates the mammary glands to produce milk and the corpus luteum of the ovary to secrete the hormone progesterone.

Prostaglandin: Any of a group of organic compounds derived from essential fatty acids and causing a range of physiological effects in animals. Prostaglandins have been detected in most body tissues. They act at very low concentrations to cause the contraction of smooth muscle.

Natural and synthetic prostaglandins are used to induce abortion or labour in humans and domestic animals. Inflammation in allergic reactions and other diseases is also thought to involve prostaglandins.

Prostate cancer: Stress can cause prostate cancer. There is nothing constructive about negative stress which affects the nerves, causing the system to lose fluid. Nerve fluid is the power of life.

Coffee, beer and the consumption of animal DNA also contribute to prostate cancer. Those who suffer prostate problems should eat about 1.5kg of tomatoes daily because they contain lycopene.

Lycopene is an antioxidant which has the ability to fight disease. It is an excellent anti-aging oxidant that prevents "harmful" cholesterol. It is a carotenoid pigment found in red, yellow and orange fruit and is one of the strongest antioxidants. A large glass of fresh tomato juice (without seeds) and a dash of chilli is an excellent way to start the day.

Protamine: Any of a group of proteins of relatively low molecular weight found in association with the chromosomal DNA of vertebrate sperm cells. They contain a single polypeptide chain comprising about 67 per cent arginine. Protamines are thought to protect and support the chromosomes.

Protease (peptidase; proteinase; proteolytic enzyme): Any enzyme that catalyses the hydrolysis of proteins into smaller peptide fractions and amino acids, a process known as *proteolysis*. Examples are pepsin and trypsin. Several proteases, acting sequentially, are normally required for the complete digestion of a protein to its constituent amino acids.

Protein: Any of the polymers formed from amino acids, which are found in all cells and which include enzymes, plasma proteins, and structural proteins such as collagen.

Ptyalin: Enzymes that digest carbohydrates. Present in the saliva of mammals. Responsible for the initial stages of starch digestion.

Radium: A radioactive metallic element. It occurs in uranium ores (e.g. pitchblende). It is used as a radioactive source in research and, to some extent in radiotherapy.

The element was isolated from pitchblende in 1898 by Marie and Pierre Curie.

Rennin: An enzyme secreted by cells lining the stomach in mammals that is responsible for clotting milk. It acts on a soluble milk protein (*caseinogen*), which it converts to the insoluble form casein. This ensures that milk remains in the stomach long enough to be acted on by protein-digesting enzymes.

Restless legs syndrome: Leg muscle contraction may be the result of pinched nerves/nerve pressing on the vertebrae. It may also be the result of spinal cord and brain damage from dehydration.

Resveratrol: Grapes, blueberries and cranberries are high in this antioxidant. Excellent for the fight against cancer.

Ribose: A monosaccharide, rarely occurring free in nature but important as a component of RNA (ribonucleic acid). Its derivative *deoxyribose,* is equally important as a constituent of DNA (deoxyribonucleic acid), which carries the genetic code in chromosomes.

Saccharide: Any of a group of water-soluble carbohydrates of relatively low molecular weight and typically having a sweet taste. The simple sugars are called mono-saccharides.

More complex sugars comprise between two and 10 monosaccharides linked together: disaccharides contain two, trisaccharides three, and so on. The name is often used to refer specifically to sucrose (processed sugar).

Saccharin: A white crystalline solid. It is made from a compound of toluene, derived from petroleum or coal tar. It is a well-known artificial sweetener, being some 500 times as sweet as sugar (sucrose) and is usually marketed as sodium salt.

Because of an association with cancer in laboratory animals, its use is restricted in some countries.

Serotonin: A hormone that stimulates happiness, induces muscular contraction, found in the brain, intestines and platelets. Found in bananas.

Skin: As we grow older, many people tend to think the skin naturally grows thinner. Dehydration is one of the main reasons why skin alters in texture.

Spectacles: Eye sight improves when one eats natural foods. It may be necessary to lessen the strength of spectacle lenses as one heals. Eye sight alters daily.

Spinal fluid: If spinal fluid is lost, the patient must remain in a horizontal position in bed for a period of four weeks for every one millilitre that is lost in order to prevent spinal damage.

Spleen: White blood cells are created within the spleen.

Sulphamic acid: A colourless crystalline solid which is extremely soluble in water. It is a strong acid, readily forming sulphamate salts. It is used in electroplating, hard-water scale removers, herbicides and artificial sweeteners.

Sulphanilic acid (4-aminobenzene sulphonic acid): A colourless crystalline solid, made by prolonged heating of phenylamine (aniline) sulphate. It readily forms diazo compounds and is used to make dyes and sulphur drugs.

Sunglasses: Muscles to the back of the eye are like the shutter of a camera. They control the amount of light that enters the eye. Sunglasses may prevent this from occurring naturally and may cause eye muscles to weaken. The higher the dependency on sunglasses, the weaker eye muscles may become.

Tartrazine: Food additive (E102). Gives foods a yellow colour. Tartrazine can cause a toxic response in the immune system. Banned in some countries. Used widely as a food colouring.

Tinea: Nylon stockings can alter the PH level of the skin to the extent of killing tinea.

Tongue: Lumps may appear at the back of the tongue during natural cleansing. This may be a build-up of calcium. To remove the build-up, rub the glands with lemon.

Uric acid: The end product of purine breakdown in most primates, birds, terrestrial reptiles and insects and also, except in primates, the major form in which metabolic nitrogen is excreted. Being fairly insoluble, uric acid can be expelled in solid form, which conserves valuable water in arid environments. The accumulation of uric acid in the synovial fluid of joints causes gout.

Vegetables: Whether they are cooked or raw, vegetables cause mouth dryness, dehydration and are difficult to digest.

Vinegar: Soak a towel in one litre of water with 100ml of vinegar added to it. Place it over bone fractures or swelling to relieve pain.

***WARNING**: Self diagnosis is dangerous. If injured seek the advice of a qualified health care professional.*

Viruses: All viruses affect the nerve system.

Warfarin 3-(alpha-acetonylbenzyl)-4-hydroxycoumarin: A synthetic anticoagulant used both therapeutically in clinical medicine, and in lethal doses as a rodenticide.

Water: Elias said not to go into an airconditioned atmosphere or ride in a car with the windows down immediately after swimming. This can cause ear damage.

If water has entered the ear during swimming, bath or shower, do not attempt to remove it because the body will absorb it.

Weight loss: Finishing a meal with two slices of pineapple may help weight loss because is hastens digestion.

“

if it is logical, it is probably true and we should keep an open mind

”

– author unknown

Chapter 7

IN THEIR WORDS

People visit Elias from all over the world in an effort to heal themselves through natural therapy.

Each and every one of them has their own experiences, their own story to tell.

Here are some of those stories.

"

you cannot heal if pride
stands in the way

"

– christopher bugeja

HEALING BREAST, LIVER AND SPINAL CANCERS

Karla was born in Zimbabwe. Her father was Rhodesian and her mother South African, both were of English decent. Her family moved to England in 1962 and returned to Zimbabwe in 1973. She moved to South Africa in 1974.

She enjoyed a happy and healthy childhood but contracted viral pneumonia in her early teens. Some years later her tonsils were removed after several bouts of tonsillitis. She began smoking in her teens and continued until November 2007.

In 1994 she and husband Nigel moved to Zimbabwe with their family. They purchased 1,000 acres of land outside Harare and built a homestead on a hill overlooking a vast picturesque valley. This was an exciting time for the family because they were building their home from scratch with a view to starting an eco-based photo safari business.

After the first year the construction of their home was well under way. They stocked the farm with 60 impala which joined the other prolific wild animals. There were dik dik, a lone sable antelope, kudu, reed buck and a vast number of smaller bush animals and birds.

Another aim was to establish an antelope park and build small lodges scattered across the surrounding hills. They were passionate about establishing a permaculture farm. Its produce was intended to sustain those who lived, worked and visited the property.

During the time they were there, Karla enjoyed good health, went for long walks with friends and felt blessed to be living in paradise. But in 1998 the political climate in Zimbabwe had changed and it became obvious problems were looming.

Those with white skin were no longer allowed to own farms and sadly, they were not going to be replaced with indigenous farmers. The corrupt had a field day.

By 2000 the situation was very worrying, but Karla and her family were not prepared to walk out of their home or off their land. She said: “In retrospect, this was a huge misjudgment”?

Even though they had made their decision, they realised after another three years of extreme worry that the situation was worsening. They then entered a six-month period of intense negotiation in an attempt to sell 75 per cent of their land. But the bargaining only served to ignite an explosive chain of horrendous events:

ZIMBABWE – MY HOME

Silver clouds drift.
Golden grasses veil the savannah.
Masasa cloak distant hills.

Skies settle,
gentle breezes abate,
another glorious sunset unfolds.

The family of three
sat on the verandah, chatting.
And counted their blessings.

Hidden beyond a garden wall,
two brutal men lie in wait.
The scent of human prey in their nostrils.

With the stealth of a panther,
and loaded guns drawn,
they attacked, without warning, without mercy.

An iron bar bounced off Nigel's head.
Bound, gagged and bleeding.
Repeatedly kicked. Muffled screams.

Theo was next.
A gentle youth of just fourteen.
He could not escape their brutal force.

Cold metal pressed against Karla's wrists.
She heard the handcuffs – click.
Bullets flew over her head.

From below his knees,
clenching his fist
he delivered a mighty blow.

A hammer-like strike to the side of her face,
was this to be her end?
Her blackened mind twinkled with stars.

The floor of their home
ran crimson with blood.
They were victims of a senseless regime.

Zimbabwe, once beautiful, once serene,
once the breadbasket of Southern Africa.
This was the cleansing of those who are white.

A terrified Karla
was dragged around her home.
"Give me cash. Cash", menaced her captor.

She was forced to the floor,
bound, gagged, locked away.
What was to be their fate?

A bathroom became her son's prison.
Doors slam, then lock,
while Nigel groaned on their living room floor.

Karla froze with fear.
"I'll be back to rape you".
An evil voice repeatedly screamed.

Her silent brave son, captive. Was he alive?
Her husband badly wounded.
"Rape! You could not hurt me more".

Nigel's pain grew. The house now quiet.
Theo stirred, he fought to be free,
and with a metal rod, broke down the door ...

The family fled their home, sought medical aid and returned during daylight hours to pack their belongings. Many have since asked: "Why did you not fight back"? But the family had made a pact just one week prior: if they were attacked they swore to each other the main objective was to survive because some who resisted did not.

Their application to migrate to Australia was successful but they had to meet the remainder of their family in New Zealand. That was the law. Nigel's head was battered and bruised, his face unrecognisable as the family embraced and reminisced.

They finally arrived in Australia with temporary residence. After taking time out to recuperate and assess their situation, they purchased a house and business.

Back in 2001, Karla had noticed a lump in her breast. It was aspirated and found to be benign. All previous mammograms were clear. She had another mammogram in 2005 but the radiologist was not satisfied with the result and she was sent for an ultra sound. Then – panic stations.

A biopsy was quickly performed in both breasts. Karla said: "At the follow-up appointment the doctor informed her that all was fine. She made no mention that anything was wrong and that the biopsy mainly showed fatty tissue. She said all was well – and I believed her".

After 18 months Karla had a mammogram, ultrasound and another biopsy of the right breast. During the procedure the radiologist quietly asked: "Why did you not return after receiving the results of the first biopsy"? She replied that she had been told there was no need to return for a follow-up as nothing had been found and the biopsy was clear of all cancer. Had she known that anything was wrong, she definitely would have returned. This series of checks once again proved negative. Even though she had "shadows" in both breasts, those who examined the x-rays and tissue samples read them as negative.

Nine months later, Karla had the flu for the fourth time that year. The business was demanding, her chest pained and lethargy was setting in.

During the next visit to the same doctor he told her a form of arthritis was present in her body. He gave her prescriptions for anti-inflammatory drugs and pain killers. Mindful of their dangerous effects, she took them with food. The result was a severe case of gastritis.

Karla was sent to a different radiology practice for another mammogram and ultrasound. The ultrasound was performed by a radiologist who asked: "Have you ever had cancer?" Karla became alarmed. A senior radiologist was asked to review the results. He said: "This looks serious. This is certainly a situation that gets the alarm bells ringing. I need to compare all your MRIs to make a diagnosis".

This was followed by a CT bone scan and a radio active isotope scan. Results indicated: what one doctor had previously diagnosed as spinal osteophytes, were tumours throughout the entire length of the spine. She also had multiple liver tumours.

The largest three were between 1 and 2cm. Bewildered and shocked, Karla questioned how and why qualified medical practitioners who were supposed to be specialists in their fields could have misinterpreted the results of their very own testing to such an alarming degree.

"I have always totally trusted doctors to the extent I put my life in their hands. I assumed they had the answers to all my problems. I assumed they were concerned, caring and committed," Karla said.

"But I did not experience that at all. In fact, I experienced the opposite. I experienced incompetence of the highest calibre. And I have to wonder just how much the cancer grew during the two years that I took prescribed hormone replacement therapy. How much did they accelerate my cancer? How much damage did their chemicals create?" A liver biopsy was performed and it was determined that she had breast cancer due to markers on the tumours. The evidence was clear – Stage 4 metastatic cancer.

Doctors told Karla the spinal cancer had seriously weakened her spine, particularly in the thoracic region. She was also told she would have to have an intravenous drug administered during chemotherapy to harden her skeletal system. These are the type of drugs that are given to those who suffer osteoporosis.

The oncologist told her she needed chemotherapy because without it she would suffer brain cancer within six months and she was to expect death within 18 months to two years. The news was devastating. But her devastation was shrouded by doubts and confusion. Until then she had endured a succession of mindless and monumental blunders by highly qualified practitioners. She said: "What was I to do? Who was I supposed to believe? Who was I to trust"?

Assuming she had no other alternative, she allowed herself to be prepared for chemotherapy. The oncologist told her to visit a dentist to have some teeth removed. He said chemotherapy made the bones brittle and the bone hardening drugs made them dense. So dense, in fact, that if she were to have tooth extractions or root canals at a later stage, the jaw bone would be very prone to breaking which in turn would create serious problems.

Karla said she agreed to have the extractions done under general anaesthetic. But doctors advised her not to waste time. She was told surgery performed in a dentist chair would be much quicker than waiting for a time slot in a hospital theatre.

Two-and-a-half hours after her dental visit saw the destruction of five relatively healthy teeth. Sickened and dispirited, she questioned yet again: "Is this the modern medical and scientific method of treating cancer: one beastly treatment after another until a person no longer looks or feels human?"

Karla slowly recovered during the days that followed. She spent many pensive hours querying the uncertainty of her future. But the decision was hers to make. Too well did she know that if she accepted chemotherapy, there was no turning back – and to her, chemotherapy and radiation felt very wrong.

During her recuperation she heard about Elias. She spoke with one of his clients who had begun working with him in 2002 and within a few months they had cured a brain tumour.

Karla investigated further and discovered much more about the excellent work he was doing. She postponed chemotherapy immediately and contacted Elias at his natural therapy clinic.

He asked if she had received chemotherapy or radiation. She had not. He asked to see all her x-rays and blood tests. After he examined them she heard the wonderful words she so desperately needed to hear: "Yes! I can help you". This was her alleluia moment.

During Karla's first consultation with Elias, they discussed her cancers and he explained the procedure of curing them through natural therapy. He said even though it sounded simple, it was not easy because the client had to do most of the work.

She learnt of the many changes she had to make in order to save her own life. Elias said her life depended on her level of discipline. The question was simple: was her belief and mental state strong enough to commit 100 per cent to the age old theories of natural healing?

Elias explained that it was not easy for some people to understand because since the end of World War II, many people had grown accustomed to modern medicine and looked no further. This was a system that did not require people to think for themselves. And it was for this reason that most of the public simply follow medical authority. Now Karla had to take back the power she was born with and she had to think for herself. He said it was imperative that she have a total understanding of the commitment, otherwise he would not accept her as a client.

Elias explained the problems that some clients created for themselves because they did not take his work seriously. He said:

"For those who believe in nature, no explanation is necessary, the body can heal itself. But for those who do not believe, nothing will convince them and they must accept the consequences of their actions."

Karla said the changes she had to make were dramatic but compared with chemotherapy, radiation therapy, and the horrendous interventions of modern medicine, the gentleness and simplicity of natural therapy was going to be a romp in the park. She said she was totally committed to following Elias's instructions so that he could help her.

He asked her to take the time and seriously think about their discussion – to relax and to eat whatever type of food she wished. After a few days of reflection she gave Elias her commitment and together they began natural therapy.

For the first seven days she was to drink three litres of water daily. During that time she was not allowed to eat any food. Karla thought the first cleansing experience was going to be very difficult but said: "It really wasn't as bad as I expected it to be". Elias gave her medical massages to her nerve system twice a day.

The following four days she had to eat as much persimmon, pineapple and papaya as she wished, as well as the water. From the fifth day onward she was to continue the water and eat as much of all varieties of fruit as she wished. Elias told her the more she ate, the sooner she would recover.

During a massage Karla asked Elias: "What triggers cancer?" He said it could be a number of factors including HRT, stress, injections, mutating viruses, electromagnetic fields, microwave oven cookery, eating animal DNA, cigarette smoking, etc.

She remembered a magpie had pecked her on the finger in 2002. Four days later she felt the tingling sensation of a nerve on the side of her face and visited a doctor. He gave her two injections: one of gamma globulin – a protein fraction of blood plasma containing antibodies – and the other for tetanus.

Elias explained the nerve pain had nothing to do with the bird – it was the body's reaction to her continuous stress. He said her stress combined with the tetanus injection was enough to trigger cancer.

Karla continued having two medical massages twice a day for three weeks, then went home for two weeks. She returned to the natural therapy clinic once again for another three weeks, then had another two-week break. During that time she had a spinal and liver MRI but without the prior contrast injection.

Test results indicated the natural therapy had put a stop to the spread of cancer. There was no increase of cancer in the liver and there were cystic changes in some of the tumours in her spine. Cystic change is evidence that tumours are dying.

Prior to natural therapy, the texture of her breasts was too dense with fatty tissue to feel lumps and she was in the group of women who have what are known as "lumpy breasts". However, after only three weeks of natural therapy, Elias felt a ductile carcinoma deep within her breast. As she lost weight, he discovered more lumps the size of walnuts in both breasts.

They began to die from the centre after only three weeks of natural therapy and her body dealt with the toxic debris via its natural drainage system. She said she thought natural therapy was incredible and incredibly simple, and was elated with the rapid progress she was making.

Once again and as usual, Elias worked on her nerve system twice a day for three weeks, after which she had a three-week break. This was followed by another series of medical massages for three weeks. She went home for a five-week break, after which a further three weeks of medical massages was necessary.

After this session Karla had another MRI but without the contrast injection. The results were outstanding. The medical massages to her nerve system, in conjunction with her well disciplined mind and commitment to healing, had not only stopped the growth of the many liver tumours, but the spinal tumours had shrunk almost 10 per cent and were seen to be turning cystic.

There were the usual and expected controversial remarks from the radiologist about the results of the liver tests. Karla said she was not concerned because she knew Elias's interpretation of images differed vastly to that of medical practitioners. None the less, the oncologist accepted the outcome as positive and told her to continue with the natural therapy if she wished.

Karla said she considered it unbelievable and unacceptable that those with cancer – especially those who make decisions on behalf of children – would choose chemotherapy over natural therapy if they realised there was a gentle and drug-free alternative available.

She said: "My grandfather was mustard-gassed during World War I. The origins of chemotherapy came from mustard gas and I find it so difficult to make the connection between chemotherapy and good health. I've seen too many people suffer so badly and have such an appalling, painful end to their lives after accepting the harsh cancer healing treatment that modern medicine has to offer.

"I just don't want to have that done to myself or my family." She continued: "I had asked many within the medical field what they would do if they were in a similar situation to myself, but I never received a straight answer. Could it be they don't have faith in it either? Have they been told they are not allowed to voice their opinion? And has this anything to do with revenue?"

After only eight months of natural therapy with Elias, she said: "I really feel fantastic. I've lost 25kg, I'm slim and have an enormous supply of energy. My skin looks and feels fantastic and the keratosis on my arms has disappeared. It's just amazing." She said she was enjoying the multiple benefits of healing the way nature intended.

With a voice of experience and humility, Karla said how sorry she felt for those who suffered unnecessarily from disease, and in particular children and those whose conditions were terminal.

She wondered how many people were enduring the ravages of chemo and radiotherapy – vomiting, and watching their hair fall out. She quietly added: "I almost feel guilty. Here I am enjoying cherries, fresh dates and other gorgeous natural food. I go to work in our business, I am getting better every day and I feel great."

Karla said she often pondered on how some in the medical fraternity had got so many health issues wrong with regards to disease. She said: "I, like so many others thought drugs were going to be my saviour, and my reliance on them was total.

"I now realise how wrong I was. I haven't taken a single chemical substance since beginning natural therapy with Elias. I had taken so many prescribed concoctions before meeting him but they did nothing to heal me. I realise I was an ongoing source of revenue for the medical and pharmaceutical industries."

She said she felt the majority of mankind had become blasé about the stranglehold the pharmaceutical industry had on the medical system. She said many people would almost be too afraid to discuss natural therapy with their doctor.

There are so many doctors who see self healing as a threat and simply shun it. Natural therapy is almost a dirty word because there is no money in it for them or the pharmaceutical industry. One feeds off the other.

She spoke about the importance of the financial demands of medicine and its connection between the cog and the wheel of the medical and pharmaceutical industries. Somewhere along the way the individual has lost out.

Since Karla was diagnosed, both she and Nigel have researched cancer continuously. One particular web site they found interesting was written by an independent and retired health industry professional.

His web site is:
www.health-science-spirit.com/cancerscience.html

In his opening statement Walter Last states:

Quote

Treatment often causes more misery then the disease itself and in most cases is unsuccessful (THE CANCER CONSPIRACY by John J. Moelaert)

How Scientific are Orthodox Cancer Treatments?
by Walter Last

The medical profession takes much pride in the rigorous scientific research that underpins its approach to cancer treatment. Someone newly diagnosed with cancer faces enormous pressure from our health care system to start immediately on a scientific medical treatment program that involves surgery, chemotherapy and radiation in various combinations. Being fearful and in shock, most individuals in this situation are no match for the overwhelming power of medical authority.

Unquote

In another part of the eight-page script, Walter Last writes:

Quote

Massaging Statistics

A recent epidemiological study confirmed the questionable value of conventional therapy by concluding that "medical interventions for cancer have had a negligible or no effect on survival". Even the conservative *New England Journal of Medicine* had an article with the headline: Cancer Undefeated.

Common ways to make medical statistics look more favourable are as follows. Patients who die during prolonged treatment with chemotherapy or radiotherapy are not counted in the statistics, because they do not receive the full treatment. In the control group everyone who dies is counted.

Further, success is judged by the percentage of temporary tumour shrinkage, regardless of survival times; if survival is measured, then only in terms of dying from the treated disease. It is not normally shown how many of the patients die due to the treatment itself.

The current trend is to pick up pre-cancerous conditions very early and treat them as cancer. While this statistically increases the number of people with cancer, it also artificially prolongs survival times and lowers death rates, thereby making medical treatments appear to be more successful. However, there may also be a genuine component of improved survival, as increasing numbers of cancer patients opt for additional natural therapies.

Unquote

Karla and Nigel agree that this web site contains a wealth of information about the negatives of medical cancer treatment and recommend it to those who wish to know some of the truths about cancer. Karla said: "At the beginning of my illness I didn't feel I had a choice. I was propelled along a well trodden path and no one was expecting me to have an opinion. I was being pushed into having chemotherapy and wasn't given enough time to make up my own mind."

Karla attends a craft workshop and is often asked about her natural food and therapy. She said: "Other members are so interested in it and they just can't believe how well I am. I told a friend that I really know that it's (natural therapy) working because my body is visibly changing."

"My friend said: 'Well, it's evident that it works because you are looking absolutely radiant'." Karla said she has had many similar comments from those who knew her before she began natural therapy and they were amazed with her results so far.

A friend of Karla's was diagnosed with breast cancer in 2006. She had both breasts removed, followed by chemotherapy and radiation. Six months later she had to have heart valve replacements because the radiation damaged the valves that had already been replaced. And she has not felt well since. Her friend said she had been told that she had congestive heart failure and could die at any time. Apparently her lungs were also irradiated. Karla said it was just so sad to see her so very unwell. Her quality of life is very poor and she is despondent because she feels so ill.

As the months go by, Karla has learnt to respect Elias's methods of medical massage and his positive and non-invasive approach to treating cancers. She said the thought of dying in abject misery and in a state of total debilitation, after countless bouts of chemotherapy and radiation, filled her with horror.

Karla is extremely grateful to Elias and said he had enormous knowledge of the human body, its nerve system and understanding of its ability to cure itself. His independence from all other authority gives him the ability to treat clients in an individual manner. This is the key to his overwhelming success.

He does not have to dance to anyone else's tune and is not driven by companies who dictate what he should do and how he should think. He has a very strong character and will not be influenced by anyone, nor will he be coerced.

She added: "It's just not possible to express my total gratitude to Elias. How can I thank him enough when he has given me back my life? I have no doubt I will be cancer free very soon and I am not living in pain. I can live life as I wish, without having had my body mutilated by mastectomies".

She said she had a totally different outlook on life. It has become very precious and does not want to waste a single day. Elias said her immune system was strong. She seems very resilient when others around her suffer colds and flu. She has had one head cold during eight months with Elias which lasted three days. Before natural therapy she spent the entire year feeling sick often.

Summing up, Karla said: "One of the most pleasant attributes of natural therapy is that my nerve system has not been burnt by chemo or radiotherapy and I haven't been poisoned by mustard gas. Elias really is a brilliant man and all his work revolves around nature and allowing the body to heal itself. "Isn't it strange that through propaganda, society highly values and willingly accepts the damaging and invasive modern scientific methods of treating cancers, rather than the gentle process of natural healing?

I certainly think I almost lost the ability to think for myself during the run-up to the chemotherapy. But the research I did on the internet and seriously assessing the situation led me to realise that there were other alternatives. It felt right when I started working with Elias."

Karla continued: "I understand how and why the body heals because I experience the phenomena daily. My dearest wish is that people give themselves time to think health issues through carefully. They should not allow the system to bully them into doing what *it* wants. The body feels entirely different after one month of natural healing. The way we deal with personal health issues is the most important decision one will ever make. The rest of one's life depends upon it."

– Karla (not her real name)

"

that which is not normal
and not natural will usually find a way
of working against the body

"

– elias ludwig schindelar

INFLUENZA A VIRUS – ITS EFFECT ON A TODDLER

"I must warn you, you may lose her".

These were the words that were spoken by a family doctor. Words that shook Heather and Ian, parents of their much loved daughter Eve, a toddler of just 16 months. This was a moment in time that they will never forget and they are grateful that the doctor spoke to them with honesty.

Heather and Ian's drama began one night during the winter of 2007. Australia was well and truly in the grip of the Influenza A virus and several people had already lost their lives. Small children and the elderly were suffering badly. Several children had already died when Heather and Ian's third child became ill.

Eve's parents put her to bed on the first night with what they thought was a head cold. But she soon became really ill. They called a medical surgery to make an appointment, but a doctor made a visit to the house in order to assess the child immediately.

The doctor advised them to have Eve admitted to a hospital as quickly as possible because she was having difficulty breathing. The child was later sent home but during that day she vomited six times. Her parents took her back to the doctor because she could not eat and was having milk only.

Eve began having fevers. By day two she was really ill with a fever of 41 degrees Celsius. Heather said she would feel hot, then she would begin to shiver. She was taken to a doctor daily and closely monitored.

During her life Eve had never once vomited but now she began vomiting in bed. Her mother said she was too sick to even cry.

Eve experienced the third day of vomiting and on the fourth day she did not have the energy to sit and was losing weight. This was of great concern to both her parents and the doctor because by this time Eve was chesty and she had a cough.

Blood tests were done and the doctor phoned to say Eve was suffering from the Influenza A virus. It was then that he said: "I must warn you, you may lose her". He also said all they could do was to put her into hospital and place her on a drip in order to counteract the loss of fluids due to her vomiting.

On the fifth day of Eve's illness, they quickly flew with her to see Elias Schindelar who had a history of helping clients especially when all else failed. Heather said it was a long and difficult flight because Eve was very ill and vomiting. "Ian and I were so afraid we were going to lose her."

They hired a car from the Cairns airport and drove to the Schindelar natural therapy clinic where Elias was waiting for them.

Heather said Eve stopped vomiting the moment Elias began working on her and her condition also began to improve immediately. He placed her on special natural foods and did natural therapy on her twice a day for 10 days.

After the 10th day they took her home. She had a cough but her chest was clear.

Elias told them to treat the cough with a natural cough mixture recipe he gave them. (Chop an onion finely and place it in a glass jar. Add two teaspoons of honey, seal the jar and allow it to stand for two hours. Take two teaspoons of the liquid four times a day for children and five times a day for adults for about four days).

Both Heather and Ian are so thankful to Elias for helping their little girl. Heather said: "He is a special man and we are so lucky to have him on our doorstep".

– Heather and Ian (not their real names)

HOPE, STRENGTH AND COURAGE – AUTISM

Joslyn is the mother of twin daughters. This is her story: autism is a severe neurological developmental disability affecting communication, sensory processing, social interaction and behaviour.

Discovering the girls had autism was a devastating and overwhelming experience. The cause is still very difficult to understand, because they were born healthy, progressed normally and spoke fluently before they were two.

Several medical treatments were tried over the years but there were no positive benefits. Many of the treatments had severe side effects and the long-term consequences of these are unknown.

When Elias Schindelar began treating the twins, they displayed many autistic characteristics such as limited eye contact, no verbal communication, attention difficulty, hyperactivity and were unresponsive to people.

Elias strongly believed their disabilities may have been caused by early childhood vaccination because dangerous levels of mercury and thimerosal are sometimes used as a preservative in several vaccines. Some also contain aluminium and formaldehyde. Test results showed they had high levels of mercury and other heavy metals in their system.

Elias explained that a strong and well disciplined commitment was essential. Food that aggravated the condition was removed from their diet and intensive behavioural management was also necessary.

It is my understanding the massage therapy Elias performs influences many body functions. Any imbalances within the nerve system can adversely affect the development of the brain and spinal cord, which can result in sensory, motor and neurological dysfunction. He massages the body's natural mechanisms to improve the functioning of the nerve system. This enhances general health and resistance to disease.

When Elias works on the children he applies highly controlled pressure on the cranial, sacrum and coccyx areas. This form of therapy has shown to be very effective because there are positive and amazing results. The girls are now displaying 100 per cent eye contact. Motor and sensory skills have improved and appropriate verbal language is no longer a problem.

They now understand spoken language and are able to perform tasks. Many behavioural problems such as tantrums and hyperactivity have been greatly reduced.

The children are being closely monitored by medical specialists who are amazed at their progress without the use of medication.

Elias is a gift to all who are committed to his style of treatment and their own wellbeing. He gives hope, strength and courage to those who believe in natural therapy and are willing to make necessary changes in their lives instead of taking the easy way out.

– Joslyn (not her real name)

THE LINK BETWEEN CHILDHOOD VACCINATIONS AND DIABETES

This story is about Jack, brother to Madison and second child of Simon and Justine who was born in May 2000. During her pregnancy Justine suffered fluid retention and as a result her unborn baby also suffered from the effects of this excess fluid.

At 28 weeks Jack was eager to draw breath. On admission to hospital, Justine was given a puffer/spray and as a consequence her body reacted violently. Her blood pressure dropped to 98 over 60. The baby was taken by Caesarean section and Justine had several transfusions to compensate her blood loss.

However, Jack was born perfectly normal and healthy and like most little boys he grew to be very busy and active. His highly motivated dad possesses an inquiring mind and Jack has followed in his footsteps. Even though they were isolated, the family shared the love of the land and the solitude of the vast outdoors.

They enjoyed good health and their isolation ensured medical visits were few and far between. As a result Jack missed out on his 18-month vaccination.

Upper and lower double teeth began to surface when he was two but they did not grow normally. Instead, they were deformed and twisted, much to the concern of his parents.

At the age of two he was taken to a doctor for a medical where he was given both 18-month and two-year vaccinations. He had two shots and oral anti-polio medication.

Justine said Jack was never the same after receiving these vaccinations. He began throwing tantrums and his behaviour was not as it had been in the past. It was a combination of rage and anger that he could not control and he would kick and scream. His parents assumed he was going through the "terrible twos" because he often threw himself on the floor and he would not go to bed at night. Justine usually retired at 8pm and little Jack would always say: "Good night mum", but he would not hop into bed until 10 o'clock.

Jack woke each morning with a healthy appetite. He had a big breakfast followed by a solid lunch and then "grazed" until 3pm. His dad said getting him to eat an evening meal was a struggle. He ate a very small meal and only did so because the family was eating and he felt he had to follow suit. His parents put it down to a perfect diet: eating as much as he wanted during the day followed by a light meal in the evening. However, there were no problems when it came to eating bread because he loved it – especially Vegemite on toast.

One day while Simon was visiting a doctor's surgery, Jack threw a tantrum in the waiting room and began screaming at the top of his voice. A doctor suggested he could have a defiant strain of Attention Deficit Disorder. Drugs were offered as a tool to curb his behaviour but they refused them. Justine said it was a constant power struggle where Jack was concerned. She fought to get him into the shower then fought to get him out. It was difficult to do simple things such as dressing him in pyjamas.

Even though he was only two-and-a-half, "things" were difficult. It was much easier to stay at home then it was to go on outings and as a result they went out only when necessary. On these occasions he refused to hop into the car without a fight but when they returned home, he would not get out of the car because he enjoyed the outing so much he did not want it to end.

Justine and Simon put his behaviour down to being strong willed and thought that little boys were "just like that". They even thought it could have been the result of their isolation where he had the freedom of running around, riding bikes and doing exactly as he wanted. His father said Jack always loved the outdoors right from when he was a baby. They transported cattle in trucks and would travel together as a family day after day. Justine breast-fed Jack in the truck and they had a crib set up in the sleeper of the rig.

Even before Jack was two years old he knew what he wanted and would not go inside the house at the end of the day until *he* was ready. Justine jokingly said she thought it was because he had been on the planet in a former life and he thought he knew more than everyone else.

Simon recalled a particular period of five days when he and several others erected a shed. Young Jack happily sat in his walker and oversaw the entire project. He even had all his meals out there because he did not want to miss anything. Justine maintained he just loved to be involved in whatever was going on around him.

Simon said Jack's level of concentration was amazing and especially if it was something he was interested in. He recalled an incident when he was carrying out maintenance on the wheels of his semi. Each tyre had to be removed and Jack replaced the nuts on the wheel studs and continued doing so for hours. He said most children would have become bored after five minutes, but not Jack, he was totally involved and he loved it. He did this when he was two, when most children that age have a short concentration span.

Even when he was 15 months old he would travel with his father in the semi for hours, passing through towns, watching the windscreen wipers beating in time, while chewing on his favourite sandwiches, totally absorbed with the passing view. As long as he was with his dad he was "as happy as Larry".

His father said: "There are not too many children of that age who are happy to be sitting in a truck and looking through a windscreen". He added: "And these were 18-hour trips". His parents are of the opinion that Jack is highly intelligent because he possesses unique powers of concentration for one so young.

Another amazing story that Simon recalled that beautifully illustrates the intellect of this precious child was when he was 18 months old. One particular evening he had almost finished his dinner and was busily chomping on the second last piece of carrot. His mother said: "Jack, if you eat that last piece of carrot you can have some sweets".

With lightning haste he spat out the mouthful he was eating, took the last piece of carrot from his plate and devoured it. He was smart enough to work out that in order to get his reward, he only had to eat the last piece. His parents still find it difficult to comprehend his level of intelligence and they recall these priceless moments with love, admiration and laughter.

As he grew older the tantrums progressively worsened. Taking him to shopping centres where there were rules and regulations was an experience to be reckoned with. He did not like the chaos of having people crowding him in supermarket aisles, nor did he like the humming sounds and bright lights associated with such venues. Even traffic lights frightened him because he did not know what they were. He must have wondered how he was supposed to fit into such a chaotic jigsaw.

They were to encounter other problems. At dusk each day they sat outside with their children and enjoyed a quiet drink while they shared the happenings of the day. If Jack had a particular type of sweet fizzy drink it would manifest into a nightmare. He grew so hyperactive it was difficult to bath and feed, and prepare him for bed.

There were many times when Simon left home at 5.30am and would not return until 6pm. One of the first things he did was to interact with the children. Jack was always overjoyed to see his father and Justine thought that this excitement may have added to his behavioural issues. She said at that stage she had not thought about the artificial sugars in their drinks until some time later.

After hearing an advertisement for packaged fruit juice, she decided to try it instead of the carbonated drinks believing they were nutritious and of benefit to her children's diet. But Jack's behaviour did not alter and she realised the juice was artificial and contained large amounts of processed sugar, additives and preservatives.

During episodes of hyperactivity, there were times when Jack ran from one end of the house to the other and it was impossible to keep up with him. It was just as difficult to put him to bed and the instant his feet touched the floor in the morning he was fully mobile. In hindsight, Justine and Simon said there was no doubt in their minds the sugar and additives in the artificial drinks contributed to their son's hyperactivity. However, they also said his hyperactivity worsened after the vaccinations at the age of two.

Justine telephoned an ADD hotline. The lady she spoke with asked for a typical example of Jack's behaviour. An incident occurred after she had set up a video for him to watch in the living area while teaching her daughter schoolwork through long distance education in another room.

Suddenly the smell of smoke wafted through the room but she thought it was someone "burning off" close by. She decided to check on Jack and discovered smouldering embers in the arm of the couch.

Jack had pushed a heavy chair 15m to the stove, climbed on the cupboard, opened the door and retrieved a "trigger" to ignite the gas stove. She believes he did not set out intentionally to burn something. He did it as an exercise to prove to himself he could achieve it.

The lady she spoke with agreed and said if Jack did suffer from ADD, he would have sat beneath the cupboard and simply screamed because children with this "syndrome" do not take the time to work things out for themselves. If what they desire is not instantly attainable they scream and perform.

Instead, he systematically worked through the process of what was necessary for him to light a fire. He needed a chair in order to reach the top cupboard. Then he had to climb, open the top cupboard door without falling, retrieve the lighter and hop off the chair. His next task was to find something he could light, then use the trigger mechanism to light a fire from a spark. Quite an achievement for a two year old!

His parents did not think he suffered from Attention Deficit Disorder. They thought he had an intelligent brain that required stimulation.

Behind everything he did was a complex mental ritual. His grandparents said Jack took after his father because as a child Simon was always "busy". They were not worried about Jack's behaviour because they felt he would settle down, but only when *he* was ready.

In time the family moved from their property to another area and life progressed as usual. Jack's behaviour continued to be busy and full on and like most responsible parents Justine and Simon tried all forms of gentle and persuasive discipline.

They took solace in the knowledge that there was a good and gentle side to his nature. He was never physically abusive and he was not a naughty child, but motivated, active and inquiring.

After the move Jack settled down for a short period which Justine attributed to the fact the family was always together and he saw a lot more of his father whom he idolised. He was never happier than when he was playing with his dad or simply basking in his presence.

Jack was four-and-a-half years old the day Madison turned 12. To mark the occasion they took their children to a water park with a group of her friends. At the end of the day the children returned home with red spots similar to that of cigarette burns the size of a thumbnail over their limbs and neck.

At first it was thought they may have suffered an allergic reaction to the chlorinated water or that the welts may have been the result of scratched mosquito bites. A doctor confirmed they were school sores. Suffering no ill effects, they were given liquid antibiotics and antibiotic cream.

About a month later, Jack began urinating four times an hour and for the first time since he was toilet trained he wet the bed twice. This was most unusual. They found it very difficult especially when driving because they had to stop every 15 minutes for him.

His parents thought he may have had a urinary tract infection so they took him to visit a doctor. After a urine test they were told he was suffering from Type 1 diabetes. They were told there are about 20 different versions of Type 1 and at that stage they had no idea what that meant. (They have since learnt much about this subject because Justine is tireless in her quest for knowledge). A specialist soon admitted Jack to hospital where he was intravenously injected with insulin.

Both parents agreed, and there were no doubts whatsoever in their minds the childhood vaccinations were responsible for Jack's new problem. The only reason they agreed to these injections in the first place was because many institutions refuse to enrol children who have not been vaccinated and Justine and Simon wanted their child to interact with others his own age. The rule is: no vaccination, no entry. However, Justine said when a child was five years old and at school entry level, parents were not asked to produce "that piece of paper". She said she felt it was the trap they fell into. She said her 12-year-old daughter had only one vaccination as an infant because she reacted violently and her arm blew up like a balloon. After that incident it was decided she would not be subjected to any more of these types of drugs.

Jack had been in hospital on intravenous insulin for three days when his blood sugar reading dropped to an alarming 2.3. Hospital staff panicked and began giving him fruit juice in an attempt to elevate his levels. Justine and Simon said there was nothing they could do but stand by and witness the horrid spectacle unfold.

Helplessly they waited out the minutes. They were reduced to tears and felt lost because there was nothing they could do to help their child. Throughout the entire ordeal Simon said Jack did not feel sick and this continued to puzzle them.

Some time later they had counselling courtesy of an organisation connected with the hospital. They were given heaps of information. Both Simon and Justine agreed: "After reading the literature it scared the living daylights out of us and we were worried because we were told: 'if you do not give your son insulin, if you do not test your son he will die within 24 hours'". Jack's parents said they found this very scary and added: "Each time we paid the centre a visit we became more stressed".

On one such visit they were given a package that contained an injection and a vial and they were to use it if their son lapsed into a coma. The injection contained liquid and in the vial was a powdered substance. They were to place the injection into the powder and withdraw it. The substances were to merge for one minute.

They were then to inject their son with the drug in order to save his life. They were told that if this was to happen it would be: "The longest minute of your life". Simon said the thought was terrifying. He did not want to see his son in a coma.

Justine said they would no sooner get over one thing then they would be hit with something else, then something else yet again.

There was always a new problem. They reached the stage where they could not tolerate the information overload any longer.

Justine said she became bewildered because they were not bad parents and they loved and cared for their son and daughter. The children did not fill up on junk food. They were careful with what foods they gave them to eat and she was baffled as to why things were going so wrong.

They spoke with a dietician who questioned their diet. He said they were abnormal because only 15 per cent of the Australian population actually sat down together at the dining table as a family and ate home cooked meals daily. This ritual is part of their daily routine. Even when they go into town to shop they order salads and eat healthy. They did not have junk foods and in the bush all meals are carefully prepared.

Justine said both she and her husband felt very uncomfortable during counselling sessions.

Simon said one would think that by now, everything would have been invented. But this is not so. Every day people are coming up with new and brilliant ideas.

On these grounds they thought "there had to be something else out there" that could help them. They never believed they had only one option. It was this thought that kept them going and they agreed they would both continue researching independent information.

Justine said: "I find it impossible to believe that the body turns against itself unless it has issues with the environment e.g. accidental absorption of chemicals, or viruses and disease". She added: "Stress and an improper diet are contributing factors as well as addictions such as social drugs, alcohol, prescription drugs, cigarettes, obesity etc".

She went on to say: "Unless foreign substances or viruses etc., actually enter the body, it will not turn on itself. I firmly believe that all human cells, whether they are the skin, hair, the liver etc., will regenerate given appropriate conditions and I find it difficult to believe the pancreas dies as a result of diabetes".

Apart from the antibiotics and prescription cream he had for the school sores, the childhood vaccinations were the only drugs Jack ever had. They did not believe in "pumping" their children with chemicals, drugs and cough mixtures and they do not believe drugs and chemicals are capable of curing the human body.

After the hospital episode, Simon and Justine had to leave their children for one week because they had pre-booked airfares. They were left in the loving care of a trusted person who was familiar with Jack's problem.

He had to be injected with insulin twice daily and his treatments placed on a sliding scale: if his blood sugar level was between 10 and 15, he had to have three units of insulin. If readings were between five and 10, he would have to have two units. There was long acting insulin and fast acting insulin.

Simon said when Jack first started having insulin injections he lost his powers of concentration. He was never one to sit and colour in or read a book because he was a "hands-on", mechanically minded child.

In the absence of their children Justine and Simon constantly thought about their situation and viewed the problem from a different perspective. They reviewed what had happened and how to manage future problems.

They recalled a session where they were told if Jack was to have physical activity, he was to compensate it with insulin. For example if he swam, the exercise would lower his blood sugar and that activity had to be compensated with carbohydrates, so they gave him a banana before the swim. Counterbalancing physical activity with carbohydrates was continuous.

During this week they realised just what was expected from the parents of a diabetic child. They were to test his blood, administer insulin, then feed him up to cover the insulin that he had just taken. They were constantly worried about him having a "low" after having had four units of fast acting and the two units of long acting insulin. They thought it may be best to give him something really sweet in order to block the fast acting insulin, such as a tub of yoghurt and hopefully this would carry him through to lunch.

They said the situation was "crazy". They were constantly thinking of insulin and food, and going to bed in a nervous state. They found themselves going to his bedside and shaking him while he slept to see if he was "all right". They turned on the light, checked his colour to ensure he was breathing. And that went on every single night.

On their return they found Jack puffy faced and looking fat. Each time he went to the toilet he complained about impacted motions because he was on a high carbohydrate diet. They were told Jack was to have four units of carbohydrates every meal. Every unit consists of 15 grams, equating to 60 grams of carbohydrates. He was to eat huge amounts of bread, potato, yoghurt, pasta, rice and various other foods, most of which caused constant constipation and contributed to the blood sugar levels.

They confided in a friend who advised them to have Jack's vertebrae checked. Justine recalled reading an article on the importance of correct spine alignment. She remembered an incident when Jack suffered a nasty fall whilst playing on his trampoline. She thought he could have suffered nerve damage that may now be contributing to his diabetes.

The family discussed the damaged nerve theory. Their friend advised them to take Jack to visit Elias because he had helped someone she knew who had suffered a pinched shoulder nerve. She said Elias treated people differently to other therapists. He works with the body holistically in conjunction with natural foods.

Justine telephoned Elias and explained Jack's problems. He asked her to fax his blood tests, all records of his vaccinations and the blood sugar level readings from the onset of the illness. They did as Elias requested and in their next telephone conversation he asked them to have a meeting with him.

They met for the first time on Saturday afternoon after Elias finished working. They did not know what to expect prior to the meeting. They thought they were going to see someone who was "way out". They were relieved to see an ordinary clean building and a man appropriately dressed in a white uniform because they expected to see someone clad in a sarong.

Simon said: "You never really know what to expect when people advise a natural therapist". They said they were prepared to take Jack anywhere for help and would explore all available avenues.

During the meeting Elias explained the task of encouraging Jack's body to heal itself naturally. He said this was not going to be easy and it would not be quick. He had helped many people to heal themselves and the key factor was *discipline*. People must give themselves time to overcome any setbacks they may encounter.

Jack was going to have to be on a strict diet and they would all have to work together. He explained the benefits of fruits and especially that of grapes to a diabetes sufferer. He explained how a bunch of grapes was even shaped like a pancreas and that the grape's natural insulin was absorbed in the mouth, then immediately travelled to the brain. Elias told them to give Jack only fruit to eat for two weeks, after which they were to revisit him.

He asked them to fax Jack's blood sugar reading every night and if the reading was more than 12, they were to give him artificial insulin. If the readings were under 12 they were not to administer insulin. Simon said Elias did not charge them for the first visit. He answered all their questions, gave them information and all the time they needed to absorb what he was telling them.

They felt nervous on the trip home because what Elias told them was almost *opposite* to the information they had received during their counselling sessions. Elias said the body required fruit and lots of water to flush impurities and toxins.

The next day they started Jack on fruit. He complained because he missed his regular food. Before he went to bed that night his blood sugar reading was 10. They did not give him artificial insulin. Simon felt relieved and thought Elias must know what he was talking about.

But Justine's thoughts were completely opposite. She thought about a hospital lecture given by a professor who specialised in diabetes. He said: "If you do not give your child insulin he will die". She was apprehensive and torn. She harked back to the initial conversation they had with Elias and remembered how knowledgeable he was in the science of fruit and nature. And to her it all made sense.

On the second night they were somewhat relieved because the fruit had worked for that day also. It worked the next and it continued to work for the first week. They realised they had stopped panicking and worrying and thought how the stressful situation had "worn them down". Prior to the diagnosis they had enjoyed a laid back lifestyle and stress had not been part of their lives. Simon's thoughts lay only with his loved ones and said: "If the family is all right, who really cares".

Two weeks later it was time for their second visit to see Elias. He massaged Jack's back and said that everything was going fine and spoke about the dangers of administering artificial insulin. He said they were doing a good job and to continue as they were.

As with most people who are introduced to this natural way of eating, they needed more information on what was a fruit and what was a vegetable. Elias explained that capsicum, tomato, avocado, pumpkin, eggplant, zucchini, chilli, squash and coconut were all fruit.

Justine was so relieved when she heard coconut, coconut milk and cream were a necessary part of a fruitarian's diet that she cried because it gave her so much scope when cooking his meals. She made smoothies, ice blocks and coconut ice cream with added fruit and Jack loved it.

Their third visit was two weeks later and like the second, all was fine. As he massaged Jack's back, Elias told them they could now introduce a few vegetables to his diet because he was progressing well and improving a lot quicker than anticipated.

It would normally take two months of eating fruit to make the progress Jack had made in only four weeks. They thought it was great and they were excited about the fact that they could now give him potatoes. Things had changed in the culinary department because Justine now had to think of new and inventive ideas to jazz up fruits and vegetables in order to entice her child to eat the food that was to heal him of diabetes.

Simon said shopping trips were completely different after they met Elias. Their cart was now filled with different varieties of fruit and vegetables and very few processed items. He said when you looked at the layout of a supermarket, the fresh food section was small compared with the processed food area.

When Jack began eating fruit only, he was four years old and he found it very hard because he was accustomed to a high carbohydrate intake. Making the switch to fruit was a culture shock for him, but by the fourth month he settled down and most times he did not even ask for other types of foods. However, he craved home made potato chips and bread. Elias said if he craved bread he could have only half a slice.

The whole family changed their eating habits in order to support him. They ate healthier and found themselves having meals similar to Jack. He was much happier with the addition of vegetables.

One day he ate a whole slice of wholemeal bread but it did not agree with him. Simon said his blood sugar levels "shot through the roof". They contacted Elias and explained what had happened. After researching the ingredients of the bread, Elias discovered there was an added preservative that caused adverse reactions to diabetes sufferers.

He said they would have to wait until Jack recovered from his setback and if they wanted him to have bread, they were going to have to grind the flour and make it themselves. After that episode they decided not to give him any more.

After his recovery, Jack's parents decided to send him to preschool because his diet was under control and they wanted him to interact with other children. However, after only a few days he returned home one afternoon sick with a flu virus. The illness elevated his blood sugar reading past 27. Concerned, they telephoned Elias who said they should give him lots of apples.

The next day he ate 10 apples and drank a lot of water and his blood sugar reading went down to 10. The illness lasted nine days and in that time Justine took him to visit Elias for four nerve massages in order to hasten the healing process. A persistent cough accompanied the virus and Elias gave her the onion and honey cough mixture recipe and it worked beautifully.

One day Jack accidentally kicked the leg of their barbecue and gashed his foot. Elias said that Jack should not be given a tetanus injection and antibiotics. A doctor at the hospital used liquid anaesthetic in droplet form and proceeded to mend the incision with six stitches. Simon said the doctor did a brilliant job. The anaesthetic elevated his blood sugar levels somewhat but the reading was not alarming. Elias also said that Jack should have chilli (to purify his blood) and avocado, and to rub the natural gel of aloe vera into the wound.

Simon and Justine said they continuously discovered ways to help their son. For example, it was important for him to chew his fruit slowly before he swallowed because this gave his tongue enough time to absorb fructose from fruit and glucose from grapes. They are constantly learning what effects different fruits have on his body.

They agreed Jack's condition impacted on the whole family and their lives. If they plan a social outing, they take his blood sugar reading before leaving and if it is elevated they feel it is safer to stay home. They find this very stressful because it dampens everyone's spirits. Even though they try really hard it does have a negative effect on the family.

They continuously search for information on diabetes. Simon said he was speaking with a lady whose blood sugar reading was constantly on 20 and she did not suffer from diabetes. He said: "Who is to say that every single person has to be exactly the same, it is impossible because every person's DNA is different. So why can't we all have a different blood sugar reading?" Justine added: "We all have different blood pressure readings because we are all different".

They agreed that Elias cared for his clients because he gave them his private telephone number and asked them to ring whenever they felt it was necessary. They said Elias telephoned them within 10 minutes of receiving their faxes if Jack's blood sugar reading was elevated. He is very dedicated and wants to help because he also sees Jack's situation as being unfair. Elias said when Jack's body cured itself he would not have to see him again and he would be well and healthy. He does not like to see people suffering from ill health. Elias's work revolves around people curing themselves with natural food and nerve massages if required.

It is about the body's ability to heal itself without drugs. The welfare of his clients comes first. Simon and Justine agreed that Elias was very much in touch with the average person and even though he was a professional, he was not a "smart alec".

Justine said diseases had fancy names. The word diabetes simply meant excessive sugar. She said: "If we were to remove the cause of the problem, diabetes as we know it would cease to exist". She added: "Osteoporosis is another prime example. It is a fancy name for brittle bones. If people stopped consuming animal DNA, ate naturally and exercised, they would not suffer this disease". She went on to say: "If we had proper names for diseases it would be easier for us to treat them. So why are we not given this information"?

Initially she felt Jack's diagnosis was accompanied by a death sentence. The things that really concerned them were the debilitating illnesses associated with diabetes such as kidney failure, eye problems that lead to blindness and the dreaded amputation of limbs etc. Justine added: "I believe these problems are not caused from the high sugars, they are caused by artificial insulin".

At the conclusion of their story they both agreed they could not thank Elias enough for all he did to help Jack. Simon said if he could afford it he would buy Elias a new car. Justine said she thanked God for Elias because even if (for some reason) it does not work, he has given them another option and showed her another path and she knows she does not have to give her son injections every day.

– Justine and Simon (not their real names)

“

fear stems from
ignorance. wisdom
and research are antidotes of
fear. we are not born with
wisdom but acquire it
through experience

”

– author unknown

THE AFTERMATH OF CHILDHOOD VACCINATIONS

We are the parents of two beautiful children, a son and daughter. Our eldest child suffered terribly from reflux as a baby and feeding him was difficult. However, in time his problem improved and he is growing into an amazing teenager.

My second pregnancy was closely monitored and throughout the eight months I had a total of four ultrasound scans. Her birth was difficult. I was violently ill and vomited uncontrollably throughout my labour. A doctor gave me an epidural injection and was concerned about damage to my spinal cord because I was in a state of agitation.

Although our daughter was born one month premature, we were told she was normal and healthy. Weighing in at almost 4kg, Emma was the perfect baby. She was contented, fed well and amused herself. She was an absolute joy.

She began having vaccinations at the age of three months. After the second shot at six months she developed a rash over her entire body. We were told it was eczema. It refused to go away and by the time our little bundle was one year old it was very severe.

I had breast-fed her from birth until she was four months old because I believed mother's milk to be the best source of nutrition for infants. A doctor gave us a prescription of a particularly potent cream and various others that I applied to her skin for two months. They did nothing to alleviate the problem so I stopped using them.

We had no luck healing her in our home town. We had exhausted all avenues so we flew her to a major city that had better medical facilities. A dermatologist prescribed more creams and as before, the rash did not improve.

Our situation continued and by the time she was two-and-a-half we realised she had other problems because she had made no effort to speak. She attended speech therapy classes but over the months that followed we saw little evidence of improvement.

We enlisted the services of a paediatrician who confirmed our fears. She said there was something wrong but did not know what her problem was.

By the time Emma was three, the rash worsened and encrusted her entire body. The same paediatrician admitted her to hospital, applied more of the potent cream, then bandaged her body ensuring it entered the skin and not the bed linen. This was done twice daily for seven days – these drugs were *heavy*. Her skin was in such a poor state it oozed from infection. She suffered terribly and itched continuously. It was heartbreaking to see her in that condition.

That treatment was unsuccessful. Again we flew to the city and saw another specialist. After the consultation we realised the visit was a waste of time, effort and money because he could not help.

We had heard of a specialist in another city who was brilliant in his field and flew to visit him. After examination and blood tests he said her kidneys were not functioning correctly and a build-up of toxins caused kidney failure. He said her kidneys were not flushing body waste, hence the build-up within her system. He said the body sought outlets for cleansing and Emma's chose the skin.

He began treating her with Chinese herbs and within two weeks of coming home we had a different child. After being on herbs for a period of 12 months her rash almost disappeared. She did not itch and was comfortable.

Some time later we noticed she had a developmental problem. We flew her to see another specialist who could not help but recommended a well-known paediatrician. He did tests on her brain because he thought she could have suffered epileptic fits. Test results cancelled out this theory, however he maintained she was autistic. We did not agree because we thought she did not fit into that "mould". On the contrary, she had excellent social skills.

He referred us to yet another specialist who ordered more blood tests. He suggested we had dust mites in the house. We went along with his assumption and leaving no stone unturned, had our carpets replaced with tiles. We installed air conditioning to alleviate dust problems and to prevent her body overheating because, despite all the herbal medicines, her eczema had returned. After making the changes Emma's situation did not alter. By the time she was five her health showed no signs of improvement. We enrolled her at a "special" school and found she was well in advance of others her own age. We soon discovered the environment did not suit her because she began mimicking habits that we considered detrimental for a child so young. We enrolled her at a local primary school and because she had such a beautiful loving nature she integrated well with her classmates.

Her caring teachers informed us she was having difficulty keeping up with her work and said she needed assistance. This cast doubts and we thought the paediatrician could have been correct when he said she was autistic. We visited another renowned paediatrician who said she was definitely not autistic. He agreed that she did have problems but like all the other medical professionals we had visited, he could not give us a diagnosis. We returned home after another unsuccessful trip and had no alternative but to allow matters rest.

When she was seven years old we heard of another specialist in a major city who believed strongly in hair follicle testing. We flew to see him and he said he did not know what was wrong with her but believed this form of testing produced very good results. We returned home and for two weeks we followed his instructions on how to prepare her hair for the test. We collected a sample and sent it to a laboratory in the United States.

The results revealed she had alarmingly high levels of copper in her system. A doctor from the laboratory telephoned me and said they had never seen such an elevated reading of heavy metal in a child her age. During our conversation he suggested our daughter be a guinea pig and participate in trials.

He suggested introducing zinc into Emma's system in an effort to balance the copper levels. He said the zinc might "eat out the copper" or at least "bring down the copper levels".

We were grateful that at last we had something tangible to work with. Even though a door had opened for us, we would not allow our daughter to participate in these trials because his suggestion sounded "way out". Our aim was to rid her body of the metal, not add to it.

Since Emma's problem began, my husband and I had tried hard to find a cure for our precious little girl's illness. Every time someone suggested a therapist, doctor or some form of treatment we followed up on the information. There was always someone trying to help. No one enjoys seeing a sick child and most of her life thus far consisted of pain and discomfort.

Even though we encountered one brick wall after another in our quest for help, we never gave up hope of eventually finding someone who could. I was a weekly visitor to doctors' surgeries and chemists for prescription drugs. The number of tubes of creams I smeared over Emma's body does not bear thinking about. It seemed she suffered one infection after another and it was of great concern when her skin opened up because we were afraid of cross infections.

I worked away from home and my husband has four jobs because bills must be paid. We had spent hundreds of thousands of dollars in an effort to find a cure for her. As parents we had no alternative and our main concern was that of our daughter and not the money we were spending. It was difficult for her because she suffered great discomfort during plane trips. When one has such a major problem with oozing skin over their entire body everything affects them – the sun, dust, hot summers, cold winters, wind, cold air-conditioning. Nothing equals the comforts of home.

There were times when her eczema was so severe I constantly changed her bed linen because there was always blood on her sheets. When her rash was at its worst she did not bother to talk to us but used hand gestures to communicate.

One day I heard of a lady who had suffered an illness that had been medically diagnosed as "incurable". I was told she was attending a natural therapy clinic and was well on the road to recovery. I visited her immediately and after an informative conversation she pointed me in the direction of Elias Schindelar. In a telephone conversation I explained Emma's condition to Elias. He said we had no time to waste and to visit him immediately. The next day we were in his clinic, that was August 2003 when Emma was eight years old.

He reviewed her blood and hair follicle test results and said he could help but recovery would take several years. He said he did not heal people because only the body could heal itself, nor did he allow drugs, supplements, herbs or spices. He said herbs and spices were natural drugs and if consumed regularly, the body became immune to them. Like prescription drugs they cease to be effective and build up in the system causing more problems.

His nerve massages and a pure food diet encourage the body to cleanse, then heal itself. When the body is in a *clean* state the immune system strengthens and automatically fights illness and infection. He said we must have patience and all work together. He said we would probably notice an improvement in her health within the first 12 months.

He also said she had liver damage and her kidney failure was the result of prescription drugs and creams. He began working on her liver. His nerve massages were to encourage the body to expel toxins, heavy metals and to assist the brain to function normally.

The first seven days were the most difficult because Emma had to have nothing more than lemon and water to cleanse the digestive system. As a result she felt weak and was very hungry but we saw Elias every day and he monitored her closely. He said the average diet consisted of animal products and processed foods that contained harmful chemicals and additives and that was the reason why so many people were ill and diseased. When he spoke he did so with such wisdom and conviction. It was no effort to place our trust in him.

When the seven days expired he placed her on a diet of soft fruits that included papaya, banana, pears, water with lemon juice and lots of fresh dates and avocado for her brain. She gained energy instantly and after one month she was able to eat all types of fruit.

Emma had natural therapy every two weeks for six months, then every three months. The treatments are now six-monthly. When we visit the clinic there are hugs and kisses all round. Her love for Elias and his family has made it easier because he tells her what she can eat and she does exactly as he says. She is so good – so accepting.

Our diet is exactly the same as hers because we must support her.

We did the lemon and water cleanse with her because we needed to know what reaction it had on the body and we wanted to know what she was experiencing. As a result we are all enjoying the benefits of good health and my husband lost all the weight he needed without trying because it happened automatically.

Our experience with natural healing has been a learning curve for our son. He knows how to cure himself if he ever got sick and he will benefit from this knowledge.

When Elias began working with Emma the eczema became more severe because her body was cleansing. However, within six months it completely disappeared except for a tiny area behind her knee. She had a planter wart the size of a 5c piece on the ball of her foot. It was so sore she began to limp. Elias said it was best left alone because he wanted to see how her immune system was going to handle it. After three months and with no interference it completely healed itself.

Six months into her natural therapy she suffered badly from a gum infection. Her pain was severe and Elias advised us against conventional medicine or dentistry because he did not want further contamination from prescription drugs or dental procedures.

Instead, we had to treat it with lots of pure fresh orange juice and I had to rub oil of cloves into the affected area for one week. I did exactly as he said and within two days the problem disappeared. It was at this time we saw a marked improvement in her speech coordination. She said she was feeling better: and she loved it.

After 12 months of natural therapy Elias wanted to gauge her progress and requested blood tests that were to include copper readings. He said testing the blood for heavy metals was more accurate than hair follicles. We were ecstatic because all her results were normal including the copper and her liver and kidneys had healed themselves.

However, the high levels of copper she had prior to seeing Elias affected her brain detrimentally. He reminded us it would be slow to repair and we had to have patience. There was no alternative to natural healing. Conventional medicine had failed and no amount of prescription drugs or cream could heal her. To the contrary, the prescription drugs had given her kidney failure and liver damage.

During a consultation, Elias said ultrasounds should be avoided during pregnancy because they interfered with both the mother and baby's electromagnetic field and killed brain cells. Had I known of this danger I would not have had them. When I had the scans they always showed the foetus as normal and healthy. He said that ultrasounds provided very limited information and at times they were responsible for premature births.

Elias continuously works on Emma's brain and estimates it will probably be a minimum of three to four years before we see major improvement. He said the body needed a long time to cleanse itself of heavy metals. Her school teachers all agree there are major improvements in her work. She is concentrating because she does not have the continuous eczema itch. Elias said when children had an itching problem, they focused on that and not their schoolwork.

In November 2004 Elias allowed her a little treat, a small serving of rice and pasta once a week. She thought she was in clover because she loves her food. In January 2005 we had more good news: she could add one piece of fish a week to her diet.

During one of our sessions Elias said many children suffered diseases such as Emma's after they received vaccinations. He also said high levels of zinc were present in children who suffered autism. Luckily Emma did not have zinc contamination.

Our children enjoy swimming in our pool during the summer. The high levels of copper sulphate in chlorinated water may have contributed to her problem because it would have entered her body through the skin and she may have swallowed the odd mouthful. When we made the discovery we replaced the water and sought alternate methods of keeping it safe.

Before going to Elias, Emma had difficulty with memory retention. Within 12 months of natural therapy we saw major improvements in her concentration and memory retention levels. She sat longer and was capable of solving problems.

She has had natural therapy for four years. Within 12 months she was composing sentences compatible with others her own age.

In the past we had to decipher her speech, now we understand her effortlessly because she has structure and speaks clearly.

She continues to improve in all facets of her life. Harking back to the way she once was, I feel she had so much courage for one so young. She continued to attend school the entire time she was sick. Full praise also must go to her teachers for their understanding, caring, love and support.

Her life is now full and interesting. As well as school, she loves going to speech and drama, singing lessons, choir practice and basketball. She also goes to tap dancing and jazz ballet classes and even though she is busy and out every day after school, she refuses to give away any of her activities.

She is pain tolerant and has always had high energy levels. Even when she was sick she found it difficult to stop because her brain was not functioning properly, it was not receiving or sending correct messages. On the rare occasion that she was still we had cause for concern. On a fruit diet her energy level is even higher because of its natural fructose content. Now that her brain is beginning to function normally, she is in control of her energy.

It is amazing to see a child of her age eat such large amounts of fruit. She does not stop eating and can devour a large watermelon after school in one sitting. Elias encourages her to eat as much as she wishes and said the more fruit she ate, the sooner she would recover. He said eating fruit was the only way to cleanse the body of heavy metals.

The constructive manner in which she is now speaking is the result of thought processes. After school she volunteers information and speaks freely about herself, her mates, teachers and her day. Before going to Elias I had to coax her to talk. Now she is also more aware of what is going on around her. In the past her dad and I were concerned because she was so trusting of everyone, now she steps back and assess situations.

She has learnt about trust and is more selective in who she allows into her life. When she was ill she had no fear and thought everyone was lovely. Now she is wary and aware of what is going on in her immediate surroundings. In the past she attempted to leave the house on many occasions without telling me and my life was a constant vigil over her. Now she organises herself and tells me before venturing out. It is a lot easier because she understands danger and the importance of communicating with me.

She knows the difference between right and wrong and has structure in her life. She understands that some people have a dark side to their nature that could harm her. Before it all went over her head.

Recently Emma had a head cold for five months and the infection produced a lot of phlegm. Elias told her to have two teaspoons of crushed papaya seeds daily for two days but she detested the taste and objected vehemently.

After five months she reluctantly did as her "hero" advised and within a few days she was well. Crushed papaya seeds are powerful natural antibiotics and should be taken only when necessary. Constant misuse will render them useless in times of need.

She is still a little behind in her schoolwork but her brain capacity is improving continuously and we have no doubt she will catch up in her own time. We believe when she is free of heavy metals and her brain recovers anything is possible. She does her homework diligently and her written work is structured.

She is well behaved, very loving and a joy to get along with. We believe with Elias's help she will grow into a healthy adult with a good attitude. Many brilliant and successful people have educated themselves later in life and time is on her side.

Emma is the apple of our eye and is developing into a lovely young lady. She is now 12 years old, 158cm tall and she weighs 40kg. Her beautiful chestnut curly hair is thickening and is healthier than ever. One would never know she was once covered in eczema because her skin is beautifully textured with a natural golden tan and has no scarring whatsoever. Her teeth are still a little off-colour – a remnant of the antibiotics. Before she went to Elias she had heavy dark circles around her eyes but they have completely vanished.

No adjective can adequately describe our gratitude for all Elias has done for our family. We feel the natural therapy he performs is absolutely phenomenal. There is no one like him: his knowledge is vast.

He genuinely cares for clients who make a genuine effort to help themselves and co-operate with him. Had he not come into our lives when he did, I shudder to think what would have happened to our precious little girl and the devastating effect it would have had on us.

Her adoring older brother was 10 years old before we met Elias. At that time he shared our desperation and summed up our situation in his usual unique style when he said: "Mum and dad, it does not matter if it costs a million dollars, you have to find someone who can help her".

– Don and Debrah (not their real names)

SURGERY NOT NECESSARY

This story is about our granddaughter who was born two years ago with blocked tear ducts. Our daughter had to wash her baby's eyes each morning because she could not open them. Her little eyelids would glue together, held tight with green mucus. A doctor prescribed antibiotic cream. Her eyes wept because she had inflammation to both upper and lower lids.

It is not uncommon for this condition to heal itself. However, if it does not heal naturally in the first year of the baby's life, surgeons operate to rectify the problem. A specialist warned my daughter if it went untreated, it could cause scar tissue within the blocked tube. If the procedure was unsuccessful, repetition was necessary and this would require a double dose of anaesthetic.

My daughter heard about Elias and took her baby to visit him when she was nine months old. On examining her, he told her to stop using the antibiotic cream immediately because it had damaged her liver. The baby was breastfed, so he put both mother and daughter on a diet of all types of fruit, especially pineapple.

My daughter also had to eat crushed papaya seeds because they are natural antibiotics and this flowed through to the baby. When the baby was weaning, my daughter had to make a substitute formula by using coconut milk, mixed with water and avocado. Very young babies are to also have banana in this mixture. These foods are excellent for the development of babies' brains.

Our granddaughter had to remain on the fruit diet for six months or until the ducts opened naturally. Then to ensure that healing had been successful, she had to remain on the diet a further four months. The first treatment for our granddaughter consisted of one massage a day for one week. He gently worked on her spine and massaged from the nose to the ducts.

Three months later, he repeated the procedure. The tear ducts opened naturally and surgery was not necessary. With his gentle massages and a fruit diet, her body healed itself. It was very important to have fruit available to her at all times. She was allowed to eat whenever she wanted it because unlike bread, fruit passes through the digestive system very quickly. Her parents said she was continuously eating.

Elias said how important this was because the more fruit enzymes her body received, the quicker it would heal. There was no such thing as three meals per day, it would not have worked and the child would have been hungry most of the time and lacking in fruit's vital nutrients.

Our granddaughter is now two years old. She is a good size, weight and height for her age and is very active. Her swimming coach often comments on her strength and excellent gross motor skills and suggested she join the kinder gym.

She still enjoys a fruit diet supplemented with vegetables and fish along with bread, pasta, dates and dried figs. Because fruit does not remain in the system for very long, her meal servings are very generous. She has the choice to basically graze all day. My daughter keeps the fruit bowl full and within reach and she helps herself to bananas and apples etc. She does not eat dairy foods. Her health is excellent. She has not suffered from ear infections, vomiting or diarrohea.

Her parents made a decision that they would not eat any sweets or biscuits in front of her to encourage their daughter to eat healthy. My granddaughter's taste buds have not become accustomed to a lot of processed sugar, though she enjoys a treat now and then with friends and visitors.

At her playschool she is exposed to some processed foods but she has little problem knowing that at home she eats well. This little girl thinks dates and figs are sweets. She helps herself to them from the refrigerator now that she can open the door.

– Loving Grandparents

STRESS – ITS EFFECT ON THE BODY

My name is Thomas and I used to be very healthy and extremely fit. In 1999 at the age of 59, I went to a doctor for a check-up. It is not something I normally do but I did so because it was a job requirement. The examining doctor said there was absolutely nothing wrong with me.

My workload was demanding and after three years my situation changed: I felt tired and drained.

I do not like hospitals or the idea of taking drugs because some years previous I had suffered a urinary tract infection. The pain was so severe it reduced me to tears. I was given a drug that badly affected my brain and I detested the nightmares. They pulled me into black swirling voids and I fought to keep myself awake. Since then I hated the feeling of losing absolute control.

I spoke with the administering doctor who said he did not realise I was drug sensitive. Another doctor at the hospital advised me to consult with a general practitioner and to have my medication reviewed. He said the drugs I was given had reduced my heart rate to 40 beats per minute.

A few years later I decided to visit a doctor for another checkup because I did not feel well. After an ECG, I was admitted to hospital immediately because I had suffered a "silent" heart attack the previous night.

A week later I left the hospital with eight types of medication. What really concerned me were the statements on the leaflets that accompanied them. Some said I would have to be on them for the rest of my life once I started. Taking drugs is something I do not agree with.

I was supposed to have an angiogram within three months but the hospital could not fit me in for seven months so I did not bother about it. I believe that whatever is broken or damaged could and should heal naturally over time.

A friend advised me to visit Elias. My first visit was in 2002. He said I could throw away all medication. I did not think twice about it and was very happy to do so. He immediately began working on my heart and within a very short period I was completely healed. I continued having therapy with Elias at six-weekly intervals for maintenance until the beginning of 2005. In that time I had no problems whatsoever.

My workload at the college increased to the point where it became too much to handle. One particular day I suffered a dizzy spell. I went to a local doctor who performed an ECG and I found myself back in hospital. (Unfortunately, I did not think about going back to Elias).

It was discovered my kidneys were causing problems: I had developed a build-up of fluid in my lungs and it had to be drained. This illness crept up ever so slowly.

I did not realise I had a problem until I began having difficulty breathing. I was also having trouble getting to sleep and became very tired. After visiting a doctor he recommended sleeping tablets. I did not take the medication through fear of my lungs filling with fluid and I had visions of drowning in my sleep. Prior to that, I had not seen Elias for some time because I had felt fine.

At the end of May 2005 I visited Elias again and he was almost cross with me after I told him about the medications and my problematic lungs. He told me I had to make a decision whether to continue taking drugs or to have natural therapy.

He said I could not switch from one form of treatment to another because taking drugs such as diuretics added to kidney problems and cancelled out natural therapy. He said my kidneys were quite happy to accept the diuretics because they did not have to work any more. The medication did all the work for them.

He said when people began taking this drug, they had to continue forever because the kidneys ceased to function. Then other problems arise because kidneys not only drain the fluid, amongst their many other functions they cleanse the body of toxins.

And to add to the problems, this drug produces harmful side effects and as a countermeasure other drugs must be taken. Then, they produce even more problems because all drugs have side effects. I discussed this with my nephew who is a doctor and he confirmed what Elias had said. It has always been my conviction that we do not have to rely on medication in order to cure. I know doctors work within a "system" and are really busy. But drugs do not fix health problems. I feel sure for quick relief some drugs may be effective. Then there are the repeat prescriptions which all cost dollars – but there is no healing.

However, I told Elias I was sick and needed his help. He said he would have to go back to the beginning and fix the damage that was caused by the drugs. This was the only way he could get the kidneys to work effectively. He said my left kidney was almost crippled and the adrenal glands were not working at all. It seems I had neglected my health and put up with the problems for too long. In hindsight I realise I should have consulted Elias much sooner.

One night I had difficulty breathing and had an uncontrollable coughing fit. I telephoned Elias who advised me to sit in a hot tub for an hour. However, this did not help so I spoke with him again and he told me to try another hot bath. That also failed and he advised me to come up for a treatment.

It was past midnight and driving up the Gillies Range in my condition was not enjoyable. (Much later, Elias said the intensive coughing fits could have ruptured my lungs. My kidneys were not functioning correctly which caused a build-up of fluid in my lungs. Strenuous coughing could have resulted in immediate death).

He said I was also suffering a flu virus that contributed greatly to the poor state of my lungs. He began working on the virus and spoke about the necessity of eating fruit only for a period of time in order to kill it. All the while the fluid in my lungs was causing problems. I asked if they could be drained and he said he needed the fluid to train the kidneys to function properly. I found it amazing just how accurate he is when massaging problem areas.

I had been having intensive therapy and it was taking quite a length of time training the kidneys to function normally. Elias said it took a long time to drain the lungs naturally compared with the methods used in hospitals. He said lungs quickly refilled after mechanical drainage because the kidneys were not working and the problems continued to escalate. The constant travel, the tropical heat and the number of hours I spent commuting to and from the clinic did not help my problem. Elias suggested I move to the Tablelands temporarily where the climate would be gentle on my cardiovascular system.

I have been having daily treatments and life on the Tablelands is a lot easier. At this stage I think I will be here for another four weeks. I feel happier closer to therapy because I may have cardiovascular complications. Elias told me to telephone him at any time of the day or night if ever I felt the need.

There is no question about what he does. What I did not realise in the beginning was that he begins treating you like a tradesman who knows exactly what he is doing. Like a carpenter he does not say I am going to do this, or I am going to do that, he just starts doing it. Later I discovered that whenever I want to know something, all I have to do is ask.

One day I asked him for some pamphlets so that I could read something about my illness. He took me into his study and pulled out some books and said all the information was there if I wanted to have a read.

Elias is a very knowledgeable man.

Now that I have got to know him, I realise with his ability and personality it is all really quite nice.

– Thomas (not his real name)

THE TRUTH MUST BE TOLD

by Elizabeth, wife of Thomas from the previous story.

I feel there is a great need to have this story published. It would not be correct if the full story were not told. If vital information is withheld, the wonderful work that Elias does would be all in vain. I believe people must understand themselves on all levels as well as their illness if they expect to heal.

I studied psychotherapy at Albert – Ludwig – University and as such I work with people who have various health issues. It is imperative that those who are ill must endeavour to heal on different levels and they must confront whatever it is that is preventing their healing.

In order to heal, people must address the physical, emotional, mental and spiritual aspect of their lives. However, I also believe that for some, this is a very difficult task. They find it easier to disguise the truth or completely forget their past than it is to confront it.

First of all I want to thank Elias for all he did in trying to save the life of my beloved husband Thomas. I also know he saved his life at least twice during the short time we were together and before I met him. Had he not done this, Thomas would have died much earlier and I would not have met him at all. This would have been absolutely catastrophic for me. At least I had him six months longer than I would have.

Thomas was a beautiful person. I loved him dearly and I am very grateful for the wonderful months we had together. But there was a good reason why he did not overcome his illness. He was tormented by the persecutions of his childhood and the loss of his natural father.

He never came to terms with his loss or his suffering and this made it extremely difficult for him to heal. I feel under such circumstances, Thomas's past must be revealed in order that others understand the importance of forgiveness, loss and coming to terms with their past. Thomas was a schoolteacher when he became very ill with a virus. He began having difficulty sleeping because he had fluid in his lungs and could not breathe properly. His breathing improved towards morning, however he could not afford to sleep in because he had to be at school by 8am. As the illness progressed, he worked less at the school and spent more hours home at his computer preparing lessons for the children.

The school medical system had been treating him as a cardiac patient. They gave him diuretics and informed him of his high blood pressure and high cholesterol level. He did not feel well at all. His health did not improve with the medication and it was evident that his breathing difficulties were escalating.

Even when he cut down on his work hours at the college, he did not get much rest because he found he was using all his spare time and energy travelling to and from therapy.

He loved teaching and his role at the college was to work with the pupils of grades 11 and 12. He put much effort into giving them an introduction to their pending professional careers and their lives after secondary education. He was very proud of his students and cared for them in every sense.

There was one particular student whose company he really enjoyed because the teenager was gifted. There were plans for Thomas to devote all his time to such children and others who chose to work hard. He was selected to fulfil this role because of his kindly nature. The school was forever growing in numbers. So much so, extensions were planned and he worked with architects to ensure the future needs of the children were adequately met.

He enjoyed teaching his crafts and it seemed there was little he could not do. He taught manual arts, fine furniture building, sculpture and mechanics. There is a little church perched on a hill on the Sunshine Coast in South East Queensland that bears witness to his gifted hands. It is adorned with his craft.

Thomas loved the children in his care and his authority over them was gentle and natural. He never became "loud". All he needed to do was to look at them with intensity.

The boys at the college had complete respect for him and in turn he respected them, other staff members and vice versa. He was loyal, modest and totally supported his colleagues and assisted those in authority.

He motivated students and strove to make their school days interesting and memorable. He ensured they did not become bored and would not allow repetition in the curriculum.

Thomas only worked with male students but he had been assigned to teach girls in the near future. He was looking forward to this and especially to teaching jewellery making. He had planned to use some of my special pieces as models.

He loved music, was a gifted musician and as a member of a band he had a vast repertoire. He made music at his school and entertained the children on special days by playing the trumpet, keyboard, harmonica and classical guitar. Thomas was a much loved and patient man. By sharing his talents with the children, I felt he was healing the "little boy" within himself.

In August 2005 he turned 65 and early the following month he celebrated the occasion with his much loved children and grandchildren. It was lovely to see him totally happy amongst those he held dear.

Thomas and I had only just married in January and it was wonderful for myself personally, because his children accepted me into the family. I arrived in Australia in June 2004 after surrendering my former life and business in Switzerland to be with the man I had chosen to love. I felt at ease in his company and with the decision I had made.

However, in the days my husband was unwell I felt sad, alone and homesick. We had a strong bond and the love we had for each other was deep. I really felt we were going to be together forever. We understood each other's "domain" and knew each other very, very well. He said he had three wonderful women in his life: his beautiful daughter, his principal and myself.

At that stage my husband thought he would recover from his illness, enabling him to return to fulltime work. There were times when he slept for 10 hours and when he woke he felt okay. However, his recovery was not clear in my mind because I felt his health was fragile and in a state of imbalance.

During October, Thomas could no longer work at the school. He decided to revisit the Schindelar clinic and on October 31, 2005, Elias asked him to move closer in order to alleviate the curse of negotiating the Gillies Range because the constant burden of travel was tiring him. He said the climate of the Tablelands would be much kinder to his cardiovascular system and he could have daily treatments.

Elias set about cleansing my husband of the drugs that had damaged vital organs. He began working on his kidneys to alleviate the fluid that by now had engulfed most of his body. Thomas started to feel somewhat better but on the whole I felt his condition did not improve.

He suffered greatly from excess fluid. It was pouring out through the pores of the skin on his legs. His body was swollen and as Elias pushed the fluid upwards, his legs did improve slightly. However, his left arm and hand began to swell and also oozed fluid. Then the right became affected. In a short while sores broke out over his skin, they became infected and Elias treated them with chemical-free ointments.

His body swelled to the point where he was having problems with his clothing. Nothing would fit, not even his shoes and he had to wear open sandals. This really troubled him because he had always been an aesthetic man who took pride in his grooming and the manner in which he dressed.

To lose this part of self was a bitter disappointment. The swelling also caused the loss of normal daily body functions that most of us take for granted. He found this shattering and difficult to deal with.

He suffered enormous personal discomfort because the swelling was so great he found even the simple task of showering impossible. To make matters worse, he found it difficult to cope with his physical weakness. His arms were so swollen and heavy he could barely feed himself. It was important that I help him with caution because I did not want him to totally surrender his dignity and independence.

It was of great concern to him that he had to rely on me as much as he did. I reassured him that what I did was out of love and concern. Helping him was easy and effortless for me because I was happy to be with him and felt the need to help as much as possible.

Elias put him on a diet of fruit to help his kidneys. He lost strength because he did not eat enough and he did not eat other foods either. I fully understood why he should have changed his diet as Elias advised.

I purchased fruit for him, however I could not force him to eat it and I did not wish to argue with him. I felt the need to love and support my husband but the decision he made about the food he ate was his own, and not mine to make.

I bought fresh fruit daily, especially grapes because their natural juice is notorious for cleansing the body of unwanted fluid. Most times he had difficulty eating them and drinking their juice. Nine times out of 10 he rejected them and I sensed he was fading away.

He did not sleep at night because the fluid drained into his lungs. He could only manage an hour here and there. He could not lie in bed and had to rest upright all night in a chair.

Towards the end of his life I had felt the decision of his survival was his own to make and in my mind I questioned what his choice was going to be. I also felt the decision had been open for some time.

During his last days he became so weak that Elias began to question himself. He could not understand why my husband was not responding normally to the treatments.

I felt there were obstacles that were preventing my husband from healing. I decided to confide in Elias and bring his past out in the open because I felt a great need to help him as much as I could. I desperately needed him to survive.

What Elias did not know was that Thomas had been molested and persecuted in his early childhood. In terror he was hung by one leg from the fifth level of an apartment building.

There were times he was deliberately buried in sand. He was also held under water until he felt his lungs would burst. From the age of five to 15, he was sexually abused. The torture continued for many years and he was shunted from institution to institution. In one instance, sadistic carers beat him with lengths of wood. There were so many terrible events that occurred in his life as a child, then later as a teenager. He carried the burden of his torments throughout his life.

After learning of my husband's unfortunate history, Elias said he would work on his "dark side" in order to help him overcome his problems. He said that it would be very difficult for my beloved husband to become healthy. His kidneys would have been under stress all his life and they would have released a natural stress hormone that is very detrimental to the body and to healing. And this would have occurred every day of his life.

Elias said the only way Thomas could get better was to forgive those who tortured him. He had to delve deep within his mind, work with his problem in order to forgive and come to terms with what had happened.

He found this very difficult because he married, had children and grandchildren whom he loved and cherished, and through them he knew children need love and support. He could not understand how adults could allow such monstrous acts to occur and even join forces with the perpetrator when the mood took them.

In order to survive, my husband had to learn to come to terms with what had happened to him early in his life, forgive, find inner peace and let go of the past. Thomas said his was a life of torment and it seemed he had to fight for everything he wanted.

He said he found it difficult to let go of the past and had difficulties within relationships but it was easy for him to love children. Even though our love was honest and deep, it may have also been confronting. He said when he met me, he learnt the meaning of true love and trust. Could it be that the honesty of our love eroded the protective barriers he built around himself throughout his vulnerable years and then his entire life? Did the genuine love we had for each other render him emotionally naked?

There is another incident that may have triggered his illness.

With total disregard for his feelings, one of the people who had been involved in the childhood atrocities contacted Thomas. That telephone conversation came four days before Thomas's birthday where he planned to introduce me to his family.

The call rekindled torturous memories. Feelings of abuse came flooding back and Thomas did not want to confront the past. Having a kindly nature, this was a very difficult period for him. The ugly memories of his childhood that were resurrected had a profound affect on him and on his health. It seems too coincidental: it was about that time his fatal illness began.

As well as working on his kidneys, Elias also planned to work on Thomas's hormones in order to help him cheer up. Elias was confident he could help overcome his suffering. However, it was necessary for them to work together. He asked Thomas to follow a strict diet which consisted only of fruit, especially grapes, their juice and lemon water. If my husband had the strength and capacity to do what was necessary, Elias could have helped him overcome the virus and other problems. But this would have taken time and time was not on his side.

Elias said that if he did not let go of the past, my husband would not become healthy. He said he had dealt with clients who had similar problems. He said people who suffered early childhood abuse must forgive and let the past go. If they harbour ill feelings towards others, they may become violent and aggressive and turn to crime, or they may turn their thoughts to suicide.

After that particular session with Elias, my husband became very quiet and said very little except that it was difficult for him to handle because he was so ill and fragile.

I felt it was all too much for him to bear. I also felt Elias was fighting for support from my husband because he needed him to "hold on" and work with him and to continue fighting for his precious life. He did not want him to surrender his valuable life to those who persecuted him. If a client does not fight to survive, Elias is powerless.

Early in his illness Thomas did not want to go into hospital because he was convinced he would have been given mind-altering drugs that would further contribute to kidney failure. He did not want to be on constant medication for the rest of his life. There were days when he thought he was going to survive but there were also times when he was doubtful. He told me he would have died earlier had I not been in his life offering love and support.

The night before he died he said his daughter would need a lot of support from me. I felt he was being philosophical when he said the world was in a very bad state because various types of wars were being fought on many fronts.

He said he had made a good life for himself and because the virus had made him so ill, he was ready to "go". My husband made an almighty effort that evening as he struggled out on to the terrace. We sat together witnessing the beautiful remnants of the day, then the sun kissed him goodbye and vanished over the horizon.

We went to sleep in our usual fashion – me on the edge of the bed and he in a chair close by. I always left a light on behind him because I did not like to sleep too deeply in case he needed me. I took his hand in mine and drifted off.

In the early hours of November 27, 2005 I woke as usual to check on Thomas. I looked over and saw my dear husband leaning to one side of his chair. I tried to wake him but he did not respond. I searched for signs of life but there were none. His body felt cold except for a tiny area of warmth above his heart.

Elias and his family were shocked and saddened to hear of my husband's death. He had helped many people overcome their illnesses and he wanted to help Thomas fight his. I was very grateful that he was always there for us, both day and night.

I am a professional person who deals with health issues and my education at university was based on traditional teachings. I am fully convinced the natural, drugless therapy Elias does is marvellous because it works and people heal themselves with his help.

I am also from Germany, I understand him and his work completely, therefore there are no doubts in my mind whatsoever how he works with his clients. His therapy works because he teaches people how to heal themselves, but they must work with him, they must have discipline, patience, the will to survive and they must heal themselves.

In the days prior to my husband's funeral ceremony, his beloved pupils composed two pieces of music. Their melodious voices resounded throughout the chapel as they sang the songs in his honour.

– Elizabeth (not her real name)

"

many a sceptic
has wasted valuable
natural healing time trying
to find contradictory
scientific evidence

"

– the author

THINGS ARE NOT ALWAYS WHAT THEY APPEAR

Sue is a young married mother. She and her family had been visiting the Schindelar clinic for maintenance for three years. She is a fruitarian and enjoys excellent health but she found it difficult to control stress. She underestimated her capabilities and overcompensated.

Sue has full-time employment as well as caring for her family. One particular hectic and work-laden week, she suffered the loss of a much loved family member. She was shocked by the sudden death and found it difficult to cope with her emotional stress.

She said in the three days between the death and the funeral she ate very little and became overtired from sleep deprivation. She also perspired profusely and became dehydrated.

After the stresses of the funeral and without warning she blacked out, hit her head and suffered mild concussion. At a local hospital she was diagnosed as an epileptic even though she had not suffered epilepsy previously and even though all her blood tests were normal.

Her family faxed Elias the blood test result immediately from the hospital. He said it was definitely not epilepsy but the end result of stress. He said this could happen to any person after only 36 hours of stress, sleep deprivation, excessive sweating, lack of food and water.

A week later Sue was given an EEG, but before the technician began the test he instructed her to breathe rapidly. An electrical apparatus was placed over her skull which was connected to monitors in order to measure brain wave patterns. She breathed as instructed, however she became nervous because she thought the rapid breathing could bring on another blackout.

Test results indicated there was a spiking effect in the brain wave pattern and again she was told she was an epileptic. She was given a prescription for epilepsy medication and instructed not to drive for six months.

Elias had been treating her for three years and said she did not have an epileptic seizure because she was not an epileptic. She had never had a seizure in her life. Just like any one else in a similar situation, she collapsed from lack of food and sleep, dehydration, and stress.

Sue said after listening to what Elias had to say, she questioned the accuracy of some forms of testing. Was it possible to measure (with 100 per cent accuracy) the activity of the brain where electrical frequencies had to penetrate the dense calcium of the human skull? She also questioned if the test measured nerve activity under the scalp during rapid breathing.

Elias said: "For those who must rely on technology in order to diagnose, the best way to accurately investigate the brain's function is to use radioactive isotopes scans and MRI. But I do not endorse these methods unless it is absolutely imperative because of possible side effects".

He suggested Sue investigate the possible side effects of this type of testing. He also suggested she investigate the side effects of each ingredient that was used in the manufacture of the substance that was injected into the body before having any tests. She did her research thoroughly and decided against them.

The list of the possible side effects from the injection which is administered prior to an MRI was freely given to Sue and is available to all who ask for it.

She was also given a prescription to alleviate the problems of epilepsy. Again Sue asked for a list of possible side effects and the information was freely given to her at a chemist shop.

She refused to take the drugs because of their side effects and she had faith in what Elias had told her. She had worked with him honestly for three years and she knew his history was one of 100 per cent accuracy.

It has been well over three years since Sue had her blackout. In that time she has worked diligently on the way she thinks and has controlled her stress. As a result she feels well and is calm. Elias told her to continue the good work she was doing and there was no need to visit him unless something unexpected occurred.

Sue said she would be forever grateful to Elias and all he has done for her and her family. She said: "Only heaven knows what would have happened to me had I not known Elias".

– Sue (not her real name)

(N.B. According to media reports, the medication that was prescribed to Sue is but one of many that are used in night clubs to spike drinks. Some women whose drinks have been spiked have suffered disorientation, impaired vision, collapse, loss of memory, paralysis and death).

IF ONLY I COULD TURN BACK THE CLOCK

In September 1999 my husband had surgery for bowel cancer. Following the surgery he had six months of chemotherapy but did not get good results from this treatment.

We started researching the problem we faced, hoping to find a cure. We began to realise there was merit in the books we were reading because the people who wrote them had suffered from cancer and cured themselves. Some books were written by doctors who had altered their ideas. We noticed a significant and amazing difference between conventional medicine and natural healing.

The advice of the doctors who were treating my husband was totally opposite to our natural healing research. In fact, one doctor confirmed our research had merit, but as there was no money to be made to verify that diet did play a huge part in repairing the body, nothing would be done about it.

One remarkable difference was found in the chemotherapy literature which encouraged and advised cancer patients to eat meat. However, it is a documented fact that cancer cells love and feed on animal protein.

Eventually we heard about Elias and my husband began visiting him in August 2000. However, he said that we were behind the eight ball because he had had surgery plus the chemotherapy. He saw my husband once a day, then twice every day including the Christmas period. He would not let my husband go without treatment no matter when it was. He always made himself available.

The disease finally became too much for my husband to cope with and no matter what Elias did, he could no longer help him. Everything that could have been done was done. If only we had known of Elias when the cancer was first diagnosed my story would be much happier. He was very honest and up front when we first visited him. He said the surgery and chemotherapy would work against him. If only we could turn back the clock.

We were very happy with the information that Elias gave us. He was unstintingly generous financially for the number of treatments he gave weekly. The compassion from he and his parents was unbelievable. My husband eventually lost the battle, but I truly believe Elias did his utmost. I also believe he has more to offer than any one I know and he knows more than any one I have ever met. What he says makes so much sense and he gives information so willingly.

During the few months that followed, the loss our family experienced was beginning to take its toll on my health. I felt unwell so I decided to visit Elias. He told me I was suffering from stress and it was interfering with my hormones. At that stage, I had also started to go through menopause.

I visited the clinic regularly then stopped for 12 months. Now that I am visiting him regularly once again, I can say that I feel wonderful. On my first visit, I told Elias that I had had surgery to remove my gall bladder many years ago and he was quite upset. He said to eat lots of pineapple.

My diet is ordinary, however he said that if I stopped eating every form of meat for a minimum of three weeks, the brown spots on my skin would begin to disappear. He said I should be eating more fruit and vegetables. Fish is okay occasionally. Unwanted body odour disappears when we eliminate animal DNA from our diet. He advised me to drink three litres of water daily.

I am also taking my young daughter to Elias when there are problems. She is wise enough to know the difference between natural healing, consuming prescription drugs and their effect on her body. The massages he gives her are quite deep and do hurt a little, however she does not complain.

My advice to those who are contemplating visiting Elias is: if you have a problem, talk it out with him. Do not allow his accent to become a barrier. If you do not understand what he is saying, tell him so. He will always repeat it.

There is no boundary to the amount of knowledge this man has about the body and natural healing. People must ask questions about themselves and their problems. He will answer any question and encourages clients to return should they have a problem after their treatment. The charge is a flat rate. There are no short or long consultations. It makes no difference if you see him before, within or after hours. He gives you the massage your body requires at the time. He does not hurry people. There are no expensive drugs to purchase and that is a great saving.

If people have problems after Elias has massaged them, they should just do what they normally do when visiting a medical practitioner. If they have issues they talk to that doctor. The same applies to Elias. Discuss your problem with him, not any one else. He knows your body and understands your problem. He will explain what is happening and why. People must be honest in order to heal.

I have absolutely no respect whatsoever for anybody who goes to Elias, has a problem after a massage, then goes elsewhere. If you show Elias the courtesy he deserves, you will reap the rewards.

– Evelyn (not her real name)

NO CANCER AND NO BACK PAIN

Some months ago I noticed a lump on the back of my hand the size of a 5c piece, 3mm high and red around its perimeter. I went to see a doctor and he said it was cancer. He wanted to cut it out immediately but I refused to have it done.

I said I needed a couple of weeks to think about it. But I was concerned because no tests were done to verify it was cancer. He said he wanted to remove it as soon as possible because it would get into my blood stream.

Acting on advice from my wife, I went to see Elias. He looked at my hand and said it was not cancer. He told me to take a piece of pineapple, place it on the lump and fasten it to the back of my hand with tape. I was to do this daily for five days, then I was to revisit him. When I went back the lump was completely gone.

Elias told me the lump was the result of eating dairy products. I had to eliminate them completely from my diet. He also said to stop eating meat for six months.

Unbeknown to me, my biggest problem was my enlarged prostate. At that stage, I had no pain in that area. Elias worked on the points in my back to alleviate the problem. I had to stop eating bread and pasta and I was to stop drinking beer and coffee for two months.

Another major problem was my cholesterol level. It was 8.5. A doctor had previously told me I was in danger of having a heart attack.

He placed me on medication to lower it. The dosage was one tablet daily. Elias told me to stop taking the drugs and eat chilli daily instead because it cleaned the arteries and lowered cholesterol.

I have had a very sore back as the result of driving heavy machinery for 30 years. In that time, I visited what seems like every chiropractor in our area but got no relief. Four discs were causing the problems and as quick as they were put in, they would pop out.

While I was visiting Elias I asked if he could help me with my back. He ran his fingers down my spine and said he could. During my massage, he worked very gently on my discs. He popped them into their correct position and I did not even know that he had done it. Since then, I have had no pain. I consider myself very fortunate because I am pain free and enjoy excellent health.

– Clive (not his real name)

"

walk your own path, not that of others

"

– author unknown

DEBILITATING VIRUSES

I was diagnosed with Post Viral (Chronic Fatigue) Syndrome which badly affected my muscles. In January 2002, I got mastitis in my left breast and needed antibiotics. But they did not agree with me.

Later I had a mammogram and an ultra sound. Both were clear, however from then on I continued contracting colds that never really left me. I would be all right for a couple of weeks then the head cold would return and my energy levels were down.

Early in November I got a really bad cough, similar to that of a smoker. By the end of the month my face took on a yellow hue. I had lost almost 6kg throughout the year. I was having trouble sitting because the muscles deep within my buttocks were very painful. The pain travelled into the back of my thighs. All the while my energy level remained low.

In the middle of December I went to a doctor. He recommended blood tests and a chest x-ray. All the results were clear. I visited a doctor in late January. By this time I stopped losing weight and the jaundice appearance had left my face. However, the muscular pains spread to the remainder of my body.

I had more blood tests and a pelvic scan that required a probe to locate my ovaries. All came back clear and some of the tests had been performed twice just to double check.

The doctor said he could find nothing wrong with me. He offered to send me to a specialist, but I declined. I saw no point in that as he had done all the tests necessary and they had all came back clear. The muscular soreness moved into the joints and they were at their worst night and morning.

A physiotherapist suggested light exercise and walking if I had the energy. He was rather concerned because I began losing weight again. It was as if my muscles were wasting away. They were very stiff, sore and painful and exercise seemed to increase my discomfort.

Getting to sleep and staying asleep were difficult. I felt as though I was an invalid. I knew something was very much amiss with my health but I had no answer. I had heard of the incredible results Elias Schindelar had been having with other peoples' ailments, so I made an appointment to see him.

It proved to be the wisest choice for me because I now had someone who knew exactly what was happening within my body. And more importantly, with his treatment my health began to improve almost immediately.

My first visit with Elias was on March 24, 2003. He told me I had a virus and he began working on it immediately. Along with the treatment, he put me on lemon juice and water for seven days. Later, he told me he would work on my liver, kidneys and nerve system because the virus had also affected them. He said my breast would heal itself in time.

I felt hot then cold, and very tired as my body journeyed through the healing process. He said I would lose more weight and that would be okay because it would return as my body healed itself. He also warned me my body would become even more tired and stressed during the healing process.

He told me if I strictly followed what he asked me to do, the virus would be gone in four-and-a-half months. After the first week I was able to have fruit. After two weeks of treatment I knew I would be doing exactly as Elias asked because for the first time in months, I knew my problem had been diagnosed. My healing had begun.

The virus was gone within the time Elias said it would. Treatment at this stage is ongoing as my body continues to heal the various organs, nerve system and other areas that were badly affected by the virus.

Had I not gone to Elias looking for help, I honestly do not know where I would be at this point in time. I had pretty much hit rock bottom. He made it very clear on my first visit that he could help me heal my body but only if I was prepared to do exactly as he asked. The choice was mine.

I was prepared to take the responsibility for my own healing.

I was also prepared to change my eating habits so as to give my body every opportunity to heal itself in conjunction with his nerve massages.

I chose to make that commitment to myself. Now I am a much healthier person. I have my life back again and I know my healing process is nearing an end. I am very, very grateful that I was fortunate enough to meet and be treated by this man who is a credit to the healing fraternity. A man who is very caring and who makes it very clear that he is available at any time should a client need him.

– Ellen (not her real name)

NERVES SEVERED DURING SURGERY

My symptoms began in 1995 when I was working. I was getting really tired, lethargic and experiencing chest pains. I had pains in my left hand, knee joints and muscles. Strength in my hand was lessening and it felt weak. In the morning, it looked like a claw and it took a while to straighten my fingers.

These symptoms continued for three years. During that time I visited doctors regularly. I visited a hospital on several occasions, because it was thought I had a heart problem. A doctor I was seeing suggested taking anti-depressant drugs because she could not pinpoint the cause of the illness. I refused to take them.

I had been a regular blood donor. Routine tests revealed I was extremely anaemic and I was advised to have further blood tests. A thyroid problem was discovered and I began taking medication. That was 13 years ago. At the same time a doctor gave me hormone implants.

My illness worsened and a doctor suggested it could be my oestrogen levels. Another suggestion was that it could be the thyroid condition.

In 1998 I began to lose faith in the medical system because I was very ill and I could not get a diagnosis. I asked for a referral to a specialist who worked in a major city because I felt I needed to visit a thyroid clinic at one of the larger hospitals.

After blood tests a specialist said I had a connective tissue disease: systemic lupus. My immune system had gone into overdrive and was attacking itself.

I returned home and visited a local physician who said I should begin taking steroids and anti-inflammatory drugs. I did not want to do that because I had heard stories of the damaging effects they have on the body.

He said lupus was an incurable disease and I felt medication was just a stop gap treatment so I decided to tolerate the pain. However, a short time later the pain became so intense, I agreed to take them.

But I had to put a stop to it because of the adverse side effects I suffered, along with headaches and dizziness. I also had to take another drug to control the high acid levels. All the while the lupus was eroding my oesophagus. I always had a burning sensation in my stomach and felt uncomfortable and suffered aches and pains.

Over the following years I spent a fortune on supplements. I sought alternative medicines and therapies. I researched my illness and visited numerous naturopaths. Acupuncture sessions helped relieve the symptoms for a little while but they always returned. I spent countless days in bed because the pain had spread to other parts of my body.

In the year 2000, my husband and I were travelling in another state and I began to experience back pain. I entered a hospital where I had an x-ray. A doctor there told me I was suffering from a bowel obstruction and that I needed surgery immediately. She said if I did not have the operation I would die.

My stress level was high at that stage and having no alternative, I agreed to have it done. Unfortunately for me, the doctor had read the x-rays incorrectly and the surgery was a complete mistake. I was far from happy because I suffered a lot of unnecessary pain and stress and was left with a large scar.

When we arrived back in our home state, I had to go into hospital because the staples and stitches had burst and my stomach became infected. It was at this time a doctor discovered I had suffered mild kidney failure.

In January 2003, a friend told me about Elias. At that stage I really did not know if he could help me. However, my friend was getting results from his massages and by eating natural food, so I decided to visit him. I told Elias about my illness and asked him if he could help. He said he could, but I would have to work with him so that the body could cure itself. I was amazed because I had been told lupus was incurable. Elias said some people cured themselves within three months and some took six, while others could take a year.

He advised me to eat fruit and vegetables. I was mainly on fruit and a small amount of vegetables. I had the vegetables lightly cooked because Elias said raw vegetables would be too harsh on my colon. I drank lots of water and three lemons daily.

In the first few months I had to visit his clinic every two weeks. Then I had monthly visits for some time, then two months and now it is four. The elimination of pain took about six months. I continued with Elias's natural therapy and travelled thousands of kilometres because I believed he could help me.

Within six months he helped my body cure itself of lupus. He had concentrated on that problem first. I asked him what caused the lupus because I suspected the hormone medication. I felt the excessive amounts of oestrogen had given it to me. In my research, I discovered this disease is also drug induced. He said viruses had also invaded my system.

Within the six months, he said my kidney problem had righted itself and so had my liver and spleen. For several years I had been on prescribed medication for my thyroid condition, taking 950mcg per week. Doctors had told me I would have to take this drug for the rest of my life. They also said without it I could not survive.

Elias was happy with my progress and began working on my thyroid. He halved my medication immediately. This was a leap of faith for me. He sensed I was apprehensive and suggested I have a blood test. Results showed that the thyroid levels were scattered and a doctor I was seeing at that time told me if I continued on such a low dose of medication, my system would close down. The situation was scary.

I spoke to Elias and he assured me that I was going to be fine. On my next visit, he halved my medication again. He halved it once again on the following visit. At that stage I was having treatments every two months. My blood tests began to stabilise and became close to normal.

It is now November 2009. I am taking 12.5mcg of the prescribed medication once every three weeks instead of the 950mcg a week I was on before Elias began working on my thyroid. During a recent visit, Elias said my thyroid was actually starting to grow.

When I was 18, I had spinal surgery. The surgeon performing the operation severed nerves to one side of my thyroid gland during the surgery. At this stage, it is a waiting game. Elias wants to see if the thyroid gland is going to function normally or partially. On the first day I went to Elias, he told me to stop taking the other medication. From the beginning of my new way of eating, I have had no stomach aches or burning sensation. I feel comfortable when I eat fruit, which surprised me because I believed it would irritate my stomach.

I have learnt to eat fruit properly in order to obtain full benefit. For breakfast, I eat a combination of fruit, not as a fruit salad, but eating melons together then moving on to another variety. Vegetables and salad are fine for me when eaten together. When I first visited Elias, I weighed 65kg. When I began eating naturally I dropped to 57kg now I am 60kg.

With my health and energy levels returning, I have decided to take up a passion of mine and start my own business. I am thankful that I met Elias because he has taught me how to take control and responsibility for my own body. Very soon I will be visiting Elias every six months.

– Lillian (not her real name)

RHEUMATOID ARTHRITIS AND THE IVF PROGRAM

It is a privilege to share my story. It is important to understand the body can heal itself when in a state of disease, especially with the support of friends, family and other realms. In order to do this we must make several decisions. The most important being total commitment.

My story begins at the age of three when my tonsils were removed. I contracted hepatitis A in my first year at school and after three-and-a-half months of bed rest I grew thin and developed dark circles under my eyes.

On my return to school I began suffering diseases such as measles, rubella and mumps along with coughs and head colds.

From the age of six through to 40, I experienced pain that felt like electric shocks shooting across my body and chest. At first they were diagnosed as growing pains but they worsened during later years. I still experience them occasionally.

By the age of 12, I had grown to a height of 170cm. One sports day I fell in the seated position and damaged my coccyx. That was the beginning of more pain.

At 18, I suffered an accident. I injured my spine and neck and despite regular visits to a chiropractor, pain relief was short lived. About that time my ankles were beginning to swell. Fluid tablets were prescribed but I refused them.

By the age of 22, I had been a hairdresser for six years and loved it. One day my fingers began to stiffen. In the morning they were like claws and during the day I accidentally dropped objects. The diagnosis was RSI and I was advised to rest.

Chronic hay fever was a nuisance, especially when working with clients. Anti-histamine medication did not work, the problem slowly worsened and I was diagnosed as borderline asthmatic. My body ached and my nostrils were so sore they bled. I visited doctors with ear infections, hay fever, sinusitis, asthma and given numerous medications. Hairdressing was blamed for my problems.

A friend advised me to place the juice and skin of a lemon in a glass of boiling water and drink it warm every morning. I felt improvement in the first week.

She advised me to stop eating dairy products in order to combat the hay fever, sinusitis and asthma. I did as suggested and noticed rapid progress. Within six weeks my symptoms disappeared. However, they reoccur when I am in a tobacco smoke-laden environment. I could not wear perfume but now I do so without ill effects.

At 23, I ate healthy, did lots of walking and life was good. I travelled the world for a year but I did not eat meat. I had stopped eating pineapple and passion fruit in my childhood because I got lumps on my tongue. At 28, I stopped eating citrus for the same reason. The morning lemon juice also became difficult.

Four years later my father was involved in a motor vehicle accident. Unable to help, we watched as he slowly slipped away. I believe this dreadful incident had an adverse reaction on my health.

The turning point in my life came soon after my 33rd birthday. I become an egg donor for my sister because she could not conceive naturally. This was to be my gift.

I was fit and healthy and health conscious. I played tennis twice a week, walked 5km daily and bubbled with good health. I owned my own business and worked long hours.

After deciding to become a donor I became even stricter with my diet. I wanted my eggs to have the best chance of success. The IVF program required at least 20 blood tests and their results would decide whether I had the necessary qualifications to become a donor. All tests were successful. I was fertile so the program began.

I contracted an influenza virus but it did not interfere with proceedings. My sister, who lived elsewhere, had already begun the necessary procedures.

My next step was to inhale a nasal spray several times daily for five days. It was to trick my body into believing it was infertile. After the fifth day I joined my sister.

The flight was long and after leaving the plane a strange feeling crept over me. I thought it was jet lag. The following morning I felt stiff and unwell. I went for a long walk thinking it would ease my stiffness, but it did not and my throat began to hurt. I thought it may be viral. I suggested seeing a doctor because the IVF program was well under way.

I was having injections in the fatty tissue around my stomach in order to trick my body into believing it was super fertile. This made my body produce the maximum amount of about 22 eggs. (Some women produce more while others less). If I could produce the required amount, I would only need to have this done once and my sister would be able to have seven deposits of three eggs.

I did not know the chemical ingredients of the injections.

I was diagnosed as having a rare type of influenza, prescribed drops for my sore throat and other medication. The next day I felt worse. My throat was swelling and I was having difficulty swallowing. The pain in my joints was worsening. I compared it to that of Ross River Fever.

Feeling even worse the following day, another doctor said I had an Asian influenza which attacks the joints. He said it was nasty and gave me stronger medication. However, my condition worsened with fevers, excessive perspiring and shivers. I could not swallow food or fluids. The pain in my throat was so intense I could barely speak.

Dehydrated from excessive perspiration and lack of fluid, an intravenous drip was inserted into my hand. The next morning I was sent home from hospital in agonising pain and high fevers. I could not eat or drink and perspired profusely.

Meanwhile, the IVF program continued. Those who ran it knew I was ill but no one knew what the problem was. Then things really began to go wrong.

With little food and drink for three days, my body and limbs began to curl. I could not straighten and breathing became difficult. My urine turned bright pink with blood, my faeces potent and black-green.

After a lengthy "debate" with a doctor I was readmitted to hospital and an intravenous drip was quickly set up. My throat worsened and much to the disappointment of both my sister and I, the IVF clinic terminated the program.

Many tests followed. Days later and without a diagnosis, I was sent to a larger hospital where I saw a specialist. There was an area of pain the size of a 50c piece in my right calf which travelled upward and remained behind my knee.

Very soon it exploded into the size of a soccer ball. Meanwhile my body continued to curl, muscles shortened and the pain was horrendous. Fevers were rampant. The specialist prescribed "heavy" medication and I was taken to isolation where I began another series of tests.

Fearful of the unknown, I was taken into a lead-lined room. A woman wearing a lead apron injected an unknown substance into my arm. In the blackness of my mind, I heard the word "radium". The formula was contained in a lead syringe. I was so ill. They placed me in a machine that scanned for "hot spots". The following day they repeated the procedure and anyone who came near me had to wear masks, gloves and aprons because I was labelled "hot".

Daily tests continued. Some time later a doctor said: "You have acute rheumatoid arthritis, fibromyalgia and chronic fatigue syndrome". I wondered how this could possibly be. Before I went to visit my sister my blood tests were normal and I was healthy enough to be an approved egg donor. How can one be perfectly healthy in the one instance and so ill the next after having done everything correctly?

Looking back over my life I believe rheumatoid arthritis lay dormant and flared at different stages. I believe the episode of the IVF program was the trigger that transformed near dormant symptoms into an acute disease.

I spent 15 days in hospitals having "heavy" medication and fluid drained from my knee. My body swelled from fluid retention caused by the strong drugs and their effect on my kidneys. These drugs induced hunger and I ate to satisfy it. In less than two weeks I had changed from a normal, vibrant and athletic person to an obese, ballooning cripple. Life consisted of eating, sleeping, pain and medication. I left the hospital with ongoing symptoms. My arrival home was very emotional because my mother did not recognise me.

Then the medical roller coaster began. I reached out to doctors, specialists, herbalists and naturopaths. I tried every known remedy. I just wanted to heal and be well. Some helped, while others did not. Some suggestions were ridiculous. There were those who did not know what they were talking about while others gave me hope.

I was bed bound for a year in enormous pain. I drank very little while my husband was at work because it was too difficult to visit the toilet. Lack of fluid caused dehydration. My painful jaws seized as I tried to chew. My food had to be strained. Meal times were unpleasant.

I could not lift my arm to scratch my nose. I became weaker and bigger from the side effects of drugs. If I allowed myself to become tired, I would "hit the wall" and would have minutes to get into bed and have my drugs. If I did not act quickly I became feverish and shaken, followed by nausea and dehydration. If that set in, I would have to go to hospital and be connected to a drip.

My husband helped enormously. I was completely dependent on him. I could not do up buttons. My hands were sore and at the top of my right hand there was a lump the size of half a tennis ball.

During this time my emotional and mental states were at their lowest ebb. I wanted to be outdoors but could not walk and felt I was going insane. I suffered in many ways, however I enjoyed Reiki and I was thankful to those who gave me love and support.

My husband was a shift worker and his hours were long. I told him I felt I was dying and he asked what he could do to help. I told him I needed to sit by the ocean and after a golden handshake he gave up what had been an excellent job.

We toured in a caravan for two years, simply following the sunshine. It kept me warm while the gentle sea breezes eased the tension in my skin. And all the while my loving husband nursed me constantly.

He carried me across the beach where I felt the sand for the first time since my illness. It was so good and it helped me enormously.

One memorable day I walked unaided down the three steps of our caravan. This meant so much because I felt independence within my grasp. Turning my back on death's door, I looked to the future with eager anticipation.

One day we met a man and his daughter who practiced massage therapy. They helped my curling wrists dramatically and their technique gave added movement to my hands. My husband was taught to massage. They gave me hope and became an important part of my life. We worked together and as a result my wrists improved to the stage where I had 30 per cent movement forward and back and 10 per cent to either side.

We then sent x-rays to a leading orthopaedic surgeon because I was desperate to have the full use of my arms and hands. He replied with a letter saying: "The only thing that I can do is to fuse it. There is nothing that can be done to save your hand". I did not believe him.

On returning home, I enjoyed loving support from family and friends and Reiki helped immensely. My situation began to turn around to the stage where my husband was able to return to work.

My hands were very sore so we purchased an electric motor scooter. It offered freedom so I took my dogs walking twice daily.

My knees were sore and swollen and my legs would not straighten so I had an arthroscopy to clean the joint. My medication intake was heavy but I improved to the stage where I was less dependant on my wheelchair. Prescription drugs abused my vital organs. At different times, I was taking a new "miracle" drug for rheumatoid arthritis and eight other types of prescription medication. I worked with Reiki and had pride in becoming a master. I believe I was healing on several levels because my condition continued to improve. This enabled me to stop one of the stronger injections.

I stopped taking three other types of drugs and I very rarely took one particular painkiller. This happened over a year. Monthly blood tests enabled the monitoring of my progress. I grew within myself, became at one with my body and allowed nature to take its course.

Those who knew me commented on visual changes and my doctor

also saw improvement through blood tests and ease of movement. My week included Tai Chi, meditation and six hours of aqua aerobic exercise. I lived one day at a time and ate healthy meals.

By this time I was in 10 per cent of constant pain but by the end of the day it would increase to 30 per cent. Some days the pain made me unwell, which prevented me from doing the things I wanted. A doctor advised me to eat animal protein three times a day for my rheumatoid arthritis and to improve my health. He said this form of arthritis wrought havoc on the body. He said animal products would help me greatly.

A blood test later showed my S-urea went from 3.1 to 6.3 in seven weeks. This is within the normal range when one eats animal DNA.

In August 2003 I began visiting Elias. I explained my illness and he understood. He said there were problems with my kidneys and liver. He said he could help fix these and I believed him. He also said: "You came to me with rheumatoid arthritis but the hormones are also a problem". (I remember a herbalist who also said my illness was brought on by a virus and that I had hormonal imbalance).

Elias pointed out that even though my blood tests looked normal, they were not. He said the combination of figures indicated I needed to change my diet. He analyses blood tests and x-rays differently to many others who work within the medical profession.

He said to eat fruit and vegetables with three lemons daily in three litres of water and to have fresh coconut. In doing so, the swelling in my joints would recede, lessening the pain. In eight weeks my blood tests improved.

At the height of my illness, my hands had curled into a 90 degree angle. Tight skin on my wrists shone and my hair stopped growing. Elias examined the x-rays we had sent the orthopaedic surgeon and then began working on my wrists. I felt movement to the back of my hand and as he massaged, blood began flowing into two affected fingers.

There had been a deep indentation where he was working. I watched the surface of my hand rise as it came back to normal. He continued to work on the affected area. He gave me instructions and together with my husband, we worked on the calcification of both wrists. Dispersion of this unwanted substance would eventually allow full wrist movement. He examined x-rays of my feet because at one stage they had also curled. He massaged them and the moment he corrected bones in my feet I felt instant relief.

I had two initial treatments then after 16 days, a further 10. When I began eating fruit I thought my tooth enamel was going to dissolve because the natural fruit acids hurt every time I ate. However, after two weeks the problem disappeared.

Elias suggested I add passionfruit and pineapple to my diet. I had not eaten these fruits for almost 30 years because they had caused lumps to grow on my tongue. When I began eating fruit only, I found I could eat them along with all other varieties.

Eighteen days after my first visit with Elias I forgot to take medication for pain because there was none. He said as my health improved I would be able to go off prescription drugs but at that stage I needed confirmation that natural therapy was going to work. Five days after the first massage I woke pain free and I did a Tai Chi class without pain. This was the day I saw the golden light at the end of what had been a very dark tunnel. It was during the second lot of visits with Elias that I found myself in 2 per cent pain.

I visited Elias for the third lot of massages. My blood tests had improved and he was happy with my progress. He examined my hip x-rays because I had pain front and back. A doctor had said there was deterioration in my right hip and a cyst on the left but Elias did not agree. The problem was in the pelvis so he worked on that area.

I made mention of a pain in my neck. He said the problem was not the neck but in the shoulder. My left elbow would not straighten. The angle was about 20 degrees. He said the problem was in the wrist and shoulder. He said muscles would relax as my health improved and problems would disappear. Elias is very happy with my progress. He advised me to eat 80 per cent fruit and 20 per cent vegetables. I am to continue drinking lemon water and eating three birdseye chilli daily to purify my blood.

During a telephone conversation I explained my right knee was swollen and sore with needling pains within the joint. He was happy because he said the knee was shifting. The problems I had, caused my right foot to turn outward but it is beginning to straighten.

In recent weeks there has been a burning sensation in my upper arm. I feel the muscle is releasing and with time it will move into its correct position. My wrist movement is also improving.

Many of the things Elias said to me I had already heard, but what he has said and done has helped me greatly. I have learnt to listen to my body. I am regaining muscle strength and the posture of my youth.

Having taken part in the IVF program, I speak with experience when I say it is not for the faint-hearted. My sister has since conceived naturally and is now the mother of two beautiful children.

Eating a healthy diet with lots of fluid will remain a way of life. My protein level is excellent. I will not eat animals or any of their by-products. I will not eat seeds, grains or nuts because I know if I do I will become unwell. I do not want to be sick again because I have already lost valuable years of my life. My old eating habits have gone. I will help myself and I will do so for me.

Being healthy is wonderful because it allows me to do the things I want and I have the ability to be the person I want to be. I live my life the way I want, not as I must.

The natural healing process of an unhealthy and diseased body does not happen overnight. Natural healing requires patience and commitment. It requires dedication and faith. When healing, we need to believe in what we are doing. There is no margin for doubt and one must understand what is happening within the body.

– Anonymous

I CAN WALK AGAIN

I graduated as a teacher of sports, art and domestic science and was employed at a local school. Working with children on a professional level was excellent. I was fit, healthy, life was full and I revelled in it.

The first time I encountered problems with my health was at the age of 32. One particular day I suffered from a high fever and it forced me to bed for eight days. Ten days later my feet began to swell and pain engulfed my joints. My entire body felt the torment, including my shoulders and jaws. I found myself in such an intense state of pain that even my eyes were hurting.

Doctors in a clinic did not know what my problem was. One said: "It could be bone cancer". However, blood tests did not verify this, nor did they reveal any form of arthritis. Another doctor I visited, who also did not know what was wrong, asked if I had a good stomach. I said I did and he suggested giving me very strong medication because he wanted to see what effect it would have. I refused them after reading the possible harmful side effects of the drug.

I continued to see many medical practitioners and specialists. I needed to get to the bottom of the problem because it was interfering with my life. However, I searched to no avail because it seemed no one could help. My symptoms were synonymous with that of rheumatoid arthritis so I enlisted the help of a specialist in that field, hoping he could give me a diagnosis and appropriate treatment. This visit brought me the certitude that this was polyarthritis, however I continued to hear the same thing: "Try this", "try that".

I stopped eating meat for 12 years in an effort to help myself. A doctor I spoke with about my diet said I needed a balance, so I resumed eating meat. However, there was no change in my condition, I felt bad as usual. In those years I drank large amounts of herbal and Chinese teas because I was told they were good for me.

Even though some of them smelt and tasted terrible, I continued to have them. However, they did not help. Another treatment I tried was Chinese acupuncture but that did not work either. Many other therapies followed.

I visited another medical practitioner who ordered me to fast. During an examination he tried to take my blood pressure but the monitor refused to work because the reading was so low. I also suffered an iron deficiency. I thought the outcome was unusual and it was difficult to understand because I felt well enough to continue working and was riding my bicycle daily to and from school at that time.

I was admitted to a clinic where I had therapy for four weeks. This included daily gentle massages to the entire body to help my aching joints that by now were badly disfigured. I was offered a mild form of chemotherapy and other strong medication which I refused, but agreed to take one drug because I felt it was not as strong as what was first offered.

But the medication had adverse reactions and it was responsible for inducing heart palpitations and fluid retention that resulted in swollen ankles and legs. The iron deficiency continued and I am led to believe this problem accompanies this type of disease.

Over the years all my joints ached and both hands and feet twisted at right angles to my ankles and wrists. As time went by the pain and disfigurement worsened. So much so, I agreed to have surgery because the pain was so intense. Surgeons operated on the big and little toes of both feet. They were swollen and painful and the doctor tried to help by relieving the joints of calcification.

In the months that followed my problems did not go away. In fact the pain intensified and the disfigurement continued and I had another issue to deal with: that of scar tissue, which was a side effect of the surgery. Surgery did not fix my problem – it added to it.

I do not know what caused my affliction, however my mother began suffering symptoms identical to mine 10 years after the onset of my disease. It was the first time in our family that anyone ever suffered these symptoms.

In 2003 a family friend came to visit. He was a professional musician and had suffered severe problems with his arms. So much so, he lost movement in his hands and fingers and could no longer play his instrument. He sought the assistance of orthopaedic specialists who offered surgery. However, a surgeon told him he would never play music as a professional again because he could lose the use of his hands as a result.

My friend heard about a medical masseur in Sindelfingen in Germany who practised natural therapy. His name was Elias Schindelar. He visited Elias and after three massages he had movement in his arm and fingers. During the course of his treatments he regained the full use of his back, arms, hands and fingers and resumed his life as a musician.

He told me Elias helped people suffering from bone diseases similar to my own. However, I did not pursue his therapy at that stage because I had already started a natural therapy program. I was visiting a naturopath who lived 250km from my home.

It was such an effort to visit his clinic every week because the pain was so severe while I drove. He said: "If you do as I suggest you will be disease and pain free within two years and capable of walking hundreds of kilometres a week".

Part of the program was a special type of sauna. I felt cosy and warm after having them because they had a calm and soothing effect. However the following morning, all would be back to normal. By the third visit subtle changes were beginning to occur. One could refer to them as "good" and it was just a little easier to move about. The saunas helped to remove unwanted toxins from my system in the form of grey matter and black fluid that oozed from my skin.

Over the months that followed there were no "marvellous" improvements to speak of. But I continued with the treatment and did exactly as the practitioner instructed in order to give my body the best opportunity to heal. It was important for me to finish the therapy because I always like to finish anything I start.

After persevering for the entire two years and doing exactly as I was told, I found this form of natural therapy had not worked and the pain and disfigurement continued to plague me. During the course of the program I had a total of 100 half-hour saunas. At that stage I was working for the limited time of 16 hours a week. I needed to continue working because I wanted to have normality in my life even though I suffered much pain. I could walk only short distances, so I could not do my own shopping.

At the end of the day the pain was so severe I could not walk at all, so I sat and read until my husband came home from work. I was limited in what I could do at home, I could not open cupboards and housework was very difficult.

At the latter stages of my illness I was given a different role at the school. Instead of teaching sport I was mostly teaching other subjects. This was easier because I was able to sit and teach. Even though I walked very little, I considered myself fortunate to have had an understanding supervisor.

The friend who had told me about Elias came to visit. During the course of our conversation I told him that my two years of therapy did not work and he said: "Now you have to go to Australia".

I decided I would visit Elias and I knew it was not going to be easy. It was difficult for my husband to understand my motivation, because over the years he had witnessed the many and varied types of treatments and therapies I had tried and nothing had worked. I had purchased expensive apparatus and machines in an effort to mobilise my body and live normally but none of them helped.

He was very aware of the vast amount of money I had spent on petrol, doctors, hospitals, surgery, clinics and specialists, all to no avail. Some specialists charge a lot of money for consultations. I was always paying out. I had to do it. One cannot simply give up on life. The total I spent trying to help myself was $A300,000. My husband said: "Now it is enough with these payments".

There were no guarantees that Mr Schindelar's therapy was going to be successful, but I had faith and hoped that it would. I witnessed the good health and normal life our friend enjoyed after visiting Elias and I was excited. I obtained an International Drivers Licence. Even though I had trouble walking, I refused a wheelchair. Instead I used a kick board. My husband pushed me through airports and wherever else I needed to go. At this time I had a lot of pain, because both feet were turned out from my ankle joints at right angles of 70 degrees and I walked down steps sideways.

My hands were in the same condition. All the while the pain was endless. My body was so sore I could not tolerate the bed covers because I could not move my hands at night. I even adopted a special way of rolling over in bed.

I first visited Mr Schindelar in August 2004 and during that visit I had two massages a day for five weeks. After three days of treatments I had had six massages, one in the morning and the other in the evening of each day.

After the third day I needed to see how far I could walk. To our surprise my husband and I walked the entire perimeter of Lake Eacham on the Atherton Tablelands. I was so happy and proud because when I was in Germany I only walked when I had to – now I had walked for pleasure and did so with much less pain.

Ten days and 20 nerve massages later, I was able to walk down the steep and rugged trail of the Palmerston Range at Crawford Lookout along the Johnstone River. I walked for three-and-a-half hours. My husband termed it: "The Miracle of Malanda".

However, those of us who have experienced the wonderful work that Elias does all know: *it is far from a miracle*. The strict fruit diet and massages to the nerve system by Elias helped me. This type of natural therapy may look simple, and one may question its success, however I am living proof that it does work.

My husband could hardly believe and I had difficulties comprehending the fact that the treatments began working in such a short time. We were both ecstatic and the walk around Lake Eacham was the first "light of hope". After the wonderful achievement of walking the trail of the Palmerston we knew Elias was capable of doing what I had always dreamed of.

The best part of what happened was that I was not tired, there was much less pain and I felt comfortable. This was a new experience for me because walking was never like this. Before seeing Elias, every time I walked I felt washed out and tired because it was so difficult and painful. In the past, walking was hard work. After that five-week visit I went back to my home in Germany. My family was surprised at my unexpected weight loss of 10kg.

I ate all types of fruit including tomatoes, cucumber, squash, eggplant, pumpkin, avocado, olives, olive oil and coconut. I did not eat any cooked fruit because Elias said all fruit had to be fresh. I consider myself very lucky and I am very grateful for all that Elias had done to encourage my body to heal itself. It is a slow process but it is happening.

In May 2005 I returned to Australia for further treatments. My husband, daughter and two family friends accompanied me. This time I had a seven-week visit. During this time I interrupted my treatment for four days and flew to Ayers Rock. It felt tremendous to be a member of a party who walked around the base of the rock.

My family and friends did a tour of the Olgas and Kings Canyon. At this canyon there is a walking trail that divides into two directions. One is for adults with children and those who have difficulties walking while the other is rough and rugged and suited to the able bodied.

On May 12, 2005, at the parting of the ways, I chose the latter. I walked the entire distance in the hottest part of the day. It was laborious and there were those in our party who struggled. I felt exhilarated because this was a great achievement and I silently thanked Elias.

I encouraged my daughter to consult Elias. He helped her to overcome a problem and even though it was of a minor nature, I feel that Elias was the best person to help her.

I also encouraged a friend to come to Australia in August 2005 because doctors had said she needed hip replacements. However, after her visit with Elias she found she did not require surgery and with his help she will be able to heal herself. I was very much against her having the operations because of what had happened to me after my surgery and deep down I was certain Elias could help her.

I do not know of any other person who is doing this type of therapy and I asked him: "Please return to Germany". Of course we know that the people who love and admire him in Australia would not like to see him leave and I know he loves this country very much. A lovely quality that Elias possesses is that he is always friendly and "in touch" with the people he helps and those who help themselves. When he walks into the consulting rooms his mood is uplifting and cheerful. I enjoy sharing a joke with him in our mother tongue. Treatments with Elias are always happy occasions.

I will do as Elias says and I am positive my health will continue to improve. My fingers and toes are straightening. I have almost full use of my wrists, arms, shoulders, legs, knees and ankle joints. I am nearly pain free and can lead a near normal life.

If I was ever unfortunate enough to be struck with another illness, there is no doubt in my mind that I will return to see Elias. I trust him and fully believe that his nerve massages in conjunction with natural foods help the body to heal itself.

During the years of my incapacitation and since I have been in Australia I have heard so many horror stories from people about their illnesses. I believe if Elias says he can help a person to overcome their illness, that person will heal themselves on one condition: they must do as he says.

I am still teaching and my body continues to heal itself. I returned to Australia to have further treatments with Elias in August 2006 and again in 2007, 2008 and 2009. It is important that I tell my story because I want others to know the facts about my illness. However, it is of greater importance that they know they can heal themselves with a correct diet, a stress-free environment and if possible, nerve massages by Elias.

I finally have a classification for my bone disease: polyarthritis. Elias said this disease was the result of eating food that did not agree with my body.

– Marion

I DID NOT HAVE MULTIPLE SCLEROSIS

My husband and I live on a cattle property with our children. We breed and train horses and have fulltime jobs away from home. Even though we are incredibly busy, our life is very interesting and rewarding.

Back in 1999 I broke my hip and pelvis when a horse rolled over the top of me. I suffered a lot of pain in the years following the accident.

I began experiencing pins and needles in my right hand in 2005. As time went by I started losing sensation in the hand. I could not feel textures and started to drop objects unintentionally.

Most of my job was at a keyboard so my employer sent me for tests because the problem was thought to be work related. The results indicated I had carpal tunnel syndrome. To confirm this, an MRI was requested and I was then sent to a specialist. He said I had a symptom of multiple sclerosis, two white dots in my brain, a lesion on my spine and of course, a hand that would not work properly.

I was advised to begin taking a heavy drug immediately in order to stop the progression of multiple sclerosis. I was to inject myself weekly but was told the side effects of the drug were not "pretty" and I would feel unwell until my body adjusted. I was not enthusiastic about the drug but thought it may be better than full blown MS.

It all scared the living daylights out of me because multiple sclerosis is very unpredictable and another attack could land me in a wheelchair for life. On the other hand, I may not have another attack for who knows how long.

I had family responsibilities, commitments to the property, the horse breeding program and full time employment. Man oh man! I did not have time to be sick, let alone confined to a wheelchair. None the less, plans were made to send out a nurse who was to educate me on the drug taking program.

A family member had moved to Malanda and told me of the wonderful work Elias Schindelar was doing while working with accident trauma clients. I did as they suggested and visited the natural therapy clinic. Elias massaged my back and said I would need a further three lots of medical massages, after which everything would be okay.

The following day – and very much against Elias's wishes – we left Malanda and began the arduous trip home. In hindsight, I wish I had heeded his advice because it may have saved me a heck of a lot of heartache, fear and money. But because of a language misunderstanding and my not grasping the importance of why it was so imperative to return for natural therapy, we returned home.

During another conversation with my Malanda relatives, they told me of the amazing work Elias was doing with his multiple sclerosis clients. They advised me to revisit him.

What was I to do? A nurse was flying out the following day to teach me how to self-administer the new drug. I telephoned her and explained my need to see Elias again. She was very supportive and said if I did not give it a go, I would always be wondering and asking myself: "What if?"

My husband and I discussed the issue because my problem was impacting on our family. If my situation with the drugs went belly-up, I could be left in a wheelchair.

We received the results of the MRI and set off for Malanda. This was two years after my first visit to the Schindelar natural therapy clinic. Elias looked at the images and said: "You do not have multiple sclerosis. You came close to breaking your neck in an accident. Two millimetres further and it would have been all over".

He was referring to an incident I had experienced in 1991. We had been holidaying on the Gold Coast at the time and enjoying a frolic in the water. My husband was up to his neck in the surf and I was in ankle deep water when a rogue wave picked me up and dumped me on my head and shoulder.

It was so long ago that I had forgotten about it. But it seems I had sustained an injury which caused the lesion that was applying pressure on the spinal cord and creating the problems within my hand. Elias said the hand would heal itself when he realigned the spine. He said the white dots in my brain were small bleeds as the result of my head impacting against the sand during the dumping by the freak wave. He said there was nothing for me to worry about because with medical massage, natural foods and discipline, the body would heal and fix itself. This was fantastic because it meant we could get on with life without drugs.

Finally! Here was someone who was capable of reading the MRI images correctly. Someone with the knowledge to understand what they were looking at.

But there was no need for him to have seen the MRI images. He had explained this to me two years earlier and before I had the MRI. His mother then produced my card from their system with this information – information he had picked up with his fingertips when he was "reading" my nerve system while working on my back. It was all there, on the card, dated two years previous. Amazing!

At that moment Elias said: "Why did you not come back when I told you?".

"Sorry, I did not realise how important it was to come back, and we live 16 hours away," I said.

"Now", he said, "it will take a very long time to heal and I will need to see you every two weeks and you will have to stop eating meat and dairy".

What a dilemma! But I had to give it a go.

I used to catch the late flight into Cairns on Friday night and hire a car. My first medical massage was early Saturday morning and another was Saturday afternoon. I flew home Sunday morning.

I did this every second weekend for about five months. Then I had a two-month break. The treatments were four months apart for the next three visits, then six months. My last visit was on August 27, 2008. My whole family accompanied me and we all had natural therapy.

As one can imagine, the expenses were astronomical. The time away from my family was tough because it put pressure on my husband. He was working rosters as well as looking after the children. Flying back and forth to Cairns in those little cigar planes was not something I looked forward to. At times we had to detour hundreds of kilometres to avoid storms and there were unexpected delays and cancellations. I had to drive long distances and there was always the late night mountain range driving. But it was all worth it. Thanks to Elias my hand is back to normal. I had another MRI at the beginning of 2008. The specialist went so far as to say I did not have multiple sclerosis or any of its obvious symptoms and that the lesion had reduced in size.

I told him about Elias and the work he was doing. He said Elias would not have done anything for me because the human body was an amazing thing and that it healed itself. But I had first hand experience of what my body was doing for me – not much at all – before I started having treatments with Elias. Mine is one body that surely needed a helping hand.

As a result of my experience, I have passed information on to many of my friends. Some have taken it on board and ran with it. They now have their own amazing stories to tell and all of them have extremely high praise for Elias and the work he does.

All I can say is: "Thank you Elias for giving me back my hand and a drug-free life. For a while there, things were very scary".

– Trudy (not her real name)

NATURAL THERAPY HEALED MY PITUARY TUMOUR

I first had symptoms of a pituitary tumour in 1992. Surgeons operated, however they were unable to remove it entirely because it was located at the base of the brain. The pituitary is a major gland that controls all other glands. Specialists said the tumour would reoccur but they did not know when. There were no ifs about it – it was only a matter of time.

After the surgery, I did not have therapy of any description but developed extremely high blood pressure with readings always around 240 over 120. Doctors were continuously increasing my medication. At that stage I was also on anti-depressants.

My immune system became depleted but the main problem was my lungs. In no time head colds would develop into pneumonia and it happened at least three times a year. For 18 months, from mid 2000 to 2001, I was having antibiotics continuously to suppress lung infections.

I had annual visits with my specialists at one of the major hospitals. These tests were vital because we needed to know whether the tumour was active. The tests proved negative until November 2002 when, after 11 years, they read positive. The tumour had reactivated and was beginning to grow.

The specialists wanted me to begin medication in an attempt to arrest it. They said I should have daily injections for three weeks. I was supposed to stay in hospital for that length of time because these injections were very dangerous and it was essential to have my condition monitored.

One of the side effects of this medication is that it causes the patient to suffer extremely high blood pressure. This was of great concern to my general practitioner because it was already too high. The next suggestion the specialists put forward was radium and chemotherapy. I found this form of treatment unacceptable.

I researched using the internet and visited libraries. I questioned chemists and doctors in an attempt to seek information on these drugs. I learnt about the horrors of their side effects. Again I visited my general practitioner who said the suggested therapy was "not a walk in the park". She said if she found herself in the same situation, she would be asking more questions. I decided to place my problems on the backburner and take a trip up north with my family to visit friends. Our friend complained of severe backache after having visited naturopaths and chiropractors for the past 18 months. I saw that he was taking so many pills and many, many concoctions. However, his back pain continued and did not show any signs of improvement.

One day in desperation he asked me for advice. I told him to throw all the pills and concoctions away because it was evident they were not working. I said he should have tests done to identify the source of the problem and to just go from there. He did as I said and the tests revealed he was suffering from liver, bowel and pancreatic cancer. Unfortunately, there was more bad news. His time was running out because he only had two months to live.

Our friend had heard of Elias and thought he may be able to help him through the dying process. My friend did not want to take the intoxicating drugs usually administered to cancer patients at the end of their life. The pain of cancer was something he did not wish to suffer and he wanted to do all he could to avoid this from occurring.

Elias told him he would do all he could to help but the liver cancer was in such an advanced stage he doubted if he could help. They worked together and they did manage to completely rid the body of the bowel and pancreatic cancer because he ate all natural foods as well as the special massages Elias was giving him.

One day my friend asked me to have a look at his liver which was protruding from his stomach. I did and when I touched it, it felt very hard. I thought: if only he had had his tests done earlier. If only he had gone to Elias earlier. The six months my friend had with Elias was quality time and initially that was what he wanted. He used to sit in a warm bath for comfort and it helped him tremendously. He eventually died drug free and without pain. Before he died, my friend asked me to visit Elias because he thought he would be able to help me with my tumour. I did as he asked. April 2002 was my first visit to the Schindelar Clinic. I told Elias I was suffering from high blood pressure and chronic sinus. He said I only needed two treatments for that and he proceeded to tell me what to do in order to help myself.

At no stage during these two visits did I offer any information on the tumour in my pituitary gland. I made no mention of it whatsoever. On the last of the scheduled two visits he asked me to send pictures of my "other problem" because he said he could help.

I did as requested and later I travelled up to Malanda to visit Elias once again. He said he could help me heal my body of the tumour. He said I had to go off all medication immediately. I was very afraid to do this because my blood pressure was very high and I thought going off all medication – cold turkey – would kill me.

I questioned him as to how I was going to cope with drug withdrawal because I had been taking them for several years. He assured me that all would be fine and I was not to worry about it. He gave me 24 hours to think about what he had said before making a decision.

I went back to him within 24 hours and he began working on me immediately. He said the tumour in my pituitary gland was a secondary cancer. He went on to say that a blockage in my adrenal glands was the primary problem. I was very sick for some days and vomited continuously because my body was cleansing itself of the toxic drugs I had taken previously.

The nerve massages continued for a period of two weeks. My body was self-cleansing because he placed me on avocado, banana, mango and lemon water. I began to feel very well and my body felt *clean* even after the first week of eating fruit.

During one particular massage, a terrible taste came into my mouth. It was that of metal. I told Elias and he became very excited because this is what he was working towards. The blockage in the adrenal glands was beginning to move.

A few months later I flew to see the specialists at the hospital I usually went to in the city. I explained I was on a self-healing and natural therapy program, off all medication and that my health had improved. They said that was fine by them because they could not offer anything more than the radium and chemotherapy. The specialists asked me to have further tests in six months and to keep in contact with them. I said I would do as they asked.

Elias had been working on me for five-and-a-half-months when I revisited the specialists to have the usual tests. The results proved excellent because there was no sign of a tumour. My blood pressure had balanced itself since I had stopped taking medication. When the specialists learnt the results they requested I visit the surgery because they wanted to interview me.

As I entered the surgery to face a panel of three, I quickly discovered one was a sceptic. I did not allow his scepticism to upset me because after all, when one stops to think about it, he must be the type of person who believes everything that he had learnt and to his way of thinking, he need not look further.

Good news always travels fast because when I arrived home, I had a telephone call from an eminent media personality. I do not know how he discovered my name or my number. He said he had only just received news that he had cancer. He asked about my illness and the healing process so I pointed him in what I personally thought was the right direction – to Elias. The rest was up to him.

My healing has been very successful. However, sometimes I do experience problems with my mind because I have difficulty controlling stress. I imagine this to be synonymous with most mothers, grandmothers and with people in general as we all tend to live hectic lifestyles.

The last time I was due to visit Elias I had to go earlier than expected because I was not at all well. He told me I was suffering from stress. He said what I was eating was fine but I had to learn about stress and its effect on the entire body. He explained that I probably did not fully understand the destructive powers of stress.

If I allowed my mind to become stressed, it adversely affected my body as well. He said when we stressed, the kidneys released a stress hormone. This hormone causes toxins to build up in the blood.

The toxin-laden blood flows at a rapid pace and as these toxins contaminate the body, every organ begins to enlarge. Ultimately these organs can close down and death occurs.

He went on to explain that the toxins in the blood were tremendously powerful and that was why it was imperative for me to balance the mind and the heart. He said when I mastered the art of balance, healing followed automatically.

– Florence (not her real name)

a message from the author:

during serious illness and when matters are grim, many entertain the idea of giving up and simply waiting for death. giving up is easy because one does not have to work any more.

the problem is: those around us also give up. but when one is strong and fights for life, others will help. most people are drawn to those who display courage and strength

to heal oneself of a life-threatening illness when all else has failed, is a major achievement

NO MORE SHINGLES

My name is Dr Gerhard Raff. I am a Doctor of Philosophy having graduated from the University of Tubingen, founded in the year 1477.

I am from Germany and I am a well-known public speaker. I travel the entire country to deliver speeches but I mainly concentrate on the areas to the south. I speak on an average of 200 nights a year in cities such as Berlin and Brussels.

I speak at various venues, from halls to universities, cathedrals and castles. My interests are varied and this enables me to speak on a different topic almost every night. However, I do this only on request and all my invitations are extended by various organisations. When newspapers advertise that Dr. Raff is delivering the presentation with free admission, the house is always full.

Most people are very happy with the content of my speeches. This prompts them to contribute generously at the door before they leave. All money is donated to charity and various worthy causes.

On many occasions I have had to drive 200km to reach my destination and the return journey is very tiring. I do not sleep at motels or hotels because I cannot afford them and prefer my own bed.

Even though my life is interesting, it is hard because I am always tired. I only manage to sleep about three hours because I arrive home at two or three in the morning. The telephone usually begins ringing at 7am and there are times when I find myself talking on the phone the entire day.

This leaves little time to write and there are occasions when I have no alternative but to work all night when I am not delivering speeches. If I do get free time, my brain will not allow itself to rest because it is accustomed to sleep deprivation.

My publisher said I could be in the *Guinness Book of Records* for being the world's most successful writer of stories in dialect. But I am unknown in Australia because people in this country are unfamiliar with my work, except for Swabian immigrants. However, I remain the most sold and the most read author in dialect and unfortunately it is impossible to translate some of my Swabian "works" into the English language. Even my own people find it difficult to read because they are no longer familiar with original dialects. But some of them have been translated and German folk enjoy them.

I earn my livelihood as a weekly columnist for a famous Stuttgart newspaper. As a writer, author and novelist I do not regard myself as successful because I have not accumulated personal wealth. However my public speeches and written works are very successful. Over the years this work has generated millions of dollars which has all been donated to worldwide charities for social, cultural and ecological projects.

I live as a member of a very old, wonderful and large family that spans three generations. In 2003 a beloved cousin died from leukaemia after three years of chemotherapy. Unfortunately, at that stage we were not familiar with Elias's natural therapy. Had we known of his wonderful work and his ability to teach people how to heal their own body, there is no doubt in my mind she would be with us today.

Watching my cousin's constant pain and her struggle to survive was devastating. There was little any of us could do to help her. The mental cruelty of seeing her daily deterioration, then finally slip away from those of us who loved her was more than I could bear. Our family was devastated.

After her death I began to feel the effects of our great loss and the trauma of the previous three years. The stress of her illness, her death and my hectic lifestyle finally caught up with me.

Almost overnight I was hit with a disease. A doctor diagnosed it as shingles virus – a virus that attacks the brain and nerve system. He said it could affect me in various ways:

- I may find myself in a wheelchair.
- I could end up in a mental institution as it affects the brain.
- I could end up in a coffin.

The symptoms were ugly. My entire face was swollen and I

looked like a monster. My forehead and eye areas were affected and my nose was enormous. I was familiar with the disease because history had taught me that we had a good and beautiful queen named Catharina who died in the year 1819 from this disease after living a very busy and hectic life. She died, although as a daughter of the Russian Emperor she could have afforded the best doctors in the country.

She was a tireless worker for children's institutions, causes and the under privileged. She was a wonderful and giving person and at times I feel she was too good for this world. She is known as "The Angel of Wurtemberg". By the way, her sister-in-law was our well-known Queen Olga of Wurtemberg, after whom the Olgas near Ayers Rock in Australia were named.

When I realised I had the same disease as our much-loved queen, I was concerned because I knew too well what could happen to me and I detested the way I looked. I was given a drug intravenously and the next day my face was a lot less swollen. However, I felt as though nails were being hammered into my head. The pain was so intense it felt like a tumour in the brain.

The torture within my skull plagued me all day but it went away at night and reoccurred at two-weekly intervals. I was given medication to try but it had harsh side effects.

The prescribing doctor warned me of its severity and told me not to take more than six tablets in six days. The medication was very expensive. The violent pain left me no alternative but to try them. I persevered for six days but the pain remained, so I stopped taking them. I began to think I had a brain tumour.

Family friends were coming to Australia for natural therapy and after learning Mr Elias Schindelar had great success helping people to heal themselves, I decided to join them. This was a golden opportunity.

During my first consultation with Elias he said I had a shingles virus and that he could help me. He said I was to avoid eating all animal protein for six months. He explained viruses required animal protein in order to survive and if I was to deprive them of their food source, they would starve to death, allowing my body sufficient time to overcome my illness. It sounded simple. This meant I had to refrain from eating foods that I loved. Chocolate, milk and yoghurt were a vital part of my daily life. The abstinence of meat did not concern me so much, but eating chocolate was a daily ritual. I loved it and wondered how I could possibly live without it for so long. Fruit and vegetables were not a major part of my diet.

Elias said I had to be very strict in order to give my body time to kill the virus. If I ate only one small piece of chocolate, the virus would rise like the Rose of Jericho and bring back the pain, because it contains animal protein and I would have to restart the six-month period. Crippling headaches and ill health were my motivation for wanting to do exactly as Elias said and I thought it was not going to be a big problem to eat natural food.

He began giving me nerve massages and from the very first treatment I lost my crippling headaches and they have not returned to this very day. I am very happy and grateful.

Three days after beginning natural therapy with Elias, my companions and I were visiting the Kuranda markets. As I walked past one particular shop, the hauntingly beautiful aroma of German sausage wafted tauntingly across my nostrils. I felt instant pangs of hunger. Next I felt my feet treading over my tattered willpower. I just had to have it. I thought: "I am only three days into my therapy. I can start all over again tomorrow. Today, I simply must have that sausage".

Involuntarily my hand slid into the darkened depths of my pocket, frantically searching for my wallet, but it was not to be found. With a rumbling stomach I retreated when I realised it was back in my room. I was too ashamed to ask my companions to loan me: "sausage money". In that instant I knew I had to stop thinking about the foods I was not supposed to eat. I knew if I was not going to be strong in this moment I would be weak in others. A silent glance and questioning smile from my friends left no doubt: they knew exactly what had crossed my mind.

I did not tell Elias I was suffering from lack of sleep and fatigue.

Unknown to me at the time, he had already established the fact for himself through his finger tips as he massaged my nerve system.

He gave me a special type of massage that enabled me to sleep like a newly born babe both day and night for a week and I only woke when it was necessary. That particular massage had the effect of sleeping tablets without the harmful side effects. The natural quality of my slumber calmed my body and brain and it felt fantastic.

On returning to my homeland I resumed life as usual. I was well rested and pain free. Six months of eating fruit soon slipped by and I felt much better because the shingles virus was gone and the fruit had regenerated my body. I happily went back to my usual food because this meant I could once again eat my beloved chocolate.

There are times when I do enjoy a meal that consists of fruit only. I was very happy that Elias gave me natural therapy and information on how to kill my virus. He helped my body to naturally heal itself of a virus that had the potential to kill or to have me committed to a mental institution. I will be forever grateful.

Since my illness I have spoken with many people about health issues. I have met several people who were successfully treated by Elias in Germany before he migrated to Australia.

In May 2005 I returned to Australia because I had had problems with one of my fingers. I had not been able to straighten it and the stiffness was accompanied by pain. The problem began in November 2004. Once again Elias gave me massages and it began improving immediately. I wish I had sought his treatments earlier because it took a long time to heal. I exercised it continuously with a rubber ball.

I cried the first day Elias began working on my hand because the pain was awful. He jokingly said if I was a tough Australian farmer my finger would have cured in two to three days and added: “Sensitive city boys require more time because they cry too much”.

I had friends with me and they were in the waiting room. They jokingly asked Elias’s mum who runs the office, if he was breaking my fingers because I must have been screaming very loudly.

Highly amused, she said: “In future I will make his appointments at

4am because his screams are frightening away all our customers".

All jokes aside, I am tremendously grateful for all that Elias has done for me. I admire him tremendously and I do agree with a statement I once heard: "Elias should be cloned". It would be fantastic if every sick person in the world had the opportunity to be treated by him or someone like him.

If ever I became afflicted with cancer or any other sinister disease, I know that Elias will be able to help me. It was a great blessing the day I discovered him. Thanks to him I am free from disease and pain and I am able to live a full and normal life.

– Dr Gerhard Raff

"

many have spent a
lifetime trying to conquer a world that is
already governed by nature

"

– the author

KNOWLEDGE AND ABILITY OF A NATURAL THERAPIST

My name is Julie. My story begins at the age of 54 when I had a near-death experience because I was unable to breathe. I had developed asthma when I was 31 years old but I absolutely refused to take steroids. Eventually the inflammation in my lung reached the stage where the spray would not open the airways to allow me to breathe.

One night I was at my very worst and an ambulance took me to the emergency ward of our local hospital. Much later, I was admitted to the intensive care section where I was informed that my lung capacity would never be any better, I had emphysema. The bad news: it was important for me to use steroid inhalers as well as the usual asthma spray plus other medication.

This did not make me feel very happy. I began searching for alternative ways to heal myself – remaining on medication for the rest of my life was not an option. The journey I was experiencing was very difficult because it involved not only the physical but the mental and the emotional aspects of my being. There was also a deep belief in my spiritual self that supported me on this path of discovery.

I believe we must explore the shadow or negative aspects of ourselves. We must befriend this aspect of self and use it as a tool to move forward rather than keep the negativity and fear locked inside at a cellular level. If we do not do this it manifests in our physical body, creating all types of problems. In my case, it affected my breathing.

The journey back led me through a world of fear. The terror of not being able to breathe was unbelievable. My search began for alternative methods of self-healing. I visited my private doctor who more or less laughed when I indicated I wanted to work towards getting off all medication.

My first port of call was a Chinese herbalist in Brisbane. I spent six months following his advice and I believe he helped me tremendously. I saw a naturopath and an acupuncturist. I then took up a breathing technique and practised it religiously. This was a very, very difficult period of my life. There were times when I could not see any way out of the dark place I was in.

The journey of self-healing led me to a doctor who spoke to me in a direct manner. He said he would support me but I was to follow his instructions. At the same time he made me aware things could go wrong. We worked together and I began cutting back on the medication and I finally got the dosage right down. However, when I got a cold or infection I had to go back to taking drugs.

I ebbed and flowed in this manner for quite some time. Eventually I managed to cease taking all medication, however when I contracted lung infections I had to revert to prescription drugs. Then as my health improved I would stop taking them.

My drug-free period had expanded to seven years with no sign of flu or chest infection. I believe I arrived at this safe place because of alternative healing methods, a total change of diet, plus total trust and faith in my healing process.

It was at this time that lesions began to develop on my skin. I did not know what had caused them but what I did know was that I did not want them surgically removed. I thought of many questions that needed addressing.

Who was going to support my way of thinking? Who was going to help me rid my body of these lesions? What would happen if I allowed surgery, would they reform and if so, would they manifest into something even more sinister?

Do not get me wrong and please understand I do not criticise the medical profession because without them I would not be here. I understand that very clearly. I take total responsibility for my own healing process. I know people can support me but I also know it is entirely up to me. I cannot afford to play games and I definitely do not want to go back to where I was before. I want to die peacefully and in my own way.

The search to find answers to my questions led me to Elias.

During the first consultation, he said: "Yes, I can support you but the healing will be a very slow process". I was fully aware of that because on my first visit to his consulting rooms, it had taken eight years to arrive at the place where I found myself.

I believe the healing journey is not a quick fix. One cannot click one's fingers and expect that everything is going to be okay. I believe we have to change the whole way of being in the world. This is not an easy task. We must change the way we think because our thoughts create who we are, our thoughts create our emotions and our emotions manifest in our physical being.

If anyone thinks they are going to go to Elias and have a couple of treatments and assume that all is well, they are wrong because it does not work that way. Since Elias started working with me and on my problems, I have felt entirely different. There have been a few difficult times as the body goes through the healing process. Even though the road to healing has not always been smooth, it has been a very interesting journey.

Since that initial visit with Elias, I have been living entirely on fruit except for a period of six weeks when I introduced vegetables and a little pasta to my diet. However, my health was not improving the way Elias intended with the introduction of the two food types. He advised me to go back to eating fruit only and I am happy to say, I feel fine.

November 2009 marked seven years since I began my new eating habits and diligently following instructions given to me by Elias. Since I started going to the Schindelar natural therapy clinic, I have met many people who have also been visiting him. As an observer, I have noticed massive changes for the better in their health.

The ability to commit to natural therapy and the whole healing process has been very, very important. I guess this process was a little easier for me because I had already eliminated many harmful foods from my diet. The journey has actually led me to a place of discovery and learning. This learning has mainly been about myself. Seeing one's body respond to the treatments and the diet and to feel and experience the healing process is wonderful.

I also chose to change my place of residence because I wanted to be able to have treatments as required. That, in itself, has been a massive change, but a very good one. I believe that Elias, because of his youth, can support me the rest of my life in a natural manner should I require it.

Quality of life to me is far more important than the quantity. Waking each morning feeling great is wonderful; to feel no aches or pains in my body; to live in a very different world is worth much more than I may ever have to give up; to be at this peaceful place within.

I am truly, truly grateful to have found this man who has such knowledge and ability to turn things around for many, many, people. God bless him.

– Julie (not her real name)

LABYRINTH OF THE SUBCONSCIOUS

Steve is a conscientious man in his late forties. He and Rose are the parents of four children. Two attend high school and two are at university. Like their parents, the children possess a strong work ethic and have part time jobs.

Steve is the manager of a large manufacturing company and Rose has a catering business which she works from home. They often find it a challenge to balance their budget. Steve stresses because he feels it is his responsibility to provide the very best for his family. And he operates on the same principle when it comes to his employment. He places a great deal of emphasis on setting a good example for those in his charge.

Contrary to Steve, Rose has an easy going disposition. She is highly creative and motivated and places all her efforts into what she is doing at the time. She lives in the moment and is of the opinion that situations usually have a way of working themselves out. To her, stress is a wasted emotion.

One night after dinner Steve went back to the office for a meeting and Rose and the children went to bed. The meeting was wrapped up at 10pm. He hopped in his car and began, what he thought, was the drive home. Meanwhile, the family slept soundly, totally oblivious of the bizarre scenario that was unfolding.

Some time later, Steve woke from a sleep to find himself driving along a dark bush road. He panicked because he did not know what was happening. The vehicle was fully mobile and traveling at 100km/h. He though he was in the middle of a nightmare. But this was not a dream, trees and guideposts were flashing by. He was at a place in his mind that was beyond comprehension, beyond fear – a place he refers to as "white terror".

"What was happening? Where am I? How did I get here? Have I killed some one?" On the cusp of lunacy, he pushed hard on the breaks and trembled as the car came to an abrupt halt. Peering into the blackness of the night he could not identify his surroundings. In horror he gazed at his watch: its hands showed … 3am. "Have I been driving for five hours"? Even though he had not had an accident, he had collided with the complexities of the human mind, and the magnitude of his own frailty. Frozen with fear, he sobbed.

Uncertain of what to do next, he continued driving in the same direction, hoping to find a landmark. Luck was on his side. Within minutes he saw a sign post. He had arrived at a small isolated cattle town, hundreds of kilometres from his home. And in order to get to this town he would have driven up a mountain range.

Confused, he drove to the outskirts of the town and refueled at a truck stop before attempting to drive the long distance home.

Steve looked like an average run-of-the-mill guy. But he was not. He put everyone else first and did not set aside a moment for himself. Never for one moment did he think that something of this magnitude could happen to him.

Days later Steve began seeking help. A naturopath advised him to stop having milk. He was told: "It is the milk that is causing the problem". On several occasions after that episode, while driving with his family, they had to make him stop the car and turn around because he was traveling in the opposite direction to where they needed to go.

The weeks went by. One morning instead of arriving at work at the usual time he woke hours later and found himself behind the steering wheel of his stationary car with the motor running. He had driven along a major highway, then under a bridge. The vehicle was surrounded by tall guinea grass on the bank of a tidal river, a short distance from his place of employment. He had no recollection of what he had done or where he had been.

Steve's stress level was high at the best of times but recent events were compounding existing problems.

He had been experiencing prostate discomfort and after much research and deliberation, visited Elias Schindelar, the natural therapist on the Atherton Tablelands.

Elias said the prostate enlargement was the end result of stress. He advised Steve to eat naturally and to simplify his lifestyle.

They discussed the memory lapses that had occurred while he had been driving. Elias explained that when the body was under duress, the front part of the brain could shut down but the subconscious mind continued to function.

Steve's major concern was the possibility of killing someone while in, what he described as, the "zone". Elias said there was little danger of harming himself or anyone else while in this state, because the subconscious continued to function normally.

Elias began working on Steve's enlarged prostate and advised him to alter his way of eating and thinking, and to reassess methods of handling stress. He said between them they could easily rectify his enlarged prostate because it was not a great problem.

The real issue lay in his mind. He warned: "You must arrest this immediately, if you do not, your situation will worsen".

Walking away from the natural therapy clinic, Steve felt he had a long trek ahead of him. He knew he must relinquish his mind-set or suffer the consequences. This was another of life's wake up and reminder calls. Ignoring it could lead to brain disorder and disease.

He was accustomed to working through issues but this was new, different and it required immediate attention. The problem was his alone and he had to take ownership of it before he could deal with it.

In the weeks that followed he learnt that stress was not compulsory. He also came to the realisation that his problems stemmed from the desire to conform to the wishes of others.

Rose was his inspiration and the love of his life. He knew she was his best tutor and together they developed strategies. Steve said she was his rock, the balance in his life because she kept things simple.

He said he was much happier now and enjoying life a great deal more then he ever did. Since he turned his life around he has never woken up lost, behind the steering wheel of his car, and in the much dreaded "zone". Even though Steve had conquered his demons, he did not forget what had happened.

He continued researching the "zone" and found others had also experienced similar events as the result of uncontrolled stress.

One particular lady had enjoyed a happy marriage until one day her husband had a heart attack and died suddenly. She said they had been so close they thought as one. His death turned her life upside down. She had assumed they would have had more time together to do the things they always planned.

But life offers no guarantees. Unable to adjust to her fears and loneliness, she quickly found herself in a dark space within her mind.

One day she began driving to a friend's home that was in the next suburb. Seven hours later she woke in a frenzy to find herself driving up a mountain range at night. She had driven over the border into another state. She had also driven along one of Australia's busiest highways …

– Steve (not his real name)

LIFE'S LESSONS

One day I spoke with a man named Joseph who was also having natural therapy. He said he had had stomach problems all his adult life. He had worked hard, stressed, and in his youth, drank with his mates on weekends. But that didn't work and his stress contributed to stomach problems. He said: "It was like a dog chasing its tail. I was crazy to worry. Looking back I see it was pointless. But you can't put an old head on young shoulders and I was impatient. I stopped drinking after five years but it didn't help my stomach.

"The worst decision I ever made was when I allowed a surgeon to remove part of my colon. I had no idea what I was letting myself in for. I believed the doctor when he said everything would be okay. But life since then has been far from okay. Most of what I ate went straight through me. I used to go to the toilet up to eight times and sometimes 12 if it was a bad day. I saw many different doctors. They all prescribed drugs which made matters worse. I weighed 48kg when I first came to Elias."

He said he had had a CT scan and was told by a doctor that everything was within normal range for his age. But when Elias examined the images he found everything was far from normal. Most of his vital organs were enlarged and he saw some that were pressing on others. Elias said that Joseph's skeletal system was also in a bad way. The surgeon had removed the part of the colon that absorbed food nutrients, which is why he had suffered most of his life. And he had not been told of the side effects of the surgery.

He was suffering from malnutrition even though he was eating enough to sustain three people. He had started having seizures and hospital staff blamed his wife for not cooking properly. And even after explaining what the problem was, he said they just didn't want to know. One doctor even said: "We don't worry about missing parts of the colon – that's nothing to worry about". "Hah! It's something to worry about all right, because if a plant lacks water and nutrients it will die. The same type of thing was happening to me. But we couldn't get the message across. I think it was all too difficult for them at the hospital and they got to the stage where they just didn't want to know. "They had to blame someone so the wife copped it. When you start getting a bit of age under your belt, and if you grow a few grey hairs and wrinkles, a lot of people seem to think you must have Alzheimer's as well," he said.

"But I lay some of the blame at my own feet because I used to visit Elias years ago and my health was improving, but I didn't have the discipline to eat as he said so I paid the price. In fact, I almost paid the ultimate price – a few more weeks and I would have been dead. But then Elias stepped in. I thank my lucky stars because he took me back." With a grin he added: "People like me are a menace to Elias because we cause him a lot of problems when we don't do as he says". He explained: "If we are treated naturally by Elias Schindelar, and if we stop doing as he says and end up in hospital, it makes him look incompetent.

"But no one else knows that we have stopped natural therapy, gone back to modern medicine and that we are taking prescription drugs once again. The problem is, after we leave the clinic and go home we do what we like behind closed doors. And many of us don't like to admit we lack discipline. But we cheat on ourselves. Then other people end up saying, 'natural therapy doesn't work'. But I know better. Unfortunately Elias gets all the blame.

"I am surprised he took me back. People who have done the wrong thing rob him of the time he could be spending with people who are fair dinkum. Now I know that people who chop and change their minds are nothing but trouble because some end up dying. In the past, Elias has even got the blame for that too. But he has no control over what people eat or the drugs they take the minute they leave his clinic".

He said he had learnt his lesson the hard way when he began taking seizures. His body had been badly affected through malnutrition. He said: "Now I will do exactly as Elias says because I have proved to myself natural therapy works when everything else failed, and without it I can't survive. Modern medicine is of no help to me. Without Elias I would be dead. That's all the evidence I need." I asked if I could write his story. He said: "Of course you can, but I doubt if anyone will believe what Elias has done for me". He went on to say that Elias had concentrated his treatment on another part of his colon. That section is now absorbing amino acids from fruit which helps his body become healthy because it does all the conversion of the acids.

Elias has now started working on his other organs and said he should have a relatively normal life. He said he now went to the toilet between one and four times daily and was gaining weight. He added: "Now it's good when I go out because I don't have to worry about whether I am going to make it to a toilet in time".

He said his stomach was tolerating the oils in avocado, coconut cream and coconut milk. And he could now tolerate and digest warm and cool cocoa drinks. The cocoa closes off the colon and helps the food remain in the digestive system longer, giving the body time to absorb and convert fruit's amino acids.

He said he had tried many types of drugs, vitamins and minerals during the last four decades. He had seen many doctors and specialists but nothing had worked. Elias told Joseph he need not revisit for six months and emphasized once again the importance of eating uncooked fruit. Joseph said he had no trouble during the first four summer months. But as April drew to a close and evenings grew crisp, he craved hot meals, especially hearty soups and potatoes. He began having a cooked Sunday lunch but after a short time he was also having steamed potatoes with his salads twice a week.

At the end of June he visited the natural therapy clinic again. Elias was shocked at the state of his health. The cooked food had caused alarming damage. Elias said he was surprised that Joseph was still alive and amazed that he had not suffered a stroke. He gave him three treatments a day but within days, Joseph suffered a heart attack and stroke early one night.

His wife quickly called Elias but by the time he arrived, Joseph had no pulse. He did not appear to be breathing, his blood pressure was dangerously low, his face had collapsed and the only life Elias had to work with were a few twitching nerves. He immediately began working on the nerve system under his arm pits, his blood pressure and heart. Within minutes, Joseph's vital signs and the left side of his body and face were back to normal. An ambulance was called because he needed oxygen. He was taken to a hospital then transferred.

Even though it was against his wife's wishes, Joseph was injected with anti-seizure medication because he had suffered another seizure which lasted several hours. At 5am a doctor said he was not responding to the drugs.

He remained in hospital for a number of days and during that time a CT scan (without contrast) was carried out on Joseph's brain. As a result of that scan, a doctor diagnosed him as having had a "fit" and that he was suffering "water on the brain" from drinking too much water (2.5lt per day). The doctor told Joseph he was to drink only one litre a day. After a routine blood test, Joseph was told his vitamin B12 level was down. He was offered injections which he refused because he was aware of the possible side effects artifical vitamin B12 may have on his brain.

Later that day he and his wife were shocked when the doctor, accompanied by two other doctors, said: "If you ever come to one of our hospitals again with the same problem, we will have you mentally assessed. If we find you are unable to make your own decisions, we have the right to inject you with whatever we feel is necessary to heal you". The three doctors then left the room but the two accompanying him soon returned and repeated what the first had said.

Joseph said both he and his wife were in a state of disbelief at what they were told and the callous manner it was said. After all, he had given his wife power of attorney and enduring power of attorney. Joseph questioned: "Does that mean when people go into hospital they no longer have rights over their own body?" He added: "The power the system has over people is frightening and we felt intimidated. I now fear doctors and their system. All I want is to be chemical and drug free. It is shocking to think a person can be certified as mental, simply because they want to be chemical and drug free". He said there were those who visited certain counters of some hospitals, asked for and received free syringes so that they could inject themselves with whatever substance they chose. They do so without questions, and its legal. He said it was unbelievable that he did not have the right to refuse vitamin injections because he believed it was healthier to have natural B12 from fruit. He added: "And Australia is supposed to be a free country.".

He left the hospital and resumed his treatment with Elias where he did not feel threatened or intimidated. On reading the blood test results, Elias said it was natural for the vitamin B12 reading to be lower than normal after such an ordeal. But there was no cause for alarm and suggested Joseph eat more pineapple because it was laden with vitamin B12. After examining the CT scan, Elias pointed out the swollen areas in the brain were blood, not water, and the result of the hemorrhage he had suffered during the two strokes.

In the days that followed, large purplish-black markings – some 10cm long – began appearing on Joseph's skin. Elias suspected the drugs may have contained a blood thinner which would have thinned his already thin blood even further. Joseph began having difficulty standing. His wife investigated the ingredients of the drugs.

Records showed of those who have been tested after having this drug, almost 90 per cent have suffered changes in T blood cells. Problems have also been reported with heart rhythm, nerves, liver, gall bladder, muscles, colon, red blood cells, vision and skin damage etc. In the weeks that followed, Elias worked on Joseph twice a day, seven days a week. With the help of natural therapy, his system drained the blood from his brain and he soon felt better. Again Elias said how important it was for him to eat uncooked fruit only and that it would take at least six months for his blood to return to normal because his body had to cleanse itself of the drugs.

Joseph said: "In future, it won't matter how cold it gets, I will not eat cooked food unless Elias says I can". He added: "I don't think anyone knows how brilliant this Mr Schindelar really is. His knowledge of forensic science is unbelievable. That's the only reason I'm still alive. "But I do not envy this man because some people have treated him very badly. Mind you, most would not treat doctors like that. Some do not work with him yet they expect him to heal them. But that's impossible because he is not God, he has always said 'only the body can heal itself'. To some of us, time is a luxury we can't afford, so we must not be ignorant of the facts.

"The key to survival and healing is to understand our illness and the way Elias works. We must work with him, not against, and we must do exactly as he says. The first thing he said to me was, 'I cannot cure you, only your body can cure itself. But if you work with me, if you fight for your life I will do all I can to help you'. He told my wife I only had a 50-50 chance of survival.

"Now I am putting in the hard yards. There are no hot breakfasts with crispy toast on chilly winter mornings. And there are no hot meals on cold nights. To stay alive and have quality of life, I have to follow the laws of nature. Elias did not make these laws.

"People must understand their illness and what they have to do to heal, especially if they have a major problem. If a person does not do exactly as Elias suggests, they might as well stay home or see someone else. When I started seeing Elias again I had to change my way of thinking – big time. I did as he suggested because the fight was mine. Elias does the ground work. We must do the rest."

Wrapping up Joseph said: "I will always be grateful to Elias because he has taught me the rules of nature. He is a unique chap because he genuinely cares for those who trust and work with him. As far as I am concerned, Elias is a gift.

"But my experience of human nature tells me there will be many who will not believe what I have said. And that's their problem because they may be blinded by ignorance. They may not know that nature could one day save their life or that of a loved one, and that's what matters. Idle jibber jabber and doubt do not save lives. "I must continue to have patience because natural therapy takes discipline and time. Many, many years in fact."

– Joseph (not his real name)

“

disease is the courier of death

”

– elias ludwig schindelar

Chapter 8

A WORD FROM ELIAS

Elias said if it was not already too late, if the immune system of the client was strong and if they had discipline, the formula for killing diseases was simple but not easy. The client must eat and drink as nature intended and they must do almost all of the work.

The key to good health is discipline and disease prevention. He said it was unfortunate when people made the wrong choices about the foods they ate. He said he could do very little to help people heal if they chose not to help themselves.

He said: "I need the client to work with me 100 per cent. I have been working a long time in my profession and I know exactly what I have to do to help my clients. But I cannot heal another human being because that is not possible. With discipline, correct information, correct foods, water and a calm environment it is possible for the body to heal itself if it is not too late.

"We must all take full responsibility of our health because our illnesses are our own. The food my clients eat and the way they choose to live their lives is totally their responsibility. I cannot do this for them. But problems arise when clients do not have discipline".

He went on to say: "The second a client dismounts my table after I have given them medical massage, I have no control over them or their health whatsoever. They must be true to themselves and their need to survive must be stronger than their lust for the foods that prevent them from healing".

He added: "I take my work very seriously and have pride in those who work with me. It is satisfying to see a client completely recover from what was once diagnosed as a terminal illness. Treating people with severe injuries, diseases and terminal illness is what my work is all about. "People must realise that some illnesses and diseases take longer than others to heal. They must not get disheartened if they see others heal before they do because our immune system is unique and the length of time it takes to heal depends on many different circumstances. Patience is a major part of the healing process and sometimes it may take years." He concluded by saying: "Where natural therapy is concerned, there is no easy way out and there is no magic formula".

"

great spirits have
always encountered violent opposition
from mediocre minds

"

– albert einstein

Chapter 9

SUMMARY

Hindsight is a luxury and a wonderful teacher. I wish I had information on the healing powers of fruit when I was bringing up my children. Things would be much different.

Like many other unfortunate people, I have had my share of surgery for problems I encountered at the time because the medical fraternity practices in the manner in which it is educated.

There is no doubt in my mind that had I lived as nature intended, most of my health problems could have been avoided. Now I clearly understand why most of these issues, the prescribed drugs I took and most of the x-rays and tests I had over the decades before I met Elias were completely unnecessary.

I have worked with Elias for more than six years and during that time I have experienced the powers of natural healing. I have seen how well natural therapy works for so many of his disciplined clients. Natural therapy has given me the freedom of not having to take prescription drugs. But there were times I suffered unnecessarily during the initial stages of my therapy through my weaknesses, insecurities, isolation and fear of the unknown. In hindsight, a little more faith and trust would have worked wonders.

However, that is all behind me. The drug-induced lupus, viruses, hepatitis, pseudomonas aeruginosa bacteria, chlamydia psittaci, bronchiectasis, blood disease and emphysema are all long gone. But had I not met Elias, I would not have survived.

I will continue to work on self discipline for the rest of my life because in order to heal and be healthy, I must cleanse daily. A clean and calm body promotes a healthy immune system.

I realise only too well it is almost impossible to have a healthy body and immune system when the world is so polluted. And no one can say how much damage electromagnetic fields are going to do to our body and brain. Fluoride, other chemicals in our water supply and genetically engineered food, are not the ideal partners for promoting good health. We have no idea what effect these are going to have on our long term health. Long term tests have not been carried out.

The human body was created by nature and nature created the perfect food to sustain and heal itself: fruit. The human body was not created to be a receptacle for genetically modified foods, electromagnetic fields, pollutants and chemicals. In light of this, commonsense tells me our clock may be ticking. But one thing is sure: certain industries are raking in serious money. They pollute the planet, which weakens the human body because they can.

I am absolutely positive there will be many people who will ridicule what I have written for their own specific reasons. And these reasons may pertain to money, pride or simple ignorance. Some may feel threatened by natural therapy because it works, if we work with it. Others may be jealous of Elias's success and they may be envious of his capabilities as a natural therapist. Some may even envy the freedom he has created for himself.

Many have already spoken out vehemently against natural therapy. To date: not one of these critics has been smart enough to offer an alternate solution. A solution that places the body in a state where it is capable of freeing itself of deadly diseases without man made substances. Substances that are usually accompanied by a litany of deadly and painful side effects which further traumatize the body, thereby hastening the death of the unfortunate victim.

I am sure also, that those who believe in drugs and oppose change, will shun this book with a vengeance, even if they know their drugs are not fixing their problems. Their opposition to natural therapy may be because they lack discipline and the inner strength to change their way of thinking and to take control of their own health issues. But they probably would not like to admit it.

And I have no doubt whatsoever there will also be those who will ridicule Elias, his work and theories. They will claim there is no scientific evidence to prove that natural therapy works. The term "scientific evidence" is always used as a back stop by those who have a point to prove. Remember this: deadly diseases do not discriminate, they do not stop at the border, they are always mutating and adapting, and time is on their side. Regardless of what argument is put forward: we can not fool nature. The bottom line is: thanks to Elias, his knowledge and natural therapy I continue to heal. But many people who are on drugs grow sicker and weaker daily, while the drugs they take seem to grow stronger.

I, and thousands like me who have worked with Elias, are living proof that his natural therapy works brilliantly if we are honest with ourselves. And his theories also work brilliantly if his clients are honest.

He has taught me to look no further than myself. When I search deep within, and with honesty, and if I can surpass my ego in moments of weakness, I can usually answer my own questions. I believe a negative ego – the way we think – can be a stumbling block and a major reason why we remain ill.

Needless to say, the food I eat is simple and to compliment this, so is my lifestyle. Many aspects of my life that were once important and complicated are no longer relevant. Living simply allows me the freedom to make my own choices. No longer am I a slave to advertising and the many industries that contribute to the pollution of the planet. Decontaminating and simplifying my kitchen was indeed a pleasure. The microwave oven was the first to go.

I am deeply grateful to Elias for showing me another way to live life. No longer do I contribute to the misery of the many animals and birds who do not even have the space to turn around in their cages, let alone see the sun. I thank my Creator for giving me determination and the strength not to throw in the towel before I met Elias, a time when matters were grim. He gave me hope in my darkest hour.

Not for a second do I take credit for healing myself and extending my life with quality, because it was Elias who gave me a priceless gift: the knowledge to self-heal. He is an extremely well educated academic and brilliant beyond belief. It was Eilas Schindelar who bore the torch that lit my path to self-healing.

TOWARDS THE LIGHT

During our lifetime many seek,
get lost and die during their journey.
We only have the here and now.

Time and life are precious.
Live for the now.
Forget not the past but learn from it.

Hunger for knowledge.
Know yourself.
Shun all fear, doubts and anger.

Fulfilment is life.
Feel alive.
Without life there is void.

In times of turmoil we may not recognise
our daily blessings of joy.
And joy must be felt.

Life is most loveable.
Fall in love with life,
not with wants or needs.

Look for signs.
They are here. They go and come.
Come and go.

Our breath came with birth.
It will go in death.
Experience it now.

Many learn to pray and continue their search.
Why do they not know
their prayers are answered daily?

Fulfilment is universal light,
the ultimate goal.
Not external notions or fantasy.

Peace and fulfilment are unmeasurable.
Timeless.
Weightless.

We were born with logic
and reason.
Why seek elsewhere?

We are the vessel.
The temple most beautiful,
our glow lives within.

In times of despair its light will shine.
In loneliest of moments
we are not alone.

We are but one.
I may feel different because the unfolding person within
is the one I have always sought.

Let me be your mirror.
Look into me and see yourself.
Evolve.

Step out of the darkness and into your light.
And have the courage to do
what you know is right.

"

when we are
hungry we seek food. when we are not,
we seek recipes

"

– elias ludwig schindelar

Chapter 10

RECIPES

A personal message from Elias: "Nature has provided us with natural food that is 100 per cent compatible with the body. That food is fruit and it should be eaten raw. Cooking fruit destroys its valuable nutrients.

"There are more than 5000 varieties and the manner in which they are prepared is limited only by one's imagination. It is up to the individual to discover as many fruits as possible and to make meals an adventure".

Those who are healing, and those who wish to lose weight should disregard the cooked foods in this chapter.

These simple and quick recipes should be used only as a point of departure. Modify them and add any other ingredients you wish. Substitute ingredients because some may not be available.

Our planet and the foods we eat are being contaminated by toxins daily. Processed foods are produced and packaged mainly for their dollar value, visual appeal, little or no preparation time and a long shelf life. Many contain chemical preservatives, colourants and additives. These ingredients may exhaust the body and disarm the immune system. As the body weakens, it may become susceptible to ill health and disease.

We must maintain our own health and welfare, and that of our families. In an effort to heal and remain healthy, there is much we can do within our lives and our kitchen to decontaminate our body. To achieve this, the foods we eat must be pure.

Raw fruit is high in fructose and glucose. This is the key to sustained energy and good health because only fruit can regenerate the immune system and heal the body.

FOOD PREPARATION AND SIMPLE RECIPES

Do not use aluminium, copper or some plastic containers for the storage, preparation or serving of food. When fruit's natural enzymes contact the toxic metals and chemicals that formulate plastics – formaldehyde, PBAs (bisphenol A), trimethyl, urea-formaldehyde, resins, urethane resins and others – they contaminate food and beverages, then the human body.

Infants and children are particularly sensitive because their bodies are immature and underdeveloped as is their immune and nerve systems. Therefore, they are more susceptible to toxic contamination which leads to serious illness, such as leukaemia. Use glass containers when storing food or water and prepare food in glass bowls.

Pots and pans have not escaped fashion modes. The trendy buzz word at the moment is titanium. On this subject Elias said: titanium weakened the blood, blood cells and the walls of arteries, veins and vessels. He said this damage was reversible by properly cleansing the body of chemical toxins, changing one's eating habits to natural fruits including a generous amount of pears daily. Some state-of-the-art and very expensive cast iron cookware may be coated with cadmium, lead and chromium.

He said good quality cast iron cookware was excellent and stainless steel a close second. But there are many grades of cast iron. If the utensil breaks when dropped on a hard surface it is of inferior quality. Choose cast iron that does not have a coating.

Fruitarians should not eat curry because it is a natural antibiotic and is addictive, as are most herbs and spices. Herbs and spices sabotage the immune system which must be allowed to stand alone in the fight against disease. Therefore, herbs and spices – like other drugs – are outside influences. For those who wish to use curry very occasionally (and if one is not sick or healing), the green variety is the safest. Those who are healing can use chilli as a substitute.

The fruits used in these recipes are mainly those in season, of the common variety and most are readily available. If the climate allows, fruit should be stored at room temperature. Freezing, chilling, heating and cooking destroy fruit's nutritional value.

Processed food, fruit nectars and fruit juice may contain processed cane sugar (sucrose) and recycled water.

Use fruit as quickly as possible after it has been picked because it loses nutritional value rapidly.

Thoroughly wash and rinse all fruit before use because it may have chemical spray on the skin. Ensure fruit such as pumpkin, apples and capsicum etc., are washed properly in the stem area. Use a stiff paint brush. Final rinse: immerse fruit in one part cider to 10 parts of water. Dry with a clean cloth or allow to air dry.

Organic fruit may have been sprayed with substances that contain copper and must be washed thoroughly.

Avocado, cucumber, zucchini and all squash, pumpkin, chilli, eggplant, capsicum, marrow, choco, olives and tomatoes etc., are regarded as fruit. A general rule of thumb: if it has a seed it is a fruit.

However, beans and peas are legumes. They have seeds but like all pulses and grains – such as wheat, corn, barley, oats, rye and rice – they contain harmful acids. When eaten over a period of time their acids accumulate in the system and become just as harmful as those produced by animal DNA.

Dates should be fresh and they should have a seed in them when purchased.

Cleaning grapes: water and natural soap will not clean grapes. They are usually sprayed with substances that may contain copper and other chemicals which adhere to their white, natural wax coating. To remove these toxins before eating, break off the required portion from the bunch and place in a tall, narrow container such as a straight sided beaker (use toughened glass). Heat water to simmering (do not boil) and pour it over the grapes. As the water cools, the natural wax and chemicals rise to the surface in the form of a scum. Rinse with cold water and wash and rinse as usual.

Cornflour may be used to thicken sauces and soups. It is made from grain therefore it contains acid. Of all the thickening agents, Elias said this was the safest but it should be used sparingly.

The chilli used in these recipes are of the birdseye variety. It is a fruit with many healing and cleansing qualities. But it can be hot on the palate and is an acquired taste. There are those who prefer their chilli hot while others mild. In these recipes add chilli to taste. When handling them, it may be wise to wear rubber gloves.

To derive the most benefit from chilli, it is best when eaten raw. To quell the heat it generates: swirl a few drops of olive, coconut or avocado oil around the mouth. Within moments the heat dissipates. One may also try coconut cream and avocado.

Do not place passionfruit, strawberries, kiwifruit or any other fruit such as cucumber, zucchini, squash and tomato etc., in a food processor because when crushed, their seeds release harmful acids. Where possible, remove the seeds before blending.

When making smoothies using berries, passionfruit and kiwifruit etc., in a blender, pulse for the shortest time possible so as not to disturb their seeds.

When we eat fruit such as tomato, cucumber, kiwifruit, passionfruit and strawberries etc., we tend not to chew the seeds and they exit the digestive system whole and uncrushed, therefore their acids do not harm the body.

Use first cold pressed extra virgin olive oil from a bottle and not from a spray can. It is high in nutrients, lowers cholesterol and has a reasonably high boiling point. First cold pressed oils are processed at room temperature. Further pressings require heat to extract the remaining oil which may destroy nutritional value. Some olive oils may contain additives. Oils in spray cans are processed and may contain chemicals.

When cooking with oil, do not overheat the pan because it will burn. Use a gentle heat to prevent food from burning and to retain as many nutrients as possible. Burnt oil is harmful to the body. If the oil accidentally burns, discard it, wash the utensil and start again.

Other excellent fruit oils are that of coconut and avocado. They have a slightly higher boiling point than olive oil. Olive, avocado and coconut oil are excellent for cooking and in salad preparation. Vinegar is excellent for household cleaning especially the bathroom and toilets. Unfortunately it has the same effect on the digestive system. A few drops of good quality cask balsamic vinegar may be used in salads but only on rare occasions. Those who are healing should *not have balsamic vinegar.*

Cook only what is required because left over food can become a haven for bacteria.

Cook fruit "firmly". Overcooked fruit loses nutritional value, it is hard on the colon, difficult to digest and does not hold its shape.

Unless otherwise stated, top and tail pineapple, peel and remove the core. Eat the core because it is very high in nutrients.

The flesh of the coconut, coconut cream and coconut milk are an excellent source of nutrition. If a recipe requires coconut, ensure it is fresh. Coconut is "frozen" during processing. It loses nutritional value and may contain harmful chemicals.

Fresh dates are used extensively throughout these recipes as a sweetener.

Sprays used on citrus trees may be harsher than other sprays because of the canker virus which infects orchards. Scrub citrus well.

Zest is the grated rind of citrus.

Place baking paper on food before baking.

Use black kalamata olives. Some olives may appear black because they are treated with caustic soda to mimic the black varieties.

When adding stock to a recipe, it should be hot.

Fruit is high in water and cooks rapidly.

Capsicum/chilli: remove the placenta and seeds before cooking.

Unless otherwise stated, peel and remove the seeds/stones from: dates, jackfruit, lychees, grapes, olives, stone fruits, custard apple, pumpkin, avocado, tomato, cucumber, squash, zucchini, marrow etc.

Tomatoes: to remove the stem area, cut three-quarters of the way up the centre of the fruit with a sharp paring knife because this area may harbour chemicals.

Skinning fruit such as tomato, peaches, apricots etc: cut a 2 to 3cm cross at the top of the fruit which should be at room temperature and allow it to stand in water that has been freshly boiled for about 10 seconds. Immerse the fruit in ice/cold water. Peel.

Press the seeds of tomato, rockmelon and cucumber etc., through a sieve and add the liquid to fruit stock, sauces or drinks.

Remove the stems of all fruit during preparation.

Peel and core fruits such as apples, pears, pineapple etc., unless otherwise stated.

Peel and seed all citrus unless otherwise stated.

The skin of tomatoes and capsicum may remain unless otherwise stated.

Do not eat more than eight brazil nuts in a week because they stimulate the nerve system.

WARNING: *To guard against food poisoning, eat food as soon as possible after it has been prepared. Cook only what is required and aim not to have left overs.*

Abbreviations

dsp = dessertspoon
tbs = tablespoon
tsp = teaspoon
ml = millilitres
dcl = decilitres
lt = litre

HOW TO USE COCONUT

(Use coconut products fresh because they sour quickly).

COCONUT CREAM

Remove the flesh from the mature coconut and grate into a bowl or blend in a processor. Pour one cup of boiled water over the coconut and allow it to stand for half an hour. Pour the mixture into a clean cloth and squeeze until the coconut pulp feels dry. Allow this to stand in order for the milk to separate from the cream.

COCONUT MILK

Coconut flesh and milk is vital in the human diet. Regarded as a nut, it is also a fruit. Avocado, coconut and dates are food for the brain and vital for babies, children and adults. Coconut milk and coconut cream should be fresh, however fresh is not always possible. A certain Malaysian brand claims their products are 100 per cent pure and do not contain water, preservatives, flavouring, thickener or whitener. Read labels carefully.

COCONUT (TOASTED)

Grate fresh coconut and place on a tray lined with baking paper. Bake until golden brown under a moderate griller or in a moderate oven. Move the flakes constantly because coconut is high in oil and burns quickly. Refrigerate for storage in a glass container. This also has a short shelf life.

TOMATO PUREE

2kg tomato: strain seeds, retain liquid, fine dice
2 tbs olive oil
balsamic vinegar to taste

Place the oil in a pan, heat and gently cook the tomato. Add the retained liquid and vinegar. Cover with a lid. Stir occasionally. Cook until smooth. Cool.

STOCK

Place raw fruit in a saucepan and cover with water. Simmer gently for about 30 minutes. Pass through a colander. Retain the liquid and discard the solids. For thicker consistency: place in a processor and puree.

DRYING FRUIT

BIRDSEYE CHILLI POWDER

Like all fruit, chilli is best eaten raw. But there are times when we have a glut. The following are some ways to keep them.

Place whole chilli (in a single layer) on a tray and place in an approx. 100 degrees Celsius oven. Turn with a fork every half hour to begin with, then about every quarter of an hour to prevent burning as it dries.

After several hours the chilli dehydrate and the skin will begin to harden. Lower the temperature to 80 degrees Celsius. It is at this point that the chilli burns very quickly. The aim is for the chilli to retain its natural colour.

Continue the dehydration process until the chilli is hard. Turn off the power to the oven and open the door for about five seconds to release some of the heat, then close it. Allow the chilli to cool in the oven.

Remove from the oven. Place the dried chilli in a blender and mix to a powder. If a blender is not available, crush with a rolling pin or a mortar and pestle. Place the powder in a dry glass container, cap and refrigerate.

When drying fruit, plan on starting early in the morning because it will take quite a number of hours. This method can be used for most fruits. The powder can then be used to flavour food.

BIRDSEYE CHILLI FLAKES

Pass chilli through the "slicer" blade of a food processor. Place on a tray (in a thin layer) and dry in an approx. 100 degrees Celsius oven until crisp. (Turn every 10 minutes with a fork to prevent burning). Allow to cool in the oven. Place in a glass jar and refrigerate.

OTHER FRUITS

If dried fruit is required, use the same principle as when drying chilli. The finished product should be dry but pliable. Place in airtight sterilised jars and store in the refrigerator.

Apples: Do not remove the skin. Core and slice. Coat with lemon juice and dry as above.

Bananas: Slice lengthways, coat with lemon juice and dry on racks in a 100 degrees Celsius oven.

Chilli (whole): Place in a baking tray. Place in a 100 degrees Celsius oven until they dry pliable.

Peaches, nectarines and apricots: Do not remove the skin. Cut into halves. Remove the stone. Coat with lemon juice and dry as above.

Pears: Do not remove the skin. Core and cut into halves or slice thinly. Coat with lemon juice and dry as above.

Tomatoes: Do not peel. Remove the seeds. Cut almost in half, rub with olive oil and sprinkle with pink sea salt (optional). Open as one would a book and place (flesh down) on racks. Place in a 100 degrees Celsius oven until dry but pliable. Turn during the drying time. Remove them as they dry. Cool. Place in a glass container and cover with olive oil. Refrigerate.

To reconstitute dried fruit, soak in water over night. Discard the water the following morning, rinse the fruit well and dry before using.

FRUIT OILS (OIL INFUSIONS)

These olive oils can be used for pan frying, baking or in salads. Allow the oils to infuse for at least two weeks before using.

- Pierce 15 birdseye chilli and place in a bottle. Add another six finely sliced. Fill with oil and seal.
- Finely chop 10 olives. Place in a bottle. Fill with oil, seal.

- Cut eight olives in half and place in a bottle. Add three finely diced dried tomatoes and six finely diced chilli. Fill with oil and seal.
- Place the finely grated rind of one lemon in a bottle. Cover with oil and seal.
- Finely slice three dried tomatoes and place in a bottle. Fill with oil and seal. Store oil in dark glass bottles in a dark place. Experiment with avocado and coconut oils using chilli and dried fruits.

PASTES

CHILLI PASTE

1 cup chilli
oil to create a paste
2 cups dates

Place ingredients in a food processor and blend to a paste. Seal in a glass container and refrigerate.

COCONUT CHILLI PASTE

2 cups finely diced coconut
chilli to taste
2 cups coconut cream

Place ingredients in a food processor, blend and serve over fruit.

CREAMED CHILLI PASTE

2 cups chilli
3 tbs olive oil

Toss the chilli in oil and place in the oven at about 100 degrees Celsius. Bake until the chilli is cooked. Cool. Place in a food processor and blend to a cream using extra oil if required. This paste can be brushed over raw fruit before baking or pan frying and it can be mixed with oil as a salad dressing. Refrigerate.

COCONUT CREAM AND TOMATO PASTE

4 tbs coconut cream
1 tbs Tomato Paste (P. 357)
1 tsp chilli powder (P. 354)

Mix ingredients and use to baste fruit before baking.

OLIVE PASTE

4 cups olives
1 cup olive oil
1 dsp balsamic vinegar (optional)

Blend the ingredients. Store in a glass container and refrigerate.

TOMATO PASTE

5kg tomato: fine dice
3 tbs olive oil
few drops balsamic vinegar

Press the tomato centres through a sieve. Discard the seeds and add the liquid to the finely diced tomatoes. Place the oil in a large saucepan over a gentle heat. Add the remaining ingredients and cook for a few minutes. Lower the heat and cover with a lid. Simmer gently until cooked and the mixture is a thick consistency. Cool, mash, bottle and refrigerate.

Measures

(imperial to metric)

Quarter of a pint = 142ml
Half a pint = 283ml
Three-quarters of a pint = 425ml
One pint = 567ml
One and three-quarter pints = 1 lt

<u>MARINADES</u> – use fresh

BRAZIL NUT MARINADE

1 tbs lemon zest
quarter cup coconut oil
half cup lemon juice
8 chopped brazil nuts
3 chopped dates

Place ingredients in a food processor and blend.

Options:

1. Baste fruit with the mix before and during baking.
2. Place ingredients in a pan, simmer over a gentle heat and reduce. Serve over cooked fruit.

HOT AND SPICY MARINADE

2 tbs chilli paste (P. 356)
1 tbs green curry
1 tbs coconut oil
1 cup coconut cream
juice of 1 lemon

Heat the oil gently. Add chilli paste, green curry and cook. Add the lemon juice and heat. Add the coconut cream and mix well. Allow to cool. Baste fruit with the mix before and during baking.

HOT CHILLI MARINADE

6 crushed chilli
3 tbs olive oil

Mix the ingredients. Coat sliced fruit and allow them to stand for 1 hour before cooking or roasting.

LEMON AND AVOCADO BASTE

juice and zest of 1 lemon
3 tbs avocado oil

Mix the ingredients. Coat sliced fruit and allow them to stand for 1 hour before cooking or roasting.

RICH TOMATO BASTE

1 capsicum: chop
150ml fruity red wine
5 tomatoes: chop
2 tbs olive oil

Place ingredients in a food processor and blend. Baste fruit before and during roasting.

MARINATES

There are several ways to marinate fruit. The following are quick and simple methods. The fruit can be used immediately and are an excellent accompaniment to salads. Processed salt and vinegar are detrimental to good health. Rinse off all traces before proceeding to the next step. Fruits can be marinated separately or together.

BLACK OLIVES

- The seed of the olive can be removed or it can remain.
- If the olive is required whole, cut it down the side using a sharp knife. If this method is used, it could take up to 8 days to properly "salt" the fruit.
- The marinating period is lessened to about 3 days when the seed is removed. To remove the seed, cut the olive around the centre and discard. A good quality seed press can save many hours of repetitive work.

Brine is salted water. To make: add a generous handful of natural sea salt to 1 litre of cold water. Mix to dissolve the salt. Boil, then cool. Brine should taste like sea water.

1. Place the prepared fruit in a bowl and cover with brine.
2. The next day, pour off the brine and make a fresh lot.
3. Continue doing this for a period of between 3 to 8 days or until the olives are to your taste.
4. Remove the brine. Rinse well. Rinse until all trace of salt is removed. Up to 12 rinses may be necessary. Or allow the olives to soak in cold water until the salt has left the fruit.

This may take minutes or hours.

5. Cover the olives with white vinegar for 8 hours.
6. Discard the vinegar and rinse well until the taste has disappeared. Twelve or more rinses may be necessary. Or allow the olives to soak in cold water until the vinegar has left the fruit. This may take minutes or hours.
7. Drain the olives in a colander.
8. Spread the olives on towels to drain and air dry.
9. Place the fruit in sterilized jars. (Fresh or dried chilli or other dried fruit may be added to taste).
10. Fill with olive oil.
11. Seal in a glass container and refrigerate for storage.

Health tip: After purchasing processed marinated olives, it may be wise to soak them in water because there is no way of knowing what type of salt was used in the process.

To eliminate salt effectively: remove the stone and slice the olives. Soak in water until the salt is removed and rinse a few times. Drain the olives in a colander and spread them out on a clean towel to dry. Place the sliced olives in a bottle and cover with first cold pressed extra virgin olive oil. Seal and store in a cool, dark place.

There are many ways to marinate olives. Manufacturers in some countries protect the marinated olives by coating them with a layer of animal fat. This makes the olives feel greasy to the touch. Always feel the texture of a purchased marinated olive before eating. There is a big difference between greasy and oily.

To remove this grease: place small portions in a colander and remove the substance by flushing the olives with hot water. Quickly rinse with cold water so as not to "cook" the olive.

If marinated olives are purchased in oil, there is no way of knowing if the oil is of good quality. It may be wise to clean the olives using the above method.

MARINATING OTHER FRUITS

1. Capsicum: remove membrane, seed, cut into thin strips.
2. Zucchini: do not peel. Remove seeds. Slice thinly.
3. Place the prepared fruit in a glass bowl and cover with brine.
4. Each day pour off the brine and make a fresh lot.
5. Do this for a total of 2 to 3 days. Ensure the fruit remains crisp.
6. Rinse well as per olive recipe.
7. Add vinegar as per olive recipe.
8. Rinse off the vinegar as per olive recipe.
9. Dry as per olive recipe.
10. Bottle as per olive recipe.
11. Seal in a glass container and refrigerate for storage.

EGGPLANT

1. Peel. Cut into half centimetre wide strips, slices or circles.
2. Prepare the brine as per the olive recipe.
3. Marinate as per above recipe.
4. Add vinegar as per the olive recipe.
5. Rinse as per olive recipe.
6. Lightly steam the eggplant or pan fry.
7. Allow to cool and bottle as per olive recipe.
8. Seal in a glass container and refrigerate for storage.

MAYONNAISE

AVOCADO MAYONNAISE

1 avocado: mash
juice of 1 lemon
2 tbs avocado oil
2 tbs coconut cream
1 cup green coconut: fine dice, mash

Mix the ingredients and serve with salads.

COCONUT MAYONNAISE

1 cup mashed green coconut
half cup coconut cream
1 tsp green curry
1 dsp coconut oil
juice of 1 lemon

Heat the oil in a pan and gently cook the curry to impart the flavours. Add the lemon and reduce by half. Cool. Add the coconut and mix. Serve with salads.

EGGPLANT MAYONNAISE

2 eggplants: dice, steam
2 tbs grapefruit juice
3 tbs coconut cream
2 tbs coconut oil

Mash the eggplant and drain the excess liquid. Cool. Combine the ingredients and beat. Serve over salads.

CHUTNEY

APPLE CHUTNEY

4 apples: fine dice
4 chilli: fine dice
three-quarter cup dates: fine dice
half tsp balsamic vinegar
juice of 1 lemon
juice of 2 oranges

Mix ingredients in a bowl. Refrigerate for one hour before serving to incorporate the flavours.

PAPAYA CHUTNEY

1 papaya: fine dice
1 tbs avocado oil
1 tsp chilli powder (P. 354)
half cup dates: fine dice

1 cup figs: fine dice
half cup lemon juice
juice of 1 lime

Options:

1. Combine the ingredients in a large saucepan and simmer gently until the fruit is cooked but firm. Serve cold.
2. Mix the ingredients in a bowl and serve.

PINEAPPLE CHUTNEY

2 cups finely diced pineapple
4 chilli: fine dice
half cup dates: fine dice
juice of 1 grapefruit
juice of 1 orange

Options:

1. Mix the ingredients and serve over fruit salads.
2. Place the ingredients in a pan. Cook over a gentle heat and simmer. Serve with steamed or baked fruit.

DIPS

The following suggestions may be used as substitutes for commercially processed crackers when serving dips.

- Smear pumpkin skins with olive oil and dry in a warm oven until crisp.
- Cut large tomatoes into wedges and remove centres.
- Slice cucumber into quarters lengthways. Remove the seeds. Cut into 4cm lengths.
- Slice apple into wedges and soak in lemon juice.
- Cut rockmelon into slices.
- Cut capsicum into wide strips.
- Slice dates lengthways.

Arrange the above fruit on platters and serve with dips.

AVOCADO AND EGGPLANT DIP

1 avocado: mash
half cup finely diced, mashed figs
1 eggplant: 1cm dice, steam, mash, cool and drain
8 olives: mash
1 tbs lemon juice
1 tbs avocado oil

Mix ingredients until smooth. Dish, garnish with sliced olives.

AVOCADO DIP (1)

1 avocado: mash
3 olives: fine dice
1 tbs coconut cream

Place ingredients in a bowl and mix. Garnish with thin slices of olives and serve.

AVOCADO DIP (2)

1 avocado: mash
2 tbs coconut cream
juice of one lemon
chilli powder to taste (P. 354)

Mix the ingredients until creamy. Garnish with a thin slice of lemon.

BANANA DIP

2 bananas: mash
1 tbs lemon juice
1 tsp Creamed Chilli Paste (P. 356)
1 tbs mashed olives

Mix the ingredients and serve with a thin slice of lime.

CAPSICUM AND OLIVE DIP

3 capsicum: halve
10 olives: mash
3 tbs olive oil

Bake the oiled capsicum in a moderate oven until their skin has blackened and blistered. Remove the skin carefully and mash. Add the olives and the remaining olive oil, mix well and serve.

CUCUMBER AND MANGO DIP

2 small cucumbers: grate, squeeze to remove liquid
2 mangoes: dice, mash, drain
2 tbs avocado oil
6 dates: fine dice, mash
1 tbs lime juice
2 tbs coconut cream

Mix the ingredients. Garnish with a swirl of coconut cream.

CUCUMBER DIP

2 cucumbers: grate, squeeze to remove liquid
4 figs: fine dice, mash
1 tbs lemon juice
1 tbs orange zest
half cup coconut cream

Mix the ingredients and serve with a sprinkle of chilli.

EGGPLANT DIP

1 eggplant: 1cm dice, lightly steam, mash, drain
1 tbs coconut oil
8 olives: fine dice, mash
juice of half lemon

Mix the ingredients. Garnish with toasted shredded coconut.

OLIVE DIP

1 cup finely diced, mashed olives
half cup grated coconut
zest of 1 orange
2 tbs olive oil

Mix the ingredients. Garnish with finely sliced orange rind.

PAPAYA DIP

1 cup mashed and drained papaya
2 dates: fine dice, mash
half capsicum: fine dice
1 small avocado: chop, mash
1 tbs lime juice
1 tbs avocado oil

Mix the ingredients. Garnish with a swirl of coconut cream.

PUMPKIN DIP

1 butternut pumpkin: steam, cool, mash, drain
3 brazil nuts: crush
2 tbs avocado oil
4 dates: fine dice

Mix the ingredients. Garnish with coarsely grated coconut.

DRESSINGS

AVOCADO DRESSING

1 avocado: mash
juice of 1 lemon
1 tsp lemon zest
pinch of Chilli Powder (P. 354)
half cup Stock (P. 354)

Mix ingredients in a bowl and serve over salads.

BANANA DRESSING

1 banana: dice, mash
juice of 1 lemon
2 dates: fine dice, mash
half tsp lemon zest

Mix ingredients in a bowl until creamy and spoon over fruit.

BASIC DRESSING

few drops balsamic vinegar (optional)

half cup olive oil
juice of 1 lemon

Place the ingredients in a jar and shake. Pour over salads.

BRAZIL NUT DRESSING

6 crushed brazil nuts
juice of half pink grape fruit
2 tbs avocado oil
4 mashed dates
juice of half orange

Place ingredients in a jar and shake. Pour over salads.

CHILLI AND DATE DRESSING

3 crushed chilli
juice of 1 lemon
3 mashed dates
half cup olive oil

Place ingredients in a jar and shake. Pour over salads.

CHILLI DRESSING

6 chilli: crush
few drops balsamic vinegar (optional)
juice of 1 lemon
quarter cup Stock (P. 354)
2 tbs olive oil

Place ingredients except the oil into a bowl and whisk. Add the oil in a fine drizzle whilst whisking. Pour over salads.

CITRUS DRESSING

juice of 1 orange
1 tsp grated lemon rind
quarter cup olive oil
Chilli Powder to taste (P. 354)

Place ingredients except the oil in a bowl and whisk. Add the oil in a fine drizzle whilst whisking. Pour over salads.

COCONUT DRESSING

half cup semidried tomatoes: fine dice, crush
half cup olive oil
few drops balsamic vinegar (optional)
juice of half lemon
3 chilli: crush

Place ingredients in a bowl and whisk. Pour over salads.

LEMON DRESSING

juice of 1 lemon
1 dsp lemon zest
quarter cup Stock (P. 354)
2 tbs avocado oil

Place ingredients in a jar and shake. Serve over salads.

OLIVE DRESSING

10 olives: fine dice, crush
1 cup olive oil

Place ingredients in a bowl and mix. Serve over salads.

PINEAPPLE DRESSING

1 cup pineapple: fine dice, mash
Chilli Powder to taste (P. 354)
8 dates: mash
juice of 1 orange

Place ingredients in a bowl and mix. Serve over salads.

TOMATO DRESSING

2 large tomatoes: fine dice, mash
chilli to taste
juice of 1 lemon

Place ingredients in a bowl and mix. Serve over salads.

TOMATO (DRIED) VINAIGRETTE

half cup semi-dried tomatoes: fine dice, crush

half cup olive oil
few drops balsamic vinegar
juice of half lemon
3 chilli: crush

Place ingredients in a bowl and whisk. Pour over salad.

TOMATO (HOT) DRESSING

3 tomatoes: chop
half cup olive oil
Chilli Powder to taste (P. 354)

Place ingredients in a processor and blend. Use over salads.

TOMATO (SWEET) DRESSING

3 tomatoes: chop
half cup olive oil
6 dates

Place ingredients in a processor and blend. Serve over salads.

SAUCES

APPLE AND PAPAYA SAUCE

1 papaya: slice
2 apples: grate
4 dates: fine dice
three-quarter cup coconut milk
1 tbs grated coconut

Gently simmer the apple and dates in a little fruit juice until softened. Remove from the heat and add the coconut milk. Cool. Arrange the papaya on a tray. Pour the sauce over the papaya, sprinkle with grated coconut and serve.

Hint

Left over roast pumpkin? Slice into pieces and add it to salads.

APPLE SAUCE

3 apples: fine dice
6 dates: fine dice
juice of 1 lemon
three-quarter cup apple juice

Place ingredients in a saucepan and simmer until tender. Cool and mash. Use to top fruit or fruit salad before serving.

APRICOT AND CITRUS SAUCE

1 cup mashed apricots
juice of 1 lemon
juice of 1 orange
1 cup figs: fine dice, mash

Place ingredients in a bowl and mix. Serve over fruit.

APRICOT SAUCE

6 apricots: fine dice
juice of 1 orange
juice of half lemon
Chilli Powder (P. 354) to taste

Place ingredients in a bowl and mix. Serve over fruit.

AVOCADO AND CHILLI SAUCE

1 avocado: mash
1 tsp Chilli Paste (P. 356)
juice of half lemon
half cup coconut cream
half cup grapefruit juice
1 tbs avocado oil

Place ingredients in a bowl and mix. Serve over salads.

COCONUT CREAM SAUCE (1)

2 cups coconut cream
2 apples: fine dice
1 tsp cornflour

quarter cup of water

Place the coconut cream and apple into a food processor and blend until smooth. Transfer to a saucepan and simmer over a gentle heat. Mix the water and cornflour to a smooth paste and thicken the coconut cream mixture. This sauce is excellent over fruit salad or dessert toppings.

COCONUT CREAM SAUCE (2)

1 cup coconut cream
half cup coconut milk
1 tsp cornflour
1 tbs coconut oil

Mix the cornflour with a little water. Place the coconut cream in a small saucepan and bring to a gentle simmer. Thicken with the cornflour mix. Do not boil. Remove from the heat. Add the coconut milk and oil (for shine). If the sauce is too thick add extra coconut milk. Serve hot over cooked fruit.

COCONUT CURRY (MILD GREEN) SAUCE

2 tbs coconut oil
1 capsicum: fine dice
3 chilli: fine dice
green curry to taste
3 tbs coconut cream

Heat the oil in a pan and gently cook the chilli and curry. Add the capsicum and cook lightly. Next add the coconut cream and heat through. Serve over cooked fruit or as a baste before roasting fruit.

Fast Food

Slice a banana lengthways three-quarters of the way through.
Fill with diced fresh chilli, chilli flakes or chilli powder
and top with coconut cream.
Enjoy.

COCONUT CURRY SAUCE

2 tbs coconut oil
1 tbs grated coconut
1 dsp green curry
1 cup coconut cream
grated rind of 1 lemon

Gently heat the oil in a pan. Add the curry and the grated lemon rind and cook to impart the flavour. Add the coconut cream and coconut. Cook gently until the mixture has thickened. Remove from the heat. Serve hot over cooked fruit.

COCONUT SAUCE

1 cup coconut cream
juice of 1 lime
juice of half orange
3 dates: fine dice
1 dsp orange zest

Place ingredients in a bowl and mix. Serve over fruit salads.

FRUIT SILK SAUCE

2 bananas: mash
4 figs: fine dice, mash
half cup pineapple juice
1 mango: fine dice, mash
juice of 1 lemon

Place ingredients in a bowl and mix well. Serve as a topping over fruit salads or sliced fruit.

FRUIT SYRUP SAUCE

1 cup coconut cream
half cup mango puree

Mix ingredients in a bowl and pour over fruit.

MELON COCONUT CREAM SAUCE

1 rockmelon: dice
1 cup diced coconut
3 figs
3 dates
1 cup coconut cream

Place ingredients in a food processor and blend. Serve with sliced fruit or as a topping over fruit salad.

MOROCCAN SAUCE

3 tbs olive oil
2 capsicum: fine dice
1 tbs green curry
6 tomatoes: retain liquid, fine dice
6 chilli: fine dice

Heat the oil in a pan and gently cook the curry and chilli. Add the capsicum and cook gently. Next add the tomato, liquid and bring to a gentle simmer. Cover and simmer gently for half an hour. Stir occasionally. Pour over steamed or roast fruit.

NUTTY COCONUT CREAM SAUCE

1 orange: chop
1 tbs coconut: fine dice
1 apple: chop
juice of 1 lemon

Blend ingredients in a food processor and pour over fruit.

Benefits of eating natural

There is no need to count calories
More time away from the kitchen
The body will find its own weight
Promotes mental alertness
Increases energy
Promotes sleep

SATAY SAUCE SUBSTITUTE

2 tbs olive oil
1 capsicum: fine dice, mash
6 brazil nuts: crush
1 cup Stock (P. 354)
3 tomatoes: fine dice, mash
half tsp balsamic vinegar
1 tsp green curry

Heat the oil in a pan. Cook the curry, then the capsicum. Add the tomato liquid and remaining ingredients. Simmer gently. Stir. If the mix is dry, add stock. This is an excellent accompaniment to skewered barbecued fruit, or over steamed or roasted fruit.

SPICY SAUCE

3 tbs olive oil
2 capsicum: fine dice
1 tbs green curry
6 tomatoes: fine dice
6 chilli: fine dice

Heat the oil in a saucepan. Add the curry and cook gently. Next, add the chilli and capsicum and cook gently. Add the tomatoes, their liquid and cook until tender. Remove from the heat and mash. Serve hot over cooked fruit or cold over salads.

STRAWBERRY SAUCE

1 cup finely diced, crushed strawberries
juice of half lemon
juice of 1 orange

Place ingredients in a bowl and mix. Serve over fruit.

TOMATO SALSA (1)

6 tomatoes: dice
2 tbs Chilli Paste (P. 356)
2 tbs Tomato Paste (P. 357)
half cup Tomato Puree (P. 353)

2 tbs olives: fine slice
1 cup dried tomato: fine dice
3 tbs olive oil

Place the oil in a pan over a gentle heat. Add the chilli paste, dried tomato, olives and cook through. Add the tomato paste and tomato. Add the tomato puree and cook until tender. Serve hot over cooked fruit or cold over salads.

TOMATO SALSA (2)

2 tomatoes: fine dice
Chilli Powder to taste (P. 354)
2 tbs Tomato Paste (P. 357)
juice of half lemon
3 tbs olive oil

Place ingredients in a bowl and mix. Serve over salad.

TOMATO SAUCE (BASIC)

3 chilli: fine dice
2 tbs olive oil
2kg tomatoes: fine dice
half cup red wine

Gently heat the oil in a saucepan. Add the chilli and cook. Add the tomatoes, their liquid, wine, and simmer gently until cooked. Serve over cooked fruit.

TOMATO SAUCE (CHILLI)

2 tbs olive oil
chilli to taste
6 olives: fine dice
3 large tomatoes: fine dice

Gently heat the oil in a pan. Add the remaining ingredients and simmer. Cook, cool and mash. Serve over cooked fruit.

TOMATO SAUCE (TANGY)

3 tomatoes: fine dice
2 tbs olive oil
1 cup Stock (P. 354)
half tsp balsamic vinegar
1 capsicum: fine dice

Heat the oil in a pan and cook the capsicum gently. Add the tomatoes, their liquid and cook through. Add the stock, vinegar, and bring to a gentle simmer. Stir. Add extra stock if necessary. Cool. This is excellent for skewered fruit cooked on the barbecue or over steamed or roasted fruit. (Substitute the stock for red wine if a fruity taste is required).

SOUPS

- Add hot Stock to soups. (P. 354)
- Simmer gently – do not boil.
- Remove from the heat soon after adding coconut milk or coconut cream. Mix well to incorporate the flavours.
- For extra flavour, bake the pumpkin and add it after the soup has cooked.

ASIAN-STYLE SOUP

1 capsicum: long fine slices
1dsp coconut oil
1 zucchini: cut into long fine slices
1 mango: cut into long fine slices
2 cups finely sliced pumpkin strips: steam firm
1 cup long and thinly sliced cucumber
finely diced chilli to taste
green curry to taste
3 cups (approx) Stock (P. 354)
1 cup coconut milk

Heat the oil in a pan and lightly cook the chilli and curry. Add capsicum. Add the zucchini and cook for about one minute. Remove from the heat and add the finely sliced cucumber and mango. Toss lightly and place portions of the mixture and pumpkin into individual soup bowls. Gently heat the stock then remove from the cook top. Add the coconut milk and stir through. Pour the liquid over the prepared fruit and serve immediately with a swirl of coconut cream.

AVOCADO CHILL SOUP

3 avocados: chop
half cup lemon juice
1 cucumber: chop
1 zucchini: chop
1 cup coconut milk

Place ingredients in a food processor and blend. Pour into a tureen. Chill. Serve with a swirl of coconut cream. (Add extra coconut milk if the consistency is too thick).

CITRUS SOUP

250ml orange juice
250ml lemon juice
6 tomatoes: chop
1 tsp olive oil

Puree the ingredients in a food processor. Pour into a tureen. Chill before serving. Garnish with a thin slice of orange.

CUCUMBER CHILL SOUP

2 cucumbers: chop
2 cups coconut milk
half cup diced green coconut

Place the ingredients in a food processor and blend. Chill. Serve with a sprinkle of toasted, grated coconut.

Hint

Add chilli sparingly.
Your can always add more but you cannot take it out.

GAZPACHO

7 tomatoes: chop
1 cucumber: chop
1 capsicum: chop
2 tbs olive oil
half cup red wine of choice
1 dsp balsamic vinegar
5 dates
juice of 1 lemon

Blend the ingredients in a food processor. Serve chilled and garnish with finely sliced cucumber.

MELON SOUP (1)

1 rockmelon: chop
1 honeydew melon: chop
2 apples: chop
juice of 1 lemon
juice of 1 orange
zest of 1 orange
1 cup white wine of choice
half cup coconut cream
6 rockmelon balls
6 honeydew melon balls

Blend the first eight ingredients in a food processor. Place in a tureen. Garnish with melon balls. Serve.

MELON SOUP (2)

1 rockmelon: dice
1 honeydew melon: dice
2 cups apple juice
1 cup white wine of choice
1 mango: dice
zest of 1 orange
6 rockmelon balls
6 honeydew melon balls

Blend the first six ingredients in a food processor. Place in a tureen. Garnish with melon balls. Serve.

MELON SOUP (3)

1 small rock melon: chop
1 ripe mango: chop
1 cup coconut cream
juice of 1 orange
juice of half lemon
6 melon balls

Blend the first five ingredients in a food processor. Place in a tureen. Garnish with melon balls. Serve.

MINISTRONE

2 zucchini: fine dice
2 cups finely diced pumpkin
5 tomatoes: fine dice
1 choko: fine dice
1 capsicum: fine dice
3 tbs Tomato Paste (P. 357)
1 cup Tomato Puree (P. 353)
2 tbs olive oil
chilli to taste
Stock (P. 354)

Gently heat the oil in a saucepan and add the capsicum, chilli and cook until tender. Add the pumpkin, choko and cook until tender. Next add the tomatoes, zucchini, tomato puree, tomato paste and simmer. Two-thirds fill with stock and cook gently. Add extra stock if necessary. Serve hot.

Measures

One decilitre = one-tenth of a litre
10 decilitres = one litre

PLOUGHMAN'S SOUP

2 zucchini: fine dice
3 tomatoes: fine dice
1 capsicum: fine dice
1 tbs olive oil
2 choko: fine dice
2 cups finely diced pumpkin
3 birdseye chilli: fine dice
Stock (P. 354)

Heat the oil gently, add the chilli and cook to impart the flavours. Add the choko, capsicum and cook through. Next add the pumpkin, tomato and zucchini and cook. Two-thirds fill with stock and gently simmer until cooked. Add extra stock if required. Serve hot.

PUMPKIN COCONUT CREAM SOUP

1 large butternut pumpkin: half cm dice
2 apples: dice
2 figs: fine dice
2 tbs avocado oil
2 zucchini: fine dice
1 cup Stock (P. 354)
1 cup coconut cream
1 cup coconut milk

Gently heat the oil in a saucepan, add the pumpkin and cook to impart the flavour. Add the zucchini, figs, apples and lightly fry. Add the hot stock and simmer until cooked. Puree in a food processor. Return to a gentle heat and add coconut cream and milk. Remove from heat. Add extra coconut milk if necessary. Serve hot.

PUMPKIN SOUP (SPICY)

3 cups 1cm diced pumpkin
3 tbs coconut oil
1 tbs Chilli Paste (P. 356)
Stock (P. 354)
1 dsp green curry (optional)

1 cup coconut cream
2 apples: fine dice
2 zucchini: chop

Heat the oil gently. Add the curry paste, chilli and cook. Add the apple, pumpkin, zucchini and cook. Half fill with stock and cook until tender. Add the coconut cream and heat. Blend until creamy. Serve hot.

TOMATO AND CAPSICUM SOUP

6 capsicum
1kg tomatoes
fruity red wine and Stock (P. 354, add extra if necessary)
3 tbs Tomato Paste (P. 355)
olive oil

Smear the capsicum and tomatoes with oil. Bake in a moderate oven until cooked. The skin of the capsicum should blister. Cool, remove the skin. Cook the tomatoes firm. Cool, remove the skin. Blend the cooked capsicum, tomato paste and tomato together. Pour into a saucepan, add the red wine/stock and simmer gently. Serve into bowls and garnish with sliced olives and a swirl of olive oil.

TOMATO SOUP (CREAMY)

1.5kg tomatoes: retain liquid, fine dice
3 tbs coconut oil
3 chilli, fine dice
1 cup dried tomatoes: fine dice
2 tbs Tomato Puree (P. 353)
Stock (P. 354)
1 cup coconut cream

Gently heat the oil in a saucepan, add the chilli and cook until tender. Add the dried tomatoes, tomato puree, tomatoes, their liquid and cook through. Add the stock. Cook and mash. If the soup is thin, return to the heat and reduce. Puree in a food processor. Return to a gentle heat and add the coconut cream. Pour into a tureen. Garnish with fine slices of chilli.

TOMATO SOUP (HOT)

8 tomatoes: fine dice
2 capsicum: fine dice
1 cup dried tomato: fine dice
2 apples: fine dice
Stock (P. 354)
3 tbs Tomato Paste (P. 357)
2 tbs olive oil
finely diced chilli to taste

Heat the oil gently, add chilli and cook. Add the capsicum, dried tomato and cook through. Add the tomatoes, apple and cook. Next add the tomato paste and two-thirds fill with hot stock. Cook and serve hot.

ZUCCHINI SOUP (THICK)

5 zucchini: grate
2 apples: grate
1 cup coconut milk
1 cup coconut cream
2 tbs coconut oil

Gently heat the oil, add the apples and zucchini. Cook until tender. Add the coconut milk, coconut cream and serve hot.

SALADS

APPLE AND BANANA SALAD

4 brazil nuts: crush
juice of 1 orange
juice of 1 lemon
2 bananas: slice
4 apples: fine slice
1 dsp avocado oil

Combine the avocado oil and citrus juices in a bowl and whisk. Coat the apples and banana with the citrus and avocado oil and arrange on a serving tray. Sprinkle crushed nuts over the top. Serve.

APPLE AND COCONUT SALAD

3 apples: fine dice
2 tbs grated coconut
juice of 2 lemons
1 tbs coconut oil
6 crushed brazil nuts
4 dsp finely diced green coconut

Gently fold the ingredients in a bowl and sprinkle with the diced green coconut.

APPLE AND CUCUMBER SALAD

1 cucumber: fine slice
juice of 2 lemons
3 apples: fine slice
2 tbs avocado oil

Place the ingredients in a bowl and fold gently. Arrange on a platter and garnish with finely sliced lime.

APPLE AND PINEAPPLE SALAD

2 apples: fine slice
1 pineapple: fine slice
half cup finely diced green coconut
2 plums: fine slice
juice of 1 lemon

Gently fold the ingredients in a bowl. Serve on a platter and sprinkle with toasted, coarsely grated coconut.

Hint

Before cooking, clean bench tops. Have knives, utensils and the ingredients at your finger tips.

APPLE, PEAR AND ZUCCHINI SALAD

2 apples: fine slice
2 pears: fine slice
1 tbs avocado oil
2 zucchini: fine slice
juice of 2 lemons

Place ingredients in a bowl and fold gently. Arrange on a platter and garnish with Chilli Flakes (P. 354).

AVOCADO AND CITRUS SALAD

1 pink grapefruit: segments
2 oranges: segments

Dressing

1 ripe avocado: mash
3 tbs olive oil
juice of 1 lime
juice of 1 lemon

Combine the dressing ingredients in a bowl and whisk until creamy. Arrange the citrus segments on a platter and pour the dressing over the top. Garnish with finely sliced orange rind.

AVOCADO AND COCONUT CREAM SALAD

1 avocado: 1cm dice
1 banana: fine slice
1 custard apple: 1cm dice
half cup lemon juice
1 cucumber: fine slice
2 tomatoes: slice
1 tbs Chilli Paste (P. 357)
half cup coconut cream

Combine the coconut cream and chilli paste in a bowl and mix well. Place the remaining ingredients in a bowl and fold gently. Coat the fruit with lemon juice and arrange on a platter. Spoon the chilli and coconut cream dressing over the top.

AVOCADO AND COCONUT SALAD

1 avocado: 1cm dice
2 tbs lemon juice
1 small cucumber: fine slice
half cup finely diced coconut
half capsicum: fine dice
10 olives: fine slice

Gently fold the ingredients in a bowl. Arrange on a platter and sprinkle with lemon zest.

AVOCADO AND MANGO SALAD

2 tomatoes: fine slice
1 avocado: slice
1 mango: slice
half cup finely diced coconut

Dressing

2 tomatoes: fine dice, mash
juice of 1 orange
juice of 1 lemon
2 chilli: crush

Arrange the tomatoes on a platter with the avocado and the mango. Whisk the dressing ingredients in a bowl and pour it over the fruit. Sprinkle with chilli flakes. Serve immediately.

AVOCADO AND PAPAYA SALAD

half papaya: slice
1 avocado: slice

Dressing

1 tsp chilli paste
1 tbs avocado oil
juice of 1 lemon
half cup pink grapefruit juice

Arrange the papaya and avocado on a platter. Place the dressing ingredients in a bowl, whisk and pour it over the fruit.

AVOCADO AND STRAWBERRY SALAD

2 cups strawberries
2 avocados: slice

Dressing

2 tbs avocado oil
juice of 1 lemon
1 tsp chilli powder

Place the avocado on a serving tray. Slice the strawberries and arrange them over the avocado. Place the oil in a bowl with the lemon and chilli powder, whisk and pour it over the fruit. Ensure the avocado is well coated.

CAPSICUM SALAD

1 capsicum: fine slice
3 tomatoes: fine slice
1 small cucumber: fine slice

Dressing

juice of 1 lemon
1 dsp chilli paste
few drops balsamic vinegar (optional)
3 tbs olive oil

Arrange the fruit on a serving dish. Place the dressing ingredients in a bowl, whisk and pour it over the fruit. Garnish with finely sliced olives.

CRISPY SALAD

half cucumber: fine slice
1 capsicum: fine slice
2 tomatoes: fine slice
1 zucchini: fine slice

Dressing

juice of 1 lemon
juice of 2 oranges
2 tbs coconut cream
2 tbs coconut milk

2 tbs grated, toasted coconut
coarsely grated lemon rind
2 tbs coconut oil

Arrange the fruit on a platter. Combine the citrus juices, coconut oil, coconut milk, coconut cream in a bowl, whisk and pour it over the fruit. Sprinkle toasted coconut over the top.

CUCUMBER SALAD (1)

1 cucumber: fine slice
2 tomatoes: wedge thinly
1 tbs avocado oil
3 tbs finely diced green coconut

Arrange the cucumber and tomato wedges on a platter and sprinkle with diced coconut. Drizzle the oil over the top.

CUCUMBER SALAD (2)

1 cucumber: fine slice
2 cups grapes: halve
half cup coconut cream
3 chilli: fine dice

Place ingredients in a bowl and fold gently. Arrange on a platter and garnish with lemon wedges.

HOT FRUIT SALAD

3 blood oranges: segment
1 large papaya: slice
2 cups lychees: halve

Dressing

juice of 1 lime
juice of 1 lemon
2 tbs avocado oil
1 tsp chilli flakes

Arrange the fruit on a platter. Combine the dressing ingredients in a bowl, whisk and pour it over the fruit.

MIXED SALAD

1 zucchini: fine slice
2 tomatoes: wedge
4 olives: fine slice
1 capsicum: fine slice
1 small cucumber: fine slice

Dressing

juice of 1 lemon
2 tbs olive oil
few drops balsamic vinegar (optional)

Arrange the fruit on a platter. Place the dressing ingredients in a bowl, whisk and pour it over the salad.

PINEAPPLE SALAD

1 cup finely diced green coconut
1 pineapple: fine slice

Place ingredients in a bowl and fold gently. Arrange on a platter and garnish with toasted, coarsely grated coconut.

PUMPKIN: Even though raw pumpkin is nutritious, it can be difficult to digest. It may be wise to have small portions during the mid-day meal. If it is eaten during dinner it could prevent sleep.

PUMPKIN SALAD (1)

half small pumpkin: 1cm cube, roast, cool
3 tomatoes: wedge
6 apricots: fine slice

Dressing

2 tbs avocado oil
juice of 1 lemon
1 dsp Creamed Chilli Paste (P. 356)
juice of half pink grapefruit

Arrange the pumpkin on a platter with the tomatoes and apricots. Place the dressing ingredients in a bowl and whisk. Pour it over the fruit.

PUMPKIN SALAD (2)

1 cup raw grated pumpkin
1 cup raw grated zucchini
2 tbs sliced olives
2 tbs olive oil

Toss the ingredients lightly in a bowl and serve (small portions) as a side salad.

PUMPKIN SALAD (CREAMY)

half small pumpkin: 1cm cube, roast, cool
1 cucumber: fine slice

Dressing

2 tbs avocado oil
3 brazil nuts: crush
half cup coconut milk
half cup coconut cream

Arrange the pumpkin and cucumber on a platter. Whisk the dressing ingredients and pour it over the pumpkin and cucumber. Garnish with finely sliced lime.

TOMATO SALAD

4 tomatoes: slice
1 cucumber: fine slice
10 olives: fine slice
4 tbs olive oil
juice of 1 lemon

Arrange the tomato on a platter and place the sliced cucumber over the top. Combine the olive oil and lemon and pour it over the fruit. Garnish with sliced olives.

Hint

Cover dishes with baking paper before baking to prevent burning. It may be wise not to allow aluminum foil to touch food.

TOMATOES (STUFFED)

6 large tomatoes
1 small zucchini: grate
half capsicum: fine dice
half cup finely diced lychees
half cup finely diced mango
half cup cucumber: grate
4 dates: fine dice
4 chilli: fine dice
10 olives: fine slice
2 apricots: fine dice
1 apple: fine dice
2 tbs coconut oil

Cut through the middle of the tomatoes. Remove centres. Place the remaining ingredients (except olives) into a bowl and mix. Pack filling into tomatoes. Arrange on a platter. Drizzle olive oil over and around the tomatoes. Sprinkle sliced olives over the tomatoes.

TROPICAL SALAD

1 cucumber: fine slice
1 cup halved lychees
1 mango: 1cm dice
three-quarter cup coconut cream
1 cup grapes: halve

Place ingredients in a bowl and fold gently. Arrange on a platter and garnish with extra grape halves.

MAINS

BANANA SURPRISE

2 bananas: slice
1 eggplant: 1cm slice
6 olives: fine dice
Creamed Chilli Paste to taste (P. 356)
3 tbs coconut oil

half cup lemon juice
juice of half orange

Whisk the citrus juice and the chilli in a bowl and coat the sliced eggplant. Place it in the refrigerator for an hour. Gently heat the oil in a pan and cook the eggplant. Place on a tray. Lightly pan-fry the bananas, diced olives and spoon over the eggplant and serve.

CAPSICUM BAKE

3 capsicum: slice
4 tomatoes: 1cm dice
2 zucchini: slice
juice of half lemon
1 tbs olive oil
half cup Stock (P. 354)

Place the ingredients in an oiled oven dish. Coat the fruit with the oil. Bake in a moderate oven for about 45 minutes. Serve with a sprinkle of sliced olives over the top.

CAPSICUM (STUFFED)

4 capsicums: remove tops (lids) and set them aside
remove the seeds and membrane

Filling:

1 apple: grate
8 olives: fine dice
1 cup grated pumpkin
2 plums: fine dice
4 dates: fine dice
2 tbs olive oil
2 zucchini: grate, squeeze to remove liquid

Place the filling ingredients in a bowl and mix well. Press the filling in the capsicum and replace the lids. Rub the capsicum with oil and stand them on an oiled baking dish. Bake in a moderate oven until they soften. Top with a drizzle of olive oil.

CURRY (BANANA)

4 bananas: slice lengthways
2 tbs avocado oil
1 dsp green curry
1 apple: fine slice
1 mango: 1cm dice
2 cups 1cm dice papaya
half cup coconut cream

Gently heat the oil and cook the curry. Add the coconut cream. Do not boil. Add the remaining ingredients and gently fold the cream mixture through the fruit. Serve in individual bowls and garnish with grated, toasted coconut.

CURRY (COCONUT 1)

1 capsicum: slice
3 zucchini: slice
1 cup coconut cream
green curry to taste
1 tsp Chilli Powder (P. 354) or Creamed Chilli Paste (P. 356)
1 tbs coconut oil
1 tbs orange peel: fine slice

Heat the oil and add the curry, chilli, orange peel and cook. Add the capsicum, cook until tender. Reduce the heat. Add the zucchini and the coconut cream. Simmer to reduce the liquid and serve.

CURRY (COCONUT 2)

2 zucchini: fine slice
quarter small pumpkin: fine slice
half cup coarsely grated coconut
4 dates: fine dice
1 tbs orange zest
4 figs: fine dice
1 dsp green curry
2 tbs coconut oil
1 cup coconut cream

Heat the oil in a pan and cook the curry gently. Add the pumpkin and cook. Add the zucchini, orange zest, dates, figs, grated coconut and cook. Fold in the coconut cream and serve.

CURRY (PINEAPPLE)

1 pineapple: cut into strips
half capsicum: cut into strips
1 banana: slice
1 tbs coconut oil
4 tbs finely diced green coconut
green curry to taste
three-quarter cup coconut milk
1 tbs finely sliced lemon peel
1 tsp dried Chilli Powder (P. 354)
1 tsp cornflour (add more if required)
2 tbs Stock (P. 354)

Gently heat the oil in a pan. Add lemon strips, dried chilli and curry. Cook to impart the flavours. Add the capsicum and cook gently. Next add the pineapple, banana, green coconut and heat through. Add the coconut milk and heat. Blend the cornflour and water and add it to the mixture. Cook gently to thicken. Serve.

Measurements

(imperial to metric)

0.039 inch = 1mm
0.078in = 2mm
0.197in = 5mm
0.39in = 1cm
1.97ins = 5cm
3.93ins = 10cm
7.86ins = 20cm
19.68ins = 50cm
39.37ins = 1 metre

EGGPLANT BAKE

2 unpeeled eggplants: slice 1cm thick
1 cup Marinade (P. 358)
2 zucchini: grate
1 choko: grate
4 cups Tomato Salsa (P. 354, 375)
2 cups grated pumpkin
4 button squash: grate
2 tbs Chilli Paste (P. 356)

Soak the eggplant in marinade and allow to stand for one hour. Squeeze the liquid from the grated choko, zucchini, pumpkin, button squash and mix together with the chilli paste. Oil the base and sides of an earthenware casserole dish and line the bottom with circles of eggplant. Press the grated mixture over the top. Spoon a layer of salsa over the grated fruit mix. Continuc layering and finish off with the salsa. Bake in a moderate oven for about 1 hour. Serve hot.

EGGPLANT (HOT AND SPICY)

1 eggplant: 1cm slice
Hot and Spicy Marinade (P. 358)
2 bananas: slice

Soak the eggplant in the marinade and refrigerate for 1 hour. Oil a baking tray and arrange the eggplant. Drizzle olive oil and remaining marinade over the top. Bake in a moderate oven until cooked. Plate the sliced banana and cover with baked eggplant. Serve with hot apple sauce.

EGGPLANT PAN-FRIED

1 eggplant: slice
6 olives: fine slice
4 tbs olive oil
half tsp balsamic vinegar (optional)
2 tomatoes: slice, pan fry
extra olive oil
1 cup heated Tomato Salsa (P. 374, 375)

Mix the oil and vinegar and coat the eggplant. Refrigerate for one hour. Pan-fry in olive oil over a gentle heat. Arrange the tomatoes on a serving platter then the eggplant. Top with salsa then sliced olives.

EGGPLANT (STEAMED 1)

1 eggplant
1 tomato: fine dice
6 olives: fine dice
half capsicum: fine dice
1 tbs Chilli Paste (P. 356)
2 tbs olive oil

Slice the eggplant in half lengthways then slice the 2 halves in half again (lengthways) to represent lids. Scoop out the centre of the 2 bottom portions and finely dice the centres. Mix the remaining ingredients and the diced eggplant in a bowl and use to fill the centres. Place the lids on the top of the filling. Rub with olive oil and steam or bake in a moderate oven until tender. Serve with hot Tomato Salsa (P. 374, 375).

EGGPLANT (STEAMED 2)

1 eggplant: fine dice
2 tbs olive oil
6 dates: fine dice
juice of 2 lemons

Mix the ingredients in a bowl and marinade for 1 hour. Place the bowl in a steamer and cook for about 20 minutes. Serve hot.

Approximate Oven Temperatures

Cool = 140 degrees Celsius
Moderate = 160 degrees Celsius
Moderately Hot = 190 degrees Celsius
Hot = 220 degrees Celsius

EGGPLANT SURPRISE

2 cups finely diced eggplant
2 cups cold mashed pumpkin, drain
juice of 3 lemons
half cup finely diced green coconut
4 figs: fine dice
half cup grated coconut
1 tbs avocado oil
1 cucumber: grate, squeeze to remove liquid
3 tomatoes: fine dice
1 avocado: sliced, coat with extra lemon juice

Mix the oil with the lemon and marinade the eggplant for one hour. Pan-fry the eggplant over a gentle heat. Drain off excess liquid. Place the eggplant, pumpkin, chopped coconut, grated coconut and the finely diced figs in a bowl and fold gently. Place egg rings on serving plates and firmly press in the mixture. Cover. Chill for a few hours. Remove the rings. Top with cucumber, diced tomatoes and avocado slices. Drizzle olive oil and sprinkle chilli flakes over the top. Serve.

FRUIT BAKE

4 cups 2cm dice pumpkin
1 eggplant: 2cm dice
2 tbs olive oil
1 choko: 1cm dice
1 capsicum: 2cm dice

Place the fruit in a large bowl and coat in oil. Place in a tray and bake in a moderate oven until cooked. Serve hot.

FRUIT CASSEROLE

4 large tomatoes: 1cm dice
2 tbs olive oil
1 eggplant: 1cm dice
2 apples: 1cm dice
2 capsicums: fine slice

2 zucchini: fine slice
1 choko: fine dice

Place the ingredients in a casserole dish and coat with oil. Bake in a moderate oven for about 45 minutes. Serve hot.

FRUIT CURRY

2 eggplant: fine slice
3 zucchini: fine slice
2 apples: fine slice
Coconut Curry (Mild Green) Sauce (P. 371)

Lightly oil a baking tray and place alternate layers of the sliced fruit. Top with Coconut Curry (Mild Green) Sauce and bake in a moderate oven until cooked.

FRUIT PAN FRY

3 zucchini: cut into lengths
2 cups finely diced pumpkin
4 figs: fine dice
1 dsp orange zest
5 dates: fine dice
2 tbs coconut oil
half cup grated coconut

Gently heat the oil in a pan, add the pumpkin and fry. Add the zucchini, cook until tender. Add the remaining ingredients and heat through. Serve immediately.

FRUIT ROAST

Large dice pumpkin, eggplant, zucchini, choko, marrow and capsicum and place in a bowl with 3 tbs olive oil. Add 2 tbs each of finely diced olives and dried tomatoes. Mix thoroughly. Place the ingredients in a dish and bake in a moderate oven until cooked. Serve hot.

FRUIT STACK

3 tbs olive oil
1 eggplant: thick slice
2 tomatoes: thick slice
12 olives: fine slice
2 capsicums: cut into quarters
2 zucchini: thick slice

Heat the oil in a pan and fry ingredients separately. Stack on a serving dish. Sprinkle with finely sliced olives and a drizzle of olive oil.

FRUITY NUT LOAF

1 eggplant: grate (using a food processor)
rind of 1 lemon
juice of 3 lemons
1 banana: fine dice
1 cup dates: fine dice, mash
4 figs: fine dice, mash
1 avocado: mash
half cup finely diced green coconut
1 cup finely grated coconut
2 tbs coconut oil
Fruit Chutney (garnish) (P. 362, 363)

Place the eggplant and lemon juice in a bowl and mix thoroughly. Cover. Refrigerate overnight. Add the remaining ingredients and mix thoroughly. Line a mould with baking paper. Press the mixture firmly into the mould and cover with a small piece of baking paper. Place a weight on the top and refrigerate overnight. Remove the loaf from the mould and slice. Place a teaspoon of chutney on each piece and serve.

GEM SQUASH (STUFFED)

4 large gem squash
1 tomato: fine dice
half cup dried tomatoes: fine dice

1 capsicum: fine dice
1 zucchini: grate
1 apple: grate
4 figs: fine dice
4 dates: fine dice
1 tsp Chilli Powder (P. 354)
1 tbs olive oil
6 olives: fine dice

Cut around the top of the gem squash to form a lid. Place the lids aside and carefully remove the centres. Place the remaining ingredients in a bowl and mix thoroughly. Press the filling into the squash and replace the tops. Secure with toothpicks. Arrange the squash on an oiled baking tray. Smear with olive oil. Bake in a moderate oven until cooked. Remove toothpicks. Top with a Sauce (P. 369-376) or a Marinade (P. 358) reduction. Serve hot.

HOT CHILLI PAN-FRY

1 eggplant: fine slice
1 capsicum: fine slice
2 zucchini: slice
6 chilli: fine slice
4 tbs olive oil

Place the oil in a pan and add the chilli. Add the eggplant and the capsicum and cook gently. Add the zucchini and heat through. Place on a dish and serve immediately.

MARROW BAKE

1 marrow: peel
2 tbs olive oil
3 tbs olives: fine dice

Slice the marrow in halves lengthways. Remove the seeds. Cut the two lengths in half and place in a baking dish. Coat with olive oil and sprinkle with olives, bake in a moderate oven until the marrow softens.

MARROW (CREAMY)

1 marrow: 1cm dice
three-quarter cup coconut cream
1 tsp cornflour blended with 1 tbs water
chilli powder to taste
4 dates: fine dice

Lightly steam the marrow and place in a serving dish. Heat the coconut cream to almost simmering and thicken with the blended cornflour and water. Stir until the cornflour has cooked. Add the dates and chilli. Pour the sauce over the marrow and serve.

MARROW (STEAMED)

1 marrow: slice lengthways
half cup coconut cream
half pineapple: fine dice
6 brazil nuts: crush

Lightly steam the marrow and place on a serving tray. Gently heat the coconut cream, add the pineapple and brazil nuts and spoon over the steamed marrow. Serve hot.

MARROW (STUFFED)

1 marrow: unpeeled

Filling:

half capsicum: fine dice
6 olives: fine dice
1 apple: fine dice
1 zucchini: fine dice
1 tbs olive oil
chilli to taste
1 cup green coconut: fine dice

Lay the marrow on a board and cut a long top section to form a lid. Place the lid aside. Scoop out the centre and discard the seeds. Place the remaining ingredients in a bowl, mix well. Pack the filling into the marrow, replace the lid and secure with toothpicks. Rub the marrow with olive oil and place in a well oiled baking tray. Bake in a moderate oven until cooked but firm. Remove the toothpicks and serve with a favourite sauce.

PUMPKIN CAKES

half small pumpkin: grate, squeeze out liquid
coconut oil
10 dates: fine dice
1.25 cups grated coconut
coconut cream for dipping
extra grated coconut for coating

Place the pumpkin, dates and grated coconut in a bowl and mix. Add extra grated coconut if necessary. Form into balls and flatten. Dip them in coconut cream and coat with grated coconut. Refrigerate for 4 hours. Gently heat coconut oil in a pan and lightly fry the pumpkin cakes. Cook on a slow heat.

PUMPKIN (CITRUS)

half small pumpkin: 1cm cube, steam, drain
2 tbs olive oil
juice of 1 orange
juice of 1 lemon
1 tsp grated lemon rind
1 tbs orange rind: fine slice

Gently heat the oil in a pan. Add the citrus rind and heat to impart the flavours. Add the juices and heat through, then the steamed pumpkin and fold gently. Serve hot.

PUMPKIN (COCONUT)

half small pumpkin: 1cm dice
juice of 1 lemon
1 cup coconut cream
1 cup grapes: halve

Place the pumpkin in a saucepan and add the coconut cream. Simmer gently. Spoon into serving dishes and top with grapes. Pour lemon juice over the pumpkin and serve hot.

PUMPKIN (NUTTY)

half small pumpkin: 1cm cube
1 cup papaya: fine dice
three-quarter cup finely diced green coconut

Lightly steam the pumpkin, mash, drain. Add the papaya, green coconut and fold gently. Serve cold.

PUMPKIN (SWEET NUTTY)

3 cups 1cm dice pumpkin
grated rind of 2 oranges
juice of 2 oranges
6 dates: fine dice
half cup finely grated coconut
half cup coconut cream

Place the orange juice, green coconut, grated coconut and the dates in a bowl and mix well. Place the pumpkin in a casserole dish and spoon the mixture over the top. Bake in a moderate oven until cooked firm.

RATATOUILLE

4 tbs olive oil
5 tomatoes: fine dice
1 eggplant: fine dice
4 figs: fine dice
2 tbs dried tomato: fine dice
2 capsicums: fine dice

Heat the oil in a pan and gently cook the capsicum. Add the eggplant and cook. Add the remaining ingredients and cover until the ingredients are cooked through. Serve hot.

TOMATOES (SLOW ROAST)

6 tomatoes: slice in half
half tsp balsamic vinegar (optional)
4 tbs olive oil
12 olives: halved

Place the tomato in an oiled baking dish. Combine the vinegar and olive oil and coat the tomatoes. Place 2 olive halves on each tomato and bake in a moderate oven until cooked. Serve hot.

WINTER HOT POT

6 olives: halve
selection of fruit: dice
4 figs: fine dice
chilli to taste
half cup red wine
half cup Stock (P. 354)

Place the ingredients in an earthenware pot and cook in a moderate oven for about 45 minutes. Serve hot.

ZUCCHINI BAKE (SWEET)

4 zucchini
1 cup coconut cream
4 dates: fine dice
4 figs: fine dice

Grate the zucchini and squeeze out the liquid. Combine the ingredients in a bowl. Spoon the mixture into ramekins and place them in a baking tray that is half full with water. Place the tray in a moderate oven and bake until golden brown. Serve hot or cold with a favourite sauce.

ZUCCHINI CASSEROLE

2 zucchini: chop
2 tbs olive oil
1 medium squash: chop
juice of half lemon
2 apples: 1cm dice
1 capsicum: slice

Place the ingredients in a bowl and coat with oil. Place in a casserole dish and cover with a lid. Bake in a moderate oven. Drizzle with a little extra lemon juice before serving.

ZUCCHINI (NUTTY)

2 tbs olive oil
chilli to taste
1 tsp green curry
juice of half orange
1 tbs Creamed Chilli Paste (P. 356)
3 zucchini: fine slice
6 brazil nuts: crush
1 tbs finely sliced orange rind

Heat the oil in a pan. Add the chilli, curry and orange rind and cook gently to impart the flavours. Add the zucchini and cook gently until tender. Add the orange juice and nuts. Remove from the heat and serve.

ZUCCHINI PAN-FRIED

4 zucchini: fine slice
3 tbs olive oil
juice of 2 lemons

Gently heat the oil in a pan and fry the zucchini. Add the lemon juice, olives and serve.

ZUCCHINI (STUFFED)

4 large zucchini

Filling:

1 apple: grate
1 capsicum: fine dice
2 apricots: fine dice
6 lychees: fine dice
8 cherries: fine dice
1 banana: mash
1 mango: fine dice
2 tbs olive oil

Sauce:

3 tomatoes: fine dice
2 tbs olive oil

2 tbs lemon juice
half cup Tomato Puree (P. 353)
1 tbs Tomato Paste (P. 357)
zest of 1 lemon
half cup Stock (P. 354)

Cut the top section of the zucchini to make a lid. Scoop out the seeds. Place the zucchini on a baking tray smeared with olive oil.

Filling: Mix the ingredients and fill the zucchini. Replace the lids and secure with toothpicks. Oil the zucchini and bake in a moderate oven until tender.

Sauce: Place the oil in a pan and heat gently. Add the tomatoes and cook through. Add the stock and reduce. Add the remaining ingredients and cook to a thick sauce. Pour the sauce over the cooked zucchini. Remove toothpicks and serve hot.

ZUCCHINI (TENDER)

1 cup Stock (P. 354)
6 olives: slice
half cup dried tomatoes: fine dice
2 large zucchini: fine slice into 4cm lengths
Chilli Powder to taste (P. 354)
2 tbs olive oil

Place the oil in a pan over a gentle heat. Add the olives, dried tomatoes, chilli and cook through. Add the stock and reduce by half. Add the zucchini and cook gently until tender. Serve.

Weights

(imperial to metric)

0.035 ounces = 1g
0.17oz = 5g
0.35oz = 10g
1.76ozs = 50g
3.52ozs = 100g
35.27ozs (2lb 4oz)= 1000g (1kg)

DESSERTS

APPLE AND PLUM BAKE

4 apples: fine slice
8 dates: fine dice
4 plums: fine slice
juice of half apple
juice of 1 lemon
2 cups shredded coconut

Place ingredients in a bowl and fold gently. Transfer to a casserole dish and bake in a moderate oven until cooked. Serve hot with Coconut Cream Sauce (P. 370, 371).

APPLE BAKE

4 apples: core
6 dates: fine dice
1 dsp grated coconut
zest of 1 orange
4 figs: fine dice
juice of 1 lemon
juice of 1 orange

Place apples in a casserole dish. Mix grated coconut, orange zest, orange juice, dates and figs in a bowl. Pack the mixture into apple centres. Spoon the lemon juice over the apples. Bake in a moderate oven until cooked. Serve hot or cold with coconut cream or Coconut Cream Sauce (P. 370-371).

APPLE CRUMBLE

6 apples: slice
juice of 2 apples
6 dates: fine dice
juice of 1 lemon
1 cup grated coconut
6 crushed brazil nuts

Place the sliced apple in a pan with the apple juice, lemon juice, dates and gently simmer until cooked firm. Chill. Mix the brazil nuts and grated coconut in a bowl. Transfer the chilled apple to an ovenproof dish and sprinkle the nut mixture over the top. Place the dish under a moderate griller until golden brown. Serve hot or cold. (The apple mix can also be thickened with cornflour blended with a little water).

APPLE DELICOUS

3 apples: halve

Filling:

6 crushed brazil nuts
4 figs: fine dice
zest of 1 orange
4 dates: fine dice

Combine the nuts, dates and the orange zest and press into the apple halves. Place on a tray and bake in a moderate until cooked. Serve hot or cold with coconut cream, Coconut Cream Sauce or Strawberry Sauce (P. 369 - 376).

APPLES (STEAMED)

half cup lemon juice
1 cup orange juice
4 apples
6 dates: fine dice, mash
3 figs: fine dice, mash
3 apricots: fine dice
1 dsp avocado oil

Coat the apples with lemon juice and place in oiled ramekins. Combine the dates, figs, apricots and avocado oil and mix well. Pack the mixture into the apple centres and spoon orange juice over the top. Steam until cooked. Serve hot or cold with coconut cream or Coconut Cream Sauce (P. 369-376).

APPLES (STUFFED)

4 apples
3 plums: fine dice
half cup finely diced green coconut
zest of 1 orange
6 dates: fine dice, mash
juice of 1 lemon

Combine the dates and juices and mix well. Mix the plums, green coconut and orange zest and fill the centre of the apples. Stand the apples in an oiled casserole dish and pour the date and citrus juice mix over the top. Bake in a moderate oven until cooked. Serve with a favourite sauce (P. 369-376).

BANANA AND BERRI

2 cups blueberries
2 bananas: slice
1 pear: dice, mash
juice of half lemon
1 small cup coconut cream
2 tbs toasted, grated coconut

Mix the pear and the lemon juice. Arrange the blueberries and bananas on a serving tray. Pour the pear and lemon sauce over the fruit. Spoon coconut cream over the top and sprinkle with toasted coconut. Serve.

BANANA FRY

4 bananas: slice diagonally

Sauce:

1 apple: grate
juice of 1 orange
zest of 1 orange
juice of 1 lemon
zest of 1 lemon
1 tbs avocado oil

Whisk the apple, citrus juice and zest. Gently heat the oil and lightly fry the bananas. Place the bananas on a serving tray and pour the sauce over the top. Serve immediately.

BANANA SPECIAL

2 bananas: slice lengthways
4 passionfruit
2 kiwifruit: fine slice
half cup lemon juice

Arrange the sliced bananas in individual serving bowls and cover with lemon juice. Place the kiwifruit over the banana and top with passionfruit pulp. Serve immediately.

BANANA TROPICAL TREAT

4 bananas: slice lengthways
2 mangoes: slice
juice of 1 lemon
3 tbs grated coconut

Coat the bananas with lemon juice and toss in grated coconut. Line a platter with sliced mango and top with banana. Garnish with chilli flakes and serve.

BANANA WITH COCONUT CREAM

3 bananas
half cup coconut cream
1 tbs shredded coconut
half cup coconut milk

Slice bananas and place in serving dishes. Combine the coconut milk and coconut cream and pour over the sliced bananas. Sprinkle with shredded coconut and serve.

Hint

Washing up will be easier if baking dishes are wiped with kitchen paper after serving and soaked in hot soapy water.

BERRY NICE

1 cup strawberries: trim
1 cup blueberries
1 cup raspberries
2 mangoes: slice
half cup coconut cream

Arrange the mangoes on a serving tray then add the berries. Pour the coconut cream over the top and serve.

FIG AND DATE SELF-SAUCING PUDDING

Sauce:

1 apple: fine dice, chop
1 pear: fine dice, chop
juice of 1 lemon
half papaya: chop
1 banana, chop
juice of 2 oranges
1 tbs lemon zest

Mix the ingredients in a blender. Place 3 tbs of the sauce into oiled ramekins and set aside.

Pudding:

2 cups grated coconut
6 brazil nuts: crush
juice of 1 orange
juice of 1 lemon
1 cup finely diced dates
three-quarter cup finely diced figs
1 tbs lemon zest
half cup finely diced apricots
2 apples: fine dice

Combine the ingredients and mix well. Spoon into the ramekins and place them in a dish that is half full of water. Bake in a moderate oven for about 45 minutes. Pour 1 tbs of coconut cream over the top of each pudding and serve.

FIGS (STUFFED)

6 figs
1 apple: grate
half cup finely diced and mashed green coconut
juice of half lemon
4 strawberries, fine dice
1 cup mango juice

Cut down the side of the figs to make a pocket. Mix the apple, coconut and lemon and stuff the figs. Place them in a dish. Mix the crushed strawberries and mango juice and pour over the figs. Place the dish in a steamer for about 10 minutes. Serve hot or cold with coconut cream.

FRUIT AND NUT PIE CRUST

2 cups grated coconut
2 tbs coconut oil
5 dates: fine dice, mash
10 brazil nuts: crush
sliced fruit of choice

Combine the ingredients in a bowl and mix thoroughly. Smear avocado oil over individual serving dishes and press the mixture into the bottom and sides. Cover and set in the refrigerator for 3 hours. Fill with sliced fruit of choice and place a spoonful of Strawberry Sauce (374), passion fruit pulp or coconut cream over the filling. Serve immediately.

Measures

1 teaspoon = 5ml
4 teaspoons = 1 tablespoon
1 tablespoon = 20ml
quarter of a cup = 63ml
half of a cup = 125ml
1 cup = 250ml

FRUIT LAYER

4 figs: fine dice
sliced pineapple
lemon juice
passionfruit pulp
sliced mango
mashed banana
sliced papaya

Press figs into the bottom of ramekins. Add the pineapple and mango. Mix the banana and lemon juice. Spread over the pineapple and mango then the papaya. Top with passionfruit pulp and serve.

FRUIT SALAD (1)

1 rockmelon: slice, retain the liquid

Dressing

1 kiwifruit: 1cm dice
1 pear: 1cm dice
1 apple: 1cm dice
2 mangoes: 1cm dice
juice of 1 lemon
juice of 1 orange

Arrange the rockmelon slices on a platter. Gently combine the remaining ingredients and spoon over the melon and garnish with halved grapes.

FRUIT SALAD (2)

1 bullock heart custard apple: 1cm dice
2 bananas: slice
2 oranges: fine slice
1 mango: slice
1 pineapple: slice
juice of 1 lemon
juice of 1 pink grapefruit

Coat the banana with lemon juice. Add the remaining ingredients and fold gently. Serve at room temperature.

GRAPES AND BERRIES

2 cups grapes: halve
2 cups strawberries: halve
2 cups lychees
1 cup orange juice

Gently fold the ingredients in a bowl and spoon into serving bowls. Top with chilled coconut cream. Serve.

ICY BLOCKS

3 strawberries
3 dates
1 cup coconut milk
1 banana

Place the ingredients in a blender and mix until smooth. Pour into an ice block tray and freeze.

JACKFRUIT DELIGHT

8 jackfruit segments
4 bananas: fine slice
juice of 1 lemon
three-quarter cup finely diced coconut
half cup coconut cream
4 figs: fine dice

Place the bananas in a bowl and coat with lemon juice. Add the remaining ingredients and fold gently. Serve.

Measures

(imperial to metric)

0.88 fluid ounce = one-quarter decilitre
1.76 fluid ounces = half a decilitre
2.66 fluid ounces = three-quarter decilitre
3.52 fluid ounces = one decilitre

MANGO AND BERRY SALAD

2 cups strawberries: halve
2 cups grapes: halve
2 bananas: fine slice
juice of 1 lemon
1 large mango: 1cm dice
2 cups watermelon balls
2 cups rockmelon balls

Place the banana in a bowl and coat with the lemon juice. Add the remaining ingredients and fold gently. Serve.

MELON DELICIOUS

3 cups watermelon balls
3 cups rockmelon balls
3 cups honeydew balls
1 cup coconut cream
6 crushed brazil nuts

Place the melon balls in serving dishes. Spoon the coconut cream over the melon and top with crushed nuts.

MELON GRAPEFUL

1 rockmelon: retain juice
2 cups grapes: halve
3 cups whole grapes
2 mangoes: 1cm dice

Serrate around the centre of the rockmelon to produce two halves. Seed. Cut flat bases. Place the halves on a serving tray. Fill with layers of grapes, mango and juice. Place the whole grapes around the base of the rockmelon and serve at room temperature.

PEACHES AND BERRIES

8 peaches: skin, halve
2 cups raspberry puree
juice of 3 lemons

Dip the peaches in lemon juice and arrange in individual dishes. Spoon raspberry puree over the top and serve.

PEACHES IN RED WINE (1)

4 peaches: skin
juice of 2 lemons
fruity red wine

Cut the peaches into quarters and arrange in brandy bubbles. Cover with lemon juice and wine. Chill and serve.

PEACHES IN RED WINE (2)

8 peaches: skin
1 cup orange juice
1 tbs lemon zest
half cup lemon juice
half cup red wine

Place the fruit in brandy bubbles. Combine the citrus, zest and red wine. Spoon the mix over the fruit and serve.

PEAR SALAD

3 pears: slice
1 tbs favoured wine
juice of 1 lemon
2 tbs grated coconut

Place the ingredients in a bowl and fold gently. Place in serving bowls and sprinkle with coconut and serve.

PEARS (STEAMED)

4 pears with core: peel and retain stems
lemon juice

Place each fruit in oiled ramekins and coat with lemon juice. Place the ramekins in a steamer and cook until tender. Serve hot or cold with Coconut Cream Sauce (P. 367-374), passionfruit pulp or pureed pineapple and a sprinkle of shredded coconut.

PINEAPPLE AND KIWIFRUIT SALAD

1 pineapple: 1cm dice
3 kiwifruit: fine dice
6 dates: fine dice
1 tbs grated, toasted coconut
1 cup red wine

Simmer the dates in wine gently until soft. Cool. Arrange the remaining fruit on a serving tray. Pour the sauce over the top and serve with a sprinkle of toasted coconut and serve.

PINEAPPLE BAKE

1 pineapple: unpeeled, remove the top
coconut cream

Place the pineapple in a baking tray. Bake in a moderate oven for 45 minutes. Cool. Peel and cut into slices. Arrange on a platter and drizzle the coconut cream over the top. Serve hot.

PINEAPPLE FLOAT

1 pineapple with top
4 apples: grate
2 tbs grated, toasted coconut
6 dates: fine dice
juice of 1 lemon
zest of 1 lemon
juice of 1 orange
zest of 1 orange

Using a sharp knife, carefully slice the pineapple lengthways including the top. Remove the core and flesh, and fine dice. Cover the two halves and refrigerate. Simmer the apples, juices and zest over a gentle heat until tender. Cool. Fill the pineapple halves with alternate layers of pineapple and the apple mixture. Top with coconut cream then toasted coconut and serve.

The pineapple shells can also be filled with any fruit or freshly made fruit salad.

PINEAPPLE PIE CRUST

1 pineapple: grate, squeeze and retain juice
1 cup grated coconut
6 brazil nuts: crush
1 cup finely diced and mashed green coconut

Place the ingredients in a bowl and mix. Add coconut cream if too dry. Oil ramekins and press the mixture into the sides and bottoms. Cover. Chill. Fill with fruit of choice. Top with passionfruit and serve.

PINEAPPLE WHIP

1 pineapple: fine dice, mash
2 bananas: mash
1 tbs crushed coconut
2 mangoes: fine dice, mash
pulp of 4 passionfruit
half cup coconut cream

Place the pineapple, bananas and mangoes in a bowl and mix. Add the passionfruit and coconut and mix. Pour into stemmed glasses and top with coconut cream and serve.

PLANTAIN BAKE

6 plantain bananas
2 tbs crushed coconut
juice of 3 limes

Bake the plantains in a moderate oven until their skin blackens. Cool. Remove the flesh from the skin. Discard the skin. Serve in individual bowls. Spoon lime juice over the top and sprinkle with crushed coconut. Garnish with thinly sliced lime and serve warm.

Hint

Keep knives well sharpened. Dull knives can be dangerous.

PUMPKIN (CREAM FRUIT BAKE)

2 cups pumpkin: grate
5 dates: mash
4 figs: fine dice, mash
1 apple: grate
1 cup grated coconut
1 cup orange juice
juice of 1 lemon
half cup brazil nuts: crush
zest of 1 lemon

Combine the ingredients in a bowl. Spoon the mixture into ramekins. Place them in a dish and half fill with water. Bake in a moderate oven for about 45 minutes. Serve hot or cold with coconut cream or a favourite sauce (P. 369-376).

PUMPKIN (SWEET BAKE)

3 cups grated pumpkin
4 dates: fine dice, mash
4 figs: fine dice, mash
half cup coconut cream
three-quarter cup grated, toasted coconut

Place the coconut cream, figs and dates in a bowl. Beat until creamy. Add the grated pumpkin and mix well. Spoon the mixture into ramekins. Half fill a large baking tray with water and place the ramekins in the water. Bake in a moderate oven until golden brown. Sprinkle with toasted, grated coconut. Serve hot or cold.

ROCKMELON SALAD

1 rockmelon: retain juice, scoop out 12 balls,
dice remainder
1 kiwifruit: fine dice
juice of 1 lemon
juice of 1 orange
1 mango: fine dice
1 pear: fine dice

1 apple: fine dice

Place the juices in a bowl. Add the remaining ingredients, fold gently and serve.

STRAWBERRY AND KIWI DELIGHT

2 cups strawberries: halve
3 kiwifruit: fine dice
juice of 2 oranges
3 figs: fine dice
zest of 1 orange

Place ingredients in a bowl and fold gently. Serve in individual bowls and top with a favourite topping.

TROPICAL DELIGHT (1)

2 oranges: segment
2 mandarins: segment
2 pink grapefruit: segment
1 bullock heart custard apple: 1cm dice
juice of 1 lemon
half cup finely diced green coconut
2 cups 1cm dice soursop
2 kiwifruit: fine dice

Place ingredients in a bowl and fold gently. Serve in individual dishes and top with coconut cream.

TROPICAL DELIGHT (2)

2 pink grapefruit: segment
half cup finely diced green coconut
2 mangoes: slice
2 oranges: segment
2 cups lychees

Arrange the sliced mango and lychees on a serving dish and place the citrus on the top. Top with finely diced coconut.

TROPICAL NUT TREAT

1 pineapple: fine slice
3 bananas: slice
1 mango: fine slice
three-quarters cup finely diced crushed coconut
juice of 1 lemon

Place the chopped banana in a bowl and coat with lemon juice. Arrange the pineapple slices on a platter. Pile the chopped banana in the centre of the pineapple and arrange the sliced mango on the top. Sprinkle with crushed coconut and serve.

TROPICAL TREAT

3 guavas: 1cm dice
half cup lemon juice
3 bananas: slice

Fold ingredients gently and serve in individual bowls. Top with pureed fruit or coconut cream.

SWEET TREATS

1 cup shredded coconut
15 dates: fine dice, mash
10 figs: fine dice
1 cup finely diced green coconut
half tsp grated lemon rind
1 tsp lemon juice
finely grated, toasted coconut

Place ingredients in a bowl (except the toasted coconut) and mix. Roll into balls and coat with the toasted coconut.

BEVERAGES

Nutritious drinks can be made using fruit juices, coconut milk or coconut cream as a base. If a sweet beverage is preferred, add finely diced dates or figs and blend.

AVOCADO SMOOTHIE

half avocado: dice
1 cup coconut milk
1 cucumber: dice

Mix ingredients in a blender. Pour into a glass and serve.

BANANA SHAKE

1 banana: chop
3 dates
1 cup coconut milk

Mix ingredients in a blender. Pour into a glass and serve.

BERRY SHAKE

1 cup strawberries
1 banana: chop
half cup coconut milk
half cup coconut cream

Mix ingredients in a blender. Pour into a glass and serve.

FRUIT PASSION

4 cups watermelon juice
pulp of 6 passionfruit (whisk to separate the seeds)
2 cups rockmelon juice
juice of 1 lemon
1 mango: fine dice
1 cup mango puree
juice of 2 oranges
1 tbs orange zest

Combine ingredients in a punch bowl and mix. Float finely sliced orange on the top and serve.

Measures

(imperial to metric)
1 gallon = 4.546 litres

FRUIT PUNCH

4 apples: puree
juice of 1 lemon
1 litre watermelon juice
1 litre orange juice
1 pineapple: puree
2 cups strawberry puree

Mix the ingredients in a punch bowl. Float finely sliced lemon on the top and serve.

KIWI SHAKE

2 kiwifruit: chop
1 cucumber: chop
1 cup coconut milk
3 dates

Mix ingredients in a blender. Pour into a glass and serve.

MANGO LASSY

2 mangoes: chop
1 cup coconut milk
1 cup coconut cream

Mix ingredients in a blender. Pour into a glass and serve.

PINEAPPLE SMOOTHIE

1 banana: chop
half cup pineapple juice
half cup coconut cream

Mix ingredients in a blender. Pour into a glass and serve.

STRAWBERRY SHAKE

6 strawberries
1 pear: chop
3 figs: chop
1 cup coconut milk

Mix ingredients in a blender. Pour into a glass and serve.

TOMATO JUICE

1kg tomatoes: half, strain and discard seeds, retain liquid
juice of 2 lemons
chilli to taste

Place the tomatoes, tomato liquid and the remaining ingredients in a blender. Serve with a swirl of coconut cream.

This drink is excellent for those who suffer prostate problems.

Temperature

Boiling point of water = 100 degrees Celsius
Rinse water temperature = 74 degrees Celsius
Wash-up water temperature = 60 degrees Celsius
Most hazardous temperature (bacteria-wise)
for storing food = 21 to 43 degrees Celsius
Fruit storage temperature = between 7 and 10 degrees Celsius
Refrigeration storage = 0 to 5 degrees Celsius
Freezing point of water = 0 degrees Celsius

"

and out of the ground
made the Lord God to grow
every tree that is pleasant to the
sight and good for food; the tree of life
also in the midst of the garden,
and the tree of knowledge
of good and evil

"

– the bible (old testament) genesis ch. 2 v. 9

BIBLIOGRAPHY AND SUGGESTED READING

Title: *"Neurochemistry"*
Author: Horst Jatzkewitz.
Publisher: Georg Thieme Verlag Stuttgart
1978 Edition

Title: *Chemie Der Zucker und Polysaccharide*
Authors: Fritz Micheel and Almuth Klemer
Publisher: Akademische Verlagsgesellschaft
Geest and Portig K.-G
Leipzec 1956

Title: *Handbuch der unerwuenschten Arzneimittel Wireungen*
Authors: B. Muller-Oerlinghausen. R. Laske. H. Duppenbecker.
K.-H. Munter (Hrsg)
Unter Mitarbeit von J.D. Tiaden
Urban and Fischer 1999

Title: *Handbuch der mikroskopischen Anotomie des Menschen*
Authors: Bergrundet von Wilhelm von Mollendorff. Fortgefuehrt
von Wolfgang Bargmann.
Herausgegeben von A. Oksche und L. Vollrath
Publisher: Springer 1979

Title: *Praktische Anatomie – Becken in der Schwangerschaft und Das Neugeborene*
Authors: *Lanz & Wachsmuth*
Publisher: Springer 1988

Title: *Neurochemie Eine Einfubrung*
Author: von Horst Jatzkewitz.
Publisher: Georg Thieme Verlag Stuttgart

Title: *Spezielle Pathologische Anatomie. Ein Lehr – und Nachschlegewerk.*
Authors: Begruendet von Wilhelm Doerr und Erwin Uehlinger
Herausgegeben von
Professor Dr. Dres.h.c. Wilhem Doerr, Heidelberg
Professor Dr. Gerhard Seifert, Hamberg
Publisher: Springer 1995

Title: *AIDS-SARS*
Author: Wolfgang Eggert
Printed in Germany
ISBN: 3935845081

Title: *The New Additive Code Breaker*
Authors: Maurice Hanssen and Jill Marsden
Publisher: Lothian Publishing Co. Pty. Ltd.
ISBN: 0850913256

Title: *Neutralization of Animal Viruses*
Author: N.J. Dimmock
Publisher: Springer-Verlag
ISSN: 0070217X
ISBN: 3540560300
ISBN: 0387560300

Title: The *Macquarie Dictionary (Third Edition)*
Publisher: The Macquarie Library Pty Ltd

Title: *The Book of Remembrance –*
THE MESSAGE TO HUMANITY
Author: F.L.A. Freytag
Publisher: Imprimerie Klausfelder S.A., Vevey
Printed in Switzerland

Foetal Alcohol and Drug Unit. Department of Psychiatry and Behavoiural Sciences/University of Washington School of Medicine. United States Department of Health and Human Services.

Title: *Die Geplanten Seuchen*
Author: Wolfgang Eggert (Hrsg)
ISBN: 3935845081

Title: *Behavioural Problems in Childhood*
= The Link to Vaccinations
Author/Distributor: Viera Scheibner Ph.D

Title: *The Prophet*
Author: Kahlil Gibran
Publisher: William Heinemann (1926)
ISBN: 043429067X

Title: *April Fool's Day*
Author: Bryce Courtney
Publisher: Reed International
ISBN: 0143004603

Title: *Scientists – The Lives and Works of 150 Scientists Volume 3*
Editors: Peggy Saari and Stephen Allison
Publisher: UXL

Title: *How Scientific Are Orthodox Cancer Treatments?*
Author: Walter Last
Web site: health-science-spirit.com/cancerscience.html

Title: *Seeds of Deception*
Author: Jeffrey M. Smith
Publisher: Chelsea Green
Printed in Canada
ISBN: 0-9729665-8-7

www.chemtrailcentral.com
www.soyonlineservice.co.nz
www.beimpropheten.com

Title: *Watt's the Buzz?*
Author: Lyn McLean
Scribe Publications 2003

Title: *Cancer Undefeated*
New England Journal of Medicine

Title: *Macmillan Dictionary of the History of Science*
Editors: W. F. Bunum. E. J. Browne. Roy Porter
Publisher: The Macmillian Press Ltd

Title: *Vaccination. The Medical Assault on the Immune System*
Author/Distributor: Dr. Viera Scheibner Ph.D.
Printer: Australia Print Group

Title: *Macmillian Profiles. Scientists and Inventors*
Publisher: The Macmillian Press Ltd

www.naturalway.net.au

Welcome to the internet home of House of eLidi.

House of eLidi is the registered brand name of our handmade, all natural and chemical free skincare products.

We use natural oils from trees and plants. They also contain aloe vera, coco and shae butters, pure essential oils and our mask contains the superfine clay from the Great Artesian Basin. Many of the products contain neem oil – a powerful and natural antiseptic, moisturiser and cleanser.

We also have a gorgeous collection of handmade and Frenchmilled specialty soaps.

These soaps also contain neem oil, pure essential oils, Norwegian seaweed, superfine clay, butters, and our special range of natural oils. Their base is coconut oil.

We offer a comprehensive range of pure essential oils and aroma therapy.

Ten very interesting years have gone into developing these products that are unique.

believe –
and it shall be given you,
although it may tarry,
it will surely come to pass

NOTES

NOTES:

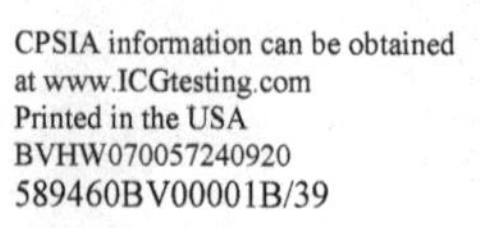
CPSIA information can be obtained
at www.ICGtesting.com
Printed in the USA
BVHW070057240920
589460BV00001B/39

9 780646 492933